The British Co-operative Movement
Film Catalogue

Dedicated to Joseph Reeves, Education Secretary of the Royal Arsenal Co-operative Society (1918-38) and Secretary-Manager of the Workers' Film Association (1938-46).

A pioneer of Co-operative film, culture and education.

Utopias are often only premature truths. (Lamartine)

When will the people wake and see
    That they must rise and help themselves
Put tyrants down, the rights assert
    Of him who toils who weaves, or delves?
When through all lands the banner floats,
    Inscribed upon "Each for All."
Then shall the cruel despots kneel,
    A smiling Peace take place of thrall.
(From the hymn, "Each for All", by Ebenezer Elliott)

The British Co-operative Movement
—————— Film Catalogue ——————

Compiled and edited by
Alan Burton

FLICKS
BOOKS

A CIP catalogue record for this book is available from the British Library.

ISBN 0-948911-77-8

First published in 1997 by

Flicks Books
29 Bradford Road
Trowbridge
Wiltshire BA14 9AN
England
tel   +44 1225 767728
fax +44 1225 760418

An edition of this book is published in North and South America by Greenwood Press, Westport, CT.

Printed and bound in Great Britain by Bookcraft (Bath) Ltd.

Contents

Acknowledgements

In 1996 British television broadcast a documentary on the well-known department store chain, John Lewis. In a rather startling and unsettling analysis, the programme concluded that the company's celebrated profit-sharing scheme had heralded an industrial experiment which represented the farthest extreme to which the British sensibility would be prepared to go with regard to collective practice – despite the evidently paternalistic regime, hierarchical structures and patronising attitude shown towards the workforce. It was rather dispiriting, after several years of actively promoting Co-operative education, that the producers failed to give any consideration whatsoever to the mighty ramifications and impressive achievements of the British consumer Co-operative Movement: a true workers' democracy which for 150 years had sought to confront capitalism, and had replaced the notion of profit (and profit-sharing!) with that of the Co-operative Commonwealth.

Admittedly, the Co-operative Movement has not had it so good in recent times. During the research and compilation of this catalogue, the ideals and practices of Co-operation and association have been the subject of a seemingly irredeemable retreat. The *Zeitgeist* has been singularly unfavourable. The Movement has continued to struggle commercially, a problem which has intensified considerably since the first significant stirrings of concern back in the 1950s. As a result, the idealistic mission of "universal provision" has been jettisoned for a more pragmatic concentration on a core business of retailing. Significantly, in 1994, the Co-operative Wholesale Society sold off its manufacturing division to an archetypical young venture capitalist weaned on the aggressive market philosophies of recent Conservative fiscal orthodoxy, and a fundamental historical tradition was reversed. More recently, the financial press has been full of details regarding a hostile takeover attempt on the Co-operative Bank, which, thankfully on this occasion, the CWS has decided to see off. This brings us to a second point of erosion: such a defiant gesture of association stands in stark contrast to the rapacious droolings typical of the rest of the banking sector. Currently, members of building societies are, with indecent haste, clamouring to trade in their status as owners, lured by the instant gratification of windfall gains. Shamefully, individualistic financial greed feeds on the corpse of mutualism.

The numerous films detailed in this catalogue offer ample evidence of a commitment by ordinary working people to take control of their own destiny, and to promote a "moral economy" of consumption in direct contrast to selfish concerns of greed. A project such as this one, primarily concerned with the raw material of film history, is greatly indebted to the tireless efforts of film archive professionals who serve film scholarship so diligently. I would like to record my grateful thanks to the archivists and assistants at the following institutions which were instrumental in the preparation of this catalogue: the East Anglian Film Archive, Educational and Television Films Ltd, the Imperial War Museum Film and Video Archive, the

National Film and Television Archive, the North West Film Archive, the Scottish Film Archive, and the Wessex Film and Sound Archive.

Film preservation is an ongoing process. The majority of films detailed in this catalogue were located by the author, formerly being in the possession of Co-operative societies and organisations. To ensure that such titles remain available to future generations of Co-operators and scholars, they have been passed forward for film preservation at the archive indicated. An expensive and time-consuming procedure, such circumstances mean that it has not been possible to state which titles are *currently* available for scrutiny. Those interested are advised to contact the film archive directly regarding the viewing status of a particular film.

Innumerable Co-operative educationalists and members have furnished me with esoteric titbits of information which have contributed to a far richer text than I could have conjured myself. The discussion of these historic films on member courses and at history events has been a distinct pleasure, as well as significantly contributing to my knowledge of the Movement.

My initial investigation into the Co-operative Movement's use of film began in 1992 while I was employed by the Co-operative Union Ltd. Mervyn Wilson has been an unflagging supporter of this work, and the management and administrative staff at the Co-operative College have given generously of their time and encouragement. Immeasurable thanks go also to Len Burch, who introduced me to the democratic structures of the Co-operative Movement and explained the philosophic basis of Co-operation. Considerable appreciation is also extended to Flicks Books for their preparedness to take on this project, and to Matthew Stevens who first presented the idea of the catalogue to me, and whose guidance and intelligent advice have contributed greatly to the publication we have before us.

The bulk of the research for this project was conducted during a Junior Research Fellowship at De Montfort University. I am grateful to the School of Humanities for their support, and for providing me with sufficient time and space to chase down both the films and the evidence so necessary to deepen our understanding of them. Gratitude also goes to my immediate colleagues who endured (almost!) my incessant tirades concerning such mundane topics as Co-op soap, the dividend, society galas, Jubilee histories, and so on.

Mark and Russell of North London tolerated my presence on numerous occasions during the genesis of the catalogue; their kindness and generosity enabled me to complete crucial aspects of the research. Most importantly, I would like to express my love and thanks to Sue, whose interest and faith in the Co-op match my own. On all occasions she has supported my ambitions and believed in my ability to realise them. The past ten years have been a joy and I look forward to the rest of our life together.

Leicester
May 1997

Abbreviations

ad	art director
BCS	Birmingham Co-operative Society
BRO	Bristol Record Office
cam	cinematographer
CCPC	Co-operative Co-Partnership Propaganda Committee
COI	Central Office of Information
comm	narrator/commentary
CPF	Co-operative Productive Federation
CWS	Co-operative Wholesale Society
CYM	Co-operative Youth Movement
d	director
EAFA	East Anglian Film Archive
ed	editor
ETV	Educational and Television Films
IAC	Institute of Amateur Cinematographers
ICA	International Co-operative Alliance
ICD	International Co-op Day
IWM	Imperial War Museum
LCS	Leicester Co-operative Society; London Co-operative Society (both societies used this acronym)
LECS	Long Eaton Co-operative Society
LJEC	London Joint Education Committee
mus	music
NCS	Nottingham Co-operative Society
NFA	Northern Film Archive
NFTVA	National Film and Television Archive
NWFA	North West Film Archive
PC	private collection
PCS	Peterborough Co-operative Society
PIMCO	Portsea Island Mutual Co-operative Society
pm	production manager
pr	production company
prod	producer
RACS	Royal Arsenal Co-operative Society
sc	scriptwriter
SCWS	Scottish Co-operative Wholesale Society
sd	sound
SFA	Scottish Film Archive
WCF	Woodcraft Folk
WCG	Women's Co-operative Guild
WFA	Welsh Film Archive / Workers' Film Association
WFSA	Wessex Film and Sound Archive

Explanatory Notes

This book contains several distinct sections:

: An introductory essay (pages xiii-xxxvi) which provides an historical context in terms both of the ideological and commercial nature of the Co-operative Movement throughout the period, and of the general trends of the Movement's film activities, in the aim of facilitating a fuller appreciation of the titles listed in the *Catalogue* section.

: A chronological listing (pages 1-154) of extant films relating to the British consumer Co-operative Movement, 1909-1980 (together with a small number of titles pertaining to other national Co-operative organisations).

: A record (pages 155-160) of titles – and subjects, where known – of Co-operative films which remain to be located.

: A listing (pages 161-163) of reference prints, held at various film archives, which are awaiting funds for preservation, and which are currently unavailable for viewing.

: Appendices (pages 164-202) containing selected press articles from 1914 to 1955, and providing a glimpse of the Co-operative Movement's response to the film medium and to its possibilities for publicity, propaganda and education.

: Indexes (pages 203-232) to the *Catalogue, Introduction, Unlocated Films* and *Reference Prints* sections, by film title; film archive; film credits; country of production; Co-operative society; brand name; product and industry; and geographical location. There is also a index of general and miscellaneous items, such as associations, companies, personalities, subjects/themes, and so on. **Please note that** numbers in the indexes refer to catalogue entries, *not* to page numbers; however, roman numerals refer to page numbers in the *Introduction*.

The entries in the main *Catalogue* section contain the following data:

NCFC number	for reference purposes within this catalogue
title (date)	this information is derived from contemporary printed sources (newspapers, journals and film catalogues). In some instances, an assumption about the date has been necessary, based on documentation, film stock, and so on. For untitled films a descriptive phrase, presented in square brackets, has been added for identification purposes.
film stock	b/w (black and white) or col (colour)
length	in minutes (m) and seconds (s)
audio track	sound or silent
country of production	unless indicated otherwise, this is England
film format	the gauge of surviving prints

archive location	where surviving prints are located
(ref)	indicates the status of a reference print, which, currently unavailable for viewing, has not been seen by the author
credits	personnel who took part in the film's production
▪ synopsis	a brief summary of the film's content
description	a break-down of the film into scenes, sequences or actions
Remarks	providing relevant background detail, and commenting on particularly notable features of content and style
See also:	reference(s) to this film in other entries in the catalogue, or in the *Introduction*
(?)	indicates that the author is not entirely certain of the preceding fact or statement

Currency

Many of the catalogue entries contain references to prices given in the currency system used in Britain before decimalisation in 1971. One pound (£) was divided into twenty shillings (s), each of which contained twelve pence (d). A price could be written as £2 10s 6d, or £2/10/6; 15s 6d or 15/6.

Foreword

Bill Lancaster

In the summer of 1958 there was a buzz around the streets of Blaydon, Tyne and Wear, that was animating the local children. Our Co-operative society was celebrating its centenary with displays, demonstrations and social events in the school hall, the largest available building in the town – the Co-operative hall now functioned as a cinema with fixed seating. Centre-stage was given to a photographic exhibition which chronicled the progress of Britain's second oldest surviving Co-operative. I have to admit that as a nine-year-old I paid scant attention to the historical section in the hall. The attraction which acted as a magnet to me and to my young comrades was the demonstration of closed-circuit television near the entrance. We collected our free centenary carrier bags stuffed with balloons and other treats, and then spent a joyous hour waving and jumping up and down in front of the camera, whilst at the same time scrutinising the monitor for our first appearance on the "telly". We were informed that this was the first public display of such equipment in the region – but this came as no surprise, because to our young eyes the "store", with its new supermarkets and chemist shop lit with fluorescent tubes, was the very essence of modernity.

I occasionally find myself telling this anecdote to young students in order to dispel their perception of the Co-op, which in my region has largely been shaped by two images: a visit to the re-created 1913 "store" at Beamish, and the remaining small supermarkets in sad decline, unable to compete with the glitzy vistas of Sainsbury's and Tescos. Sometimes I manage to kindle sufficient interest in the Co-operative Movement for a student to choose the history of a local society as the subject for dissertation work. Students have often sat in my room reporting on the progress of their research. After accounting their perusal of minute-books and jubilee histories, they relate their interviews with elderly Co-operators, ending with "Oh – and one said there was a film which featured the society". This did not surprise me; indeed, it served to confirm my argument about the dynamic nature of Co-operation during most of its history.

But where were these films, I often wondered. Did they disappear with so much other material during the mergers and closures of societies that has been a feature of the Movement during recent decades? Moreover, film, especially old stock, is a notoriously difficult medium to preserve. My despair at the potential loss of an obviously important source was alleviated five or six years ago when I became aware of Alan Burton's project of locating old Co-operative films and transferring them onto videotape. With his lectures, displays and presentations at workshops, conferences and regional cinemas, Alan has both whetted our historical appetite with the gems that he has rediscovered, and given us progress reports of his work towards establishing a Co-operative film archive at the International Co-operative College. This vast catalogue and his judicious introduction represent the completion of the first stage of Alan's project.

We will, of course, never have a complete collection of Co-operative films, which were first produced in 1899, but I am sure that we will see future supplements to the present catalogue. In the meantime, social, economic, labour, design and film historians and their students have a treasure-trove of visual source material dealing with the most important popular movement of the last century. We are all indebted to Alan Burton and his colleagues at the International Co-operative College: they deserve our warmest congratulations for producing this volume and securing an important archive.

My interest in Alan's work in the enlargement of the archive is set to continue – he may even turn up some old television footage of a group of short-trousered nine-year-old boys waving into posterity.

Bill Lancaster teaches labour and retail history at the University of Northumbria. He is the author of *The Department Store: A Social History* (1995) and of *Radicalism, Co-operation and Socialism: Leicester Working-Class Politics 1860-1906* (1987).

Introduction

Films were first projected to general audiences in Britain in the spring of 1896. Only three years later, the new medium had been adopted by the Co-operative Movement to show views of the factories operated by the Co-operative Wholesale Society (CWS) to gatherings of Co-operative society members. By the late-19th century, the Co-operative Movement had become an integral component of the industrial and commercial landscape, and an important element in the burgeoning Labour Movement. (The Labour Representation Committee was founded in 1900, and would become the Labour Party in 1906.) As the Co-operative Movement entered the 20th century, membership stood at 1 707 000, combined in 1434 retail societies, and with an annual turnover of £50 million. Membership would continue to grow throughout the first half of the century (3 million members in 1914; 8 million members in 1939; 12 million members in 1958), whilst, conversely, the number of consumer Co-operatives reduced as rationalisation led to a strategy of amalgamation and the emergence of larger, more diverse retail societies (1385 societies in 1914 with a turnover of £88 million, 1100 in 1939 with a turnover of £272 million; and 988 in 1953 with a turnover of £764 million). The statistics publicised by the Co-operative Independent Commission in 1958 were undoubtedly impressive: the Movement operated over 30 000 shops and controlled 60% of the nation's self-service outlets; its 250 factories manufactured a wide variety of products, and it was still the largest wholesaler in the country.

During this period, the Movement played an important role in the daily lives of innumerable working-class families. Its commitment to the consumer made it their champion, and it was in the interwar period that Co-operation really began to attract the semi-skilled and unskilled as members. By 1939, the Movement controlled 25% of the nation's milk distribution, 40% of butter sales, 20% of tea, sugar and cheese, and 10% of bread and bacon. Larger societies had begun to establish imposing department stores in addition to their numerous branch outlets. A member of such a society was part of an impressive commercial organisation:

> [T]he Society would have had its own gigantic bakery, flour mill, refrigeration store, coal wharfs, canal boats, railway trucks, motor lorries, even its own electr ic power plant. You might be renting a cottage from the Society, built by its own building department, having your clothes made in the Co-op tailoring workshop, and cleaned in the Society laundry. The Society might have been so big it had ceased to rely on the CWS, making its own jams, pickles, sweets, furniture, and providing food from its own farms and nurseries. From the society's milk rounds to its funeral undertaking department, you would be receiving literally a 'cradle to the grave' service.[1]

One recent historian of the Movement has indicated how significant Co-operative expansion in the service sector continued to be: "the formation of dairies, bakeries, laundries, funeral services and hairdressing departments were amongst the co-operative success stories of the inter-war period accounting for much of the growth of co-operative trade".[2]

The Co-op both responded to and led developments in retailing. Principal amongst the various innovations were the rise of hire purchase, the development of department stores (and self-service stores in the postwar period), the development of doorstep delivery services, canvassing campaigns, and the growth of the funeral business. Since the beginning of the century, large-scale city societies had become the most "dynamic form", and industrial towns such as Birmingham, Leeds, Liverpool and Plymouth counted their membership in tens of thousands. The London Co-operative Society (LCS), which traded on the north bank of the Thames, could claim to be the largest Co-operative society in the world, with a membership of nearly 800 000 by the outbreak of the Second World War. The most striking expansion in Co-operative membership and trade was apparent in the south, where total sales more than doubled in that area between 1919 and 1936.[3]

The expanding historiography of the Labour Movement since the 1960s has shown comparatively little regard for the role and contribution of the Co-operative Movement.[4] Critics of the New Left have exhibited little enthusiasm for an institution which they perceived as reformist and seeking gradual change within existing economic and political structures – accommodating rather than confronting capitalism. However, such analysis disregards the actual penetration the Movement attained in the daily routine of working people. For the active member, that meant participation in a "Co-operative community" of meetings, rallies, guilds, cultural activities, youth groups and educational classes. The fundamental contribution by the Co-operative Movement to Labour activities should be stressed. Socialist historians Raphael Samuel and Gareth S Jones have commented on that disregard of Co-operation:

> It is usually treated as a nineteenth-century remnant harking back to the remote days of Robert Owen and the Rochdale pioneers and this picture is reinforced by its nineteenth-century historians who conceive its evolution to be that from community-building to shopkeeping. But in fact the greatest period of the growth of co-operation was the first thirty years of this century, not only as a form of retailing, but also as a social and political movement. The Utopia of most Labour Party activists at least until the Second World War was entitled the 'Co-operative Commonwealth'. Nearly all Labour families were convinced co-operators. Thus co-ops were represented on the National Executive Committee, not out of deference to the pre-history of the Labour Party, but because they represented a crucial component of Labour's inter-war strength. The largest women's organisation in the Labour Party was the Co-operative Women's Guild. Meetings of local Labour Parties often took place in recently-built Co-op halls.[5]

The actual nature of Co-operative ideology remains contentious. For example, what exactly was the Movement's relationship to the dominant capitalist economy? Before such a question is addressed, it must be appreciated that a body of Co-operative theory was never fully formulated, and it would be misleading to suggest that all members were identical, embracing a clearly articulated set of political ideas, and active for social and economic change. Indeed, it is often noted that the British Labour Movement never embraced theoretical doctrines as readily as did its continental counterparts. A dogmatic pragmatism was valued over and above a theoretical rigour. However, some basic points should suffice to illustrate that the aims and intentions of Co-operation and capitalism are mutually opposed; as the Christian Socialists used to maintain, Co-operators believe in self-help but not in selfish help. Co-operative principles of equality and democracy contrast with capitalist business ethics, and reflect the defining structure of Co-operative organisation. Co-operation was founded on the ideal of assisting consumers, whilst capitalism exists to exploit them. That distinctive contrast was encapsulated in Co-operation's maxim: production for use, not for profit.

Despite the initial encouragement of the virtues of mutuality, thrift and self-help from influential sectors of society who were supportive of "respectable" activities of the impoverished, Co-operation soon came into conflict with the dominant elites within society. A typical attack on the Co-op took the form of a boycott, whether initiated by manufacturers (as in 1905, when the Proprietary Articles Trade Association objected to the Co-operative dividend), or by local traders who put pressure on their customers and employees not to trade with the local Co-operative society. At times, the Movement was goaded into the manufacture of certain items to which it was systematically denied access. In the 1930s, it began to manufacture both radio sets and light bulbs, as their respective cartels, protective of their pricing arrangement, refused to deal with the Co-op which offered the inducement of a cash dividend on purchases. Indicative of their action, the Co-op marketed both its radios and light bulbs under the brand name of "Defiant".

A decisive period in the conflict between Co-operation and private trade was the First World War. The bias against and maltreatment of the Movement by offices of the state has been summed up by Sidney Elliott: "Every action of the Government seemed to indicate a 'latent hostility' to co-operators, and an assumption that the only system for the distribution of commodities was that of the private merchant, wholesale dealer and shopkeeper".[6] The prejudicial motivations of the central distributive and productive policies wrought a fundamental reversal of the Movement's traditional stance on political neutrality. At the 1917 Co-operative Congress, a motion was carried to seek parliamentary representation, and, in the 1918 General Election, Alfred Waterson became the first Co-operative Member of Parliament, elected for Kettering. Soon after its establishment, the Co-operative Party worked in alliance with the Labour Party, and eventually an electoral scheme was worked out for the efficient contesting of elections.

As Stephen Yeo has dryly pointed out in reference to the mounting opposition, there were "those in twentieth-century Britain who thought Co-operation more powerful than many co-operators did".[7] Perceived as an economic and political threat by powerful interests, the Co-operative Movement was bound to evoke a reaction. In 1933, *The Economist* commented: "The policy of the Co-operators has been openly declared to be the elimination of the profit-maker and the capitalist middleman. The recent advance of the Movement is the measure of its success."[8] Neil Killingback has shown how, throughout the 1920s and 1930s, the Movement was systematically attacked by private interests, and a long campaign was waged to impose a more restrictive taxation burden on mutuality trading. In 1933, a partial success was claimed when legislation was introduced with the Budget, which:

[A]ssimilated mutual organizations to joint-stock companies. For tax purposes, they were supposed to be the same, and so the trading surplus of a society was equivalent to the profits of a private business...The result was that co-operative societies were now liable to an increased tax burden under Schedules C and D of the income tax.[9]

Private traders had long inveigled against the Co-operative dividend as "unfair competition", and had now, with Government support, imposed a tax burden on an element of the surplus achieved by Co-operative societies; the savings of working people who often earned so little that they did not qualify to pay income tax.[10] In 1937, Hall and Watkins summarised the situation:

To-day, when its membership represents more then one-half of Great Britain's population, whose purchases from its shops represent at least 15 per cent of the country's retail trade in some commodities, and a larger percentage in others, when its purchases in the world's markets makes an appreciable difference to price levels, and its use of certain raw materials interferes with monopoly control by private interests, large-scale business and the world of finance as well as the retail trader take notice of it, and range themselves in opposition to it.[11]

Faith in the ultimate outcome of the conflict was embodied in the slogan, "Towards the Co-operative Commonwealth":

The Movement thus tends to diminish the power and authority of the capitalist and private enterpriser by setting consumers, and producers also, free from dependence upon them, and making them masters of their own economic destinies. The stores displace the private baker, the wholesale societies the private miller, and the Wheat Pools, the grain dealer and speculator. The logical end of all this is clear. If all consumers and producers were co-operators, loyal to their organisations, and closely linked together, the capitalist would be no longer master because he would be superfluous.[12]

Central to the Co-operative mission was education; indeed, Co-operative educationalists often considered themselves "missionaries". The belief that education was essential to achieve social progress was the basis of Owenism, and the ideas of Robert Owen continued to be influential in Co-operative thinking. The fundamental aim of Co-operative education was "the making of Co-operators",[13] and in practice there were two main thrusts: courses in professional subjects such as management, book-keeping and accounting were crucial in maintaining the commercial efficiency of the organisation; and classes promoting an awareness of the history, aims and ideals of the Movement were essential in maintaining the democratic structures of societies through the encouragement of active participation by the membership. To that effort, libraries and reading rooms were established by Co-operative societies, classes were organised, and, by the late-19th century, an educational framework was in place involving the local society, regional associations and, nationally, the Co-operative Union. Important also were the women's, men's and mixed guilds for adults, promoting discussion and campaigning on issues, and various youth formations such as the British Federation of Co-operative Youth, Pathfinder groups, Comrades Circles and the Woodcraft Folk, which sought to make "Co-operators for life".

Communication with members and employees was clearly essential, and, to that end, numerous publications and journals were launched. Pre-eminent amongst these was the weekly newspaper, *The Co-operative News*, founded in 1870, which had attained a circulation of 50 000 by the end of the century. The value of bringing members together on a regular basis was recognised, and the leisure and recreational needs of the membership were catered for, as well as their material ones:

> [I]n any case Co-operation is something more than buying butter and sugar collectively; it is the working together of individuals for the common good; they have to learn how to work together effectively; and it is necessary to meet together in order to learn.[14]

Co-operative choirs, orchestras, dramatic groups and sports and leisure clubs were the components of a vibrant "Co-operative Culture". In the sense that Peter Gurney uses the phrase, "Co-operative Culture" embraced the neo-Owenite vision of a Co-operative community – indeed a Socialist Utopia. He questions the "passivity school" of Labour historians, who sensed in the Co-ops a greater concern with commerce than with social responsibility: "The dividend was not regarded as a sign of 'embourgeoisement' but rather as a stepping-stone to the co-operative community of the future".[15] Cultural and educational activities were crucial in developing an awareness of those ideals. Propaganda was widely disseminated, and film played an important role. Gurney's analysis illustrates the integrated nature of Co-operative trade, culture and education, and how each was informed by faith in an ideal:

> [T]he practice of consumer co-operation led co-operators like Ben Jones and Percy Redfern thoroughly to reject capitalist forms of trade. The majority of members may not have all shared this explicit and developed critique, but many had glimpsed an alternative, anti-competitive future in fragmentary form. The movement culture built around the social nexus of the store was important here. Co-operative values and beliefs were communicated through a wide repertoire of cultural forms: the press, libraries, classes, demonstrations, choirs, tea parties, exhibitions, festivals. The scale of this provision was remarkable and makes the better-known activities of the Clarion Clubs look like very small beer; here was the British equivalent of the cultural construction which characterised the SPD in Germany before the First World War. 10,000 voices made up the United Choir which sang at the National Co-operative Festival at the Crystal Palace in 1897. At this time more than 130 societies supported libraries with a total stock of nearly 350,000 volumes. By 1914 there were nearly 4,500 adults and 17,000 children taking classes organised by the movement. The latter studied the history of co-operation from Isa Nicholson's *Our Story* (1903). This text was republished for the ninth time in 1911 in a penny illustrated edition which ran to 250,000 copies.[16]

Co-operative educationalists and propagandists of the interwar period had been sure of their convictions regarding the nature of Co-operation, and determined in their promotion of their Co-operative mission:

> It needs no great vision to realise that a world in which co-operation was the guiding social principle would be a very different one from that in which competition rules and dominates people's actions, even if it is modified, controlled or restrained here and there by legislation and custom. In this sense the claims that Co-operative education is education for social change is fully justified; and the

future of Co-operative Education, indeed the future of the Co-operative Movement itself, depends upon the success of co-operative leaders in convincing non-co-operators that social change on co-operative lines is desirable. Herein lies the importance of Co-operative Propaganda.[17]

Film was to become an integral element of that propaganda. Before the 19th century had ended, film was being used to promote Co-operative history, trade and ideals; members meetings were enlivened by Cinématographe shows; and cinema was working towards the maintenance of a vibrant "Co-operative Culture". In the following sections, I will examine the uses which Co-operation put to film: films for publicity; films for propaganda; films for cultural and educational purposes. The actual films rarely conformed to any simplistic schematic distinctions of trade, politics and instruction. Indeed, as I have argued, a more sophisticated notion of "Co-operative Culture" is required – one that integrates commercial activity with political aspirations, and that recognises Co-operative business organisation as "a standing challenge to capitalist business, just as co-operative ideas form a criticism of capitalist economics".[18]

The problem of separating the individual intentions of a film is readily evident with an apparently "entertaining" and "harmless" film such as *Sam Goes Shopping* (1939; NCFC 084). Structured around a monologue on the Co-op by the renowned music-hall star, Stanley Holloway, hapless shopper Sam can only remember that whatever he has been sent by his wife to collect begins with a "d". As he travels through the store, Sam is offered a multitude of "d" things, all of which he rejects. He spends several hours in the store, keeping the staff well back after closing time. The dilemma is finally resolved by the manager, who is able to prompt Sam into recollecting that, after all, it was only the "Divi" that he was supposed to withdraw.

The film was released as a short into cinemas, and hence offered a general appeal in its utilisation of a celebrity and of amusing material. It was recognised at an early stage that entertainment was a necessary ally of propaganda; ultimately, that was what the film was – propaganda for Co-operative trade and ideals. The film is set almost entirely in a Co-op store, and Co-operative products are plainly evident. A final title card emphasises that fact, informing audiences that the items on view are "Only Available in Co-operative Stores". Moreover, the film expounds a fundamental ideological point, the existence of the "Co-operative Difference"; Sam discovers that he is one of the owners of the shop, and that the "Co-operative Dividend" is his reward. Therefore, an amusing, short five-minute film such as *Sam Goes Shopping* could be mobilised for publicity, political and educational purposes, and attractively packaged as an entertaining comedy sketch.

Although *Sam Goes Shopping* has both a political and an educational dimension, it is pre-eminently concerned with tempting general audiences to shop at the Co-op, and, for that reason, will be considered a publicity film for the purposes of this catalogue. I recognise that such categorisation is somewhat arbitrary; indeed, modern film studies and its concern with the audience alert us to another matter: it is probable that a film was read differently by individual members of the audience. For example, the CWS's *The King and the Cakes* (1930; NCFC 022), made for cinema release, would mainly have impressed general audiences in terms of its promotion of CWS flour. Co-operators, on the other hand, may have been more attentive to the model conditions of "their" factories, as depicted in the long middle section, and consequently accepted the film for its instructive nature.

With these difficulties in mind, I will now proceed to examine the films of the Co-operative Movement in terms of their evident functions: publicity, propaganda and education.

Films for publicity

The matter of clearly designating a function for a film is made harder by the convention, in the first third of the century, whereby the term "propaganda" was synonymous with publicity and promotion as far as the Movement was concerned. Therefore, the annual "Propaganda Week", inaugurated by the Co-operative Union in 1927 and later extended to a fortnight, was primarily concerned with boosting trade. However, the word also retained its more characteristic meaning, that of political persuasion, and hence the Joint Propaganda Committee of the Co-operative Union and the CWS sought to propagate the Co-operative message in areas where the Movement was weakly established or non-existent (so-called "deserts"). Again, the intimate link between business and ideals was evident in such circumstances. It was recognised in 1937 that "propaganda takes many forms, and whilst on the one side it impinges upon education, it impinges on the other side upon advertising and publicity work generally",[19] and that the role of the propagandist was to "visit districts untapped by co-operative societies in order to establish the Movement in them, and [to] help societies which need strengthening or are making a special effort to increase their membership or trade".[20]

Improving Co-operative trade, therefore, *was* conducting the Co-operative mission. As the supplier of Co-op brand products, the CWS was particularly active in promotional work and publicity, establishing a Publicity Department in 1916. In fact, films had been utilised in publicity work as early as 1898, primarily to illustrate lectures given by the publicity staff at members' meetings convened by local societies.[21] The practice eventually emerged of distributing CWS samples to audiences to aid in the promotion of its products. Films were made to record the various productive activities of the CWS: tea; biscuits; tobacco; confectionery; polishes, and so on. Gifts would reflect the subject of the film presentation. The practice was developed and was a basis for film publicity work well into the 1960s. A particularly striking and humorous early campaign involved the promotion of CWS soap in 1914, for which both the lantern slide and Cinématographe film were brought to aid:

> The Lecturer, Mr Crowther, (CWS)...gave a most interesting account of the manufacture of soap at the Irlam Works which was greatly enjoyed by the large audience present. The lecture concluded with a washing competition for men. The competitors were allowed five minutes in which to wash an article of domestic use...Samples of CWS soap, &c., were distributed at the close.[22]

Unfortunately, none of the many films detailing the productive work of CWS factories from the pre-First World War period appears to have survived.

An important innovation with respect to film publicity commenced early in 1928. A series of short-story films was commissioned by the CWS from a leading producer of commercial films, Publicity Films. Distribution was handled by the Co-operative Press Agency, an adjunct of the CWS Publicity Department, who secured exhibition for each film at 1000 cinemas. Each week, *The Co-operative News* printed the play dates and venues so that Co-operators were informed of screenings and could ensure their attendance when the film played their neighbourhood. The first film was *The Magic Basket* (NCFC 015), released on 13 February 1928 and lasting six minutes. The film introduced a style that would serve as a basis of the series for the next five years: brief dramatic sequences involving the ideal Co-operative couple or family, and framing the obligatory documentary sequences of CWS factory production. The flavour of the film was given in a pronouncement provided by a CWS trade journal:

> Glimpses of the actual productions will be shown, the finished product in each case being made a component of the content of the housewife's shopping basket. The audience will have a view of the interior of a Co-operative Store where the member is withdrawing her dividend. She ultimately finds her way into the drapery department, where a selection of co-operative clothing gives her a new interest in the society of which she is a member.[23]

The "magic basket" in question was thus the collected purchases of a contented Co-operative housewife, and, for the general cinema audience, the film offered the vicarious pleasures of the Co-operative shopping experience. It is evident that the interest of the potential member was being aroused by representations of the Co-operative experience with which they would be most familiar: popular retail products; a typical Co-op store; fashion; and the dividend. It was hoped that "non-co-operators who see the film, if they are wise people, will follow the example of 'Mrs Everett' – they will become loyal purchasing members of a co-operative society, and either save the dividend or put it to the same good use".[24] Further films were released on a regular basis and tended to promote a particular product – examples being *Bubbles* (soap, 1928; NCFC 012); *A Matter of Form* (corsets, 1929; NCFC 018) and *The Bright Side of Things* (polish, 1930; NCFC 020). The first sound film of the cycle was *Her Dress Allowance* (drapery; NCFC 021), released in December 1930, and subsequent titles were released in both sound and silent versions for an appreciable period. Most of the CWS publicity films are collected at the North West Film Archive, but unfortunately only in their silent form.

Furthermore, the CWS Publicity Department developed its cinema lecture programme for member societies. A provision was launched simultaneous with the cinema campaign of 1928, whereby "societies could have the services of lecturer, operator and all the requirements for an evening's cinema lecture for the inclusive fee of 35s".[25]

During the 1937-38 season, 1196 screenings were recorded for an estimated audience of 237 000. The products of the CWS Lowestoft pure foods factories were the promotional focus; in order to facilitate that, a new talking film was produced.[26] The publicity value of the occasion was fully exploited:

> [F]ar from being merely educational gatherings, these lectures were closely allied to the trading activities of the retail societies concerned. Publicity films, coupons and window displays, together with a systematic visitation of societies by CWS travellers before each event, produced a chain between propaganda and trade which reflected beneficially on sales.[27]

Over 4000 specially-prepared window displays were made available to participating societies:

> [T]he problem of inducing audiences to visit the local co-operative stores soon after the lecture was solved by presenting all who attended with a coupon entitling the holder to purchase a box of Waveney Sandwich Cheese or Cheddar Cheese at the reduced price of 3d.[28]

Such was the basic pattern of CWS film activity in the 1930s. The 1938-39 season was devoted to promoting CWS soap. Two films suitable for that task had been produced in 1936 – *"Postman's Knock"* (NCFC 063) and *Merry Mondays* (NCFC 356).[29] Innovations such as colour were readily incorporated, and the Co-op claimed at the time to be "the only organisation in the country using colour cartoons on the lines of 'Mickey Mouse' for film propaganda".[30] The first was *Sweets of Victory* (1937; NCFC 365), which lasted 5½ minutes and promoted Lutona chocolates. Over 6000 cinema screenings were secured for the film.[31]

Two particularly striking films were produced towards the end of the 1930s. *Co-operette* (1938; NCFC 071) and *Sam Goes Shopping* were both shot in an innovative British colour process, Dufaycolor, and featured star performers. The former represented the Movement's first musical, with tunes by the notable DeBroy Somers and his band, and dancing by the Co-operettes (six of C B Cochran's Young Ladies). Stanley Holloway participated in both projects, delivering one of his famous comedy monologues, this time on "'T' Co-op", in the latter film.[32] These two films were important attempts by the Movement to broaden the appeal of its publicity films through the utilisation of star performers and popular forms. CWS products featured prominently in both films.

Although progress was halted by the outbreak of war in September 1939, one significant achievement was the establishment of the CWS Film Unit in 1940:

> [T]he CWS has always aimed to manufacture as many as possible of the products they supply to Societies and through the Societies to co-operators in general so it was not surprising when the CWS Directors decided that the time had come for them to produce their own films.[33]

Many wartime and postwar productions were capably undertaken by the Unit. One innovation was the preparation of two films on that staple Co-operative product, milk. Milk salesmen and milk sales were the target of a film campaign in 1947. The two resulting films, *Milk Salesmanship* (NCFC 112) and *The Milk We Drink* (NCFC 113), although similar in theme, were aimed at distinct audiences: employees and general audiences, respectively.

Film distribution and exhibition were also subject to some attention. In 1950, the CWS commenced a scheme of mobile film units, developing upon a practice inaugurated by the SCWS in 1948, whereby cinema provision had become possible in remote villages and hamlets. The new-style displays differed from previous schemes in that they were offered free of charge to Co-operative and progressive organisations, provided they could supply a suitable venue. The system was based on fleets of vans equipped with films and projection equipment, and operating out of regional publicity offices. The CWS Publicity Department would also provide the requisite promotional material such as posters and handbills. Average annual audiences were about 250 000 throughout the 1950s. By 1962, sixteen roadshow operators were putting on 2600 shows a year for Co-operative societies. Three kinds of show were available: a women's show lasting 75 minutes; a children's show of 60 minutes; and a mixed adults' show lasting 105 minutes.[34] Publicity films would be only one element of the programme, which also comprised short pictures, cartoons, travelogues and so on, included to "sweeten" the Movement's own promotional material. It is instructive to note that the publicity film shows continued "a direct link-up with one of the CWS factories [whereby] examples of their products are given away",[35] a policy well-established before the First World War.

Typical product films that would clearly have lent themselves to the practice included: *Seal of Success* (margarine, 1954; NCFC 159); *Father Takes the Cake* (baking ingredients, 1957; NCFC 200); *Halcyon Days* (paints, c.1962; NCFC 253); and *It's In the Can* (processed foods, 1963; NCFC 257). The style of many of these films varied remarkably little from the first wave of CWS publicity films commenced in 1928. Generally, they centred on the industrial processes involved in the manufacture of Co-operative products. A simple framing sequence clearly delineated the actual brand products. Altogether more ingenious was a film designed to promote CWS household cleaning products, *The Handy Manns* (c.1963; NCFC 263). A witty script by Bob Monkhouse and Denis Gifford dispensed with the documentary scenes of industrial manufacture and concentrated on the comedy to be extracted from the friendly "battle of the sexes" conflict centring on household chores. In such a manner, memorable CWS products such as Spel, Pulvo and Miracle Mil were efficiently placed before audiences.

The SCWS was also active in promoting its trade through film. A large collection of extant films is preserved at the Scottish Film Archive; however, the context of their actual production, distribution and exhibition remains properly to be explored. Of particular note are a number of "spot" advertisements commissioned for use in cinemas, publicising such products as Unitas oats, Bluebell margarine and Pioneer custard. Moreover, the local cinema was occasionally utilised by a Co-op society for its promotional potential. For instance, 169 cinema slides were issued to Co-operative societies for the Ninth National Co-operative Propaganda Campaign in 1936.[36] Some local societies commissioned short films for screening in local cinemas, promoting the central store or perhaps a seasonal sale. So far, only a very small number of such films have come to light, most notably several made for the Newcastle Co-operative Society in the late-1950s. Additionally, societies were encouraged to organise their window displays to tie-in with local film releases. Horace Masterman, manager of the Pioneer Cinema operated by the Dewsbury Pioneers Industrial Society, was particularly active in that respect, and a winner of national prizes for his imaginative campaigns.[37]

In some cases, film was recognised as a valuable aid to trade by the local society. One of the earliest direct engagements in film production at the local level came in the summer of 1914. To help launch a new store, the Lowestoft Co-operative Society

[A]dopted the cinematographic film for advertising purposes. Striking films have been obtained of the central premises showing the movement of members in and out of the buildings, and also being served in the grocery department; the process of bread making and despatching also have been filmed. The scenes are being shown three times daily to crowded houses at the Picture Palace. This is an innovation that other societies might well initiate; it has already given a fillip to the society's trade.[38]

As familiarity with the medium of film developed, a number of societies began to explore its potential. In terms of publicity, the work of the Portsea Island Mutual Co-operative Society (PIMCO) and the Long Eaton Co-operative Society (LECS) in the 1930s are of particular note. Both had on-hand a cine-enthusiast: Reginald Denny, Publicity Manager of PIMCO;[39] and J H Poyser, member of LECS. Certain subjects seemed to lend themselves to those filmmakers, and each produced a "bread" film, a "milk" film and a "mannequin parade" (fashion) film. However, their imagination and skills were not confined to trade films, and sterling work was also undertaken on political and educational subjects. The filmmakers would tour ceaselessly around the society's trading area, giving film shows (Poyser gave 60 shows between October 1936 and February 1937) and no doubt performing an invaluable communication service with members and public alike.

The central experience of the ordinary person's involvement with the Co-op was as a customer of its goods and services. As we have seen, films were valued for the role they played in improving the society's trade. It was equally recognised that films could promote ideas, and the Movement's use of film for political purposes is examined in the next section.

Films for propaganda

Over the last two decades, there has emerged an impressive bibliography on workers' cinema during the interwar years; correspondingly, studies have appeared of labour and radical filmmaking in the United States, France, Germany and Great Britain.[40] Scholarship has invariably focused on the attention paid to cinema by overtly radical groups, and the historiography suggests that the revolutionary events in Russia towards the end of the First World War were instrumental in bringing about that activity. American film historian Jonathan Buchsbaum thus boldly concludes that "[w]ithout question it was the stunning impact of Soviet filmmaking that mobilized concerted left interest in film in the West".[41] Left political film activity, both theoretical and practical, evidently coalesced around the attempts to screen such masterpieces of heroic Soviet cinema as *Bronenosets Potemkin* (*Battleship Potemkin*, 1925).

Such a reading of events of course parallels the historiography of the Labour Movement in Britain, in which the Co-operative Movement is accorded at best a marginal role. Histories of the British workers' cinema provide only a partial consideration of the Co-op's contribution to the discourse on Labour cinema, and largely concentrate on that most politically committed of decades, the 1930s.[42] Accordingly, emphasis has been given to the Labour Party's circular on "Labour Cinema Propaganda", issued in March 1920, as signalling an awareness on the Left of the political value of film.[43] In fact, six years earlier, an editorial in *The Co-operative News* had explored the potential of cinema to advance the cause of Co-operation. Posing the question "The Cinema. Should It be Used for Co-operative Purposes?", the article was unequivocal in its praise and advocated

[T]hat the cinema might be used, with much advantage, for spreading a knowledge of co-operative activities. We are always looking about us for features that will not only bring people into our ranks, but that disseminate information about our great undertakings, and by that means convey something of the extent of our operations and their possibilities in the near and the distant future. Why not bring the cinema to aid?

In a remarkably prescient passage, the anonymous author recognised the unique visual appeal of cinema, and appreciated the opportunities presented by the new media of mass communication:

The great advantage to us would be its spread of a knowledge of co-operative activities in a way that the rank-and-file of the movement would come to see and learn. We are always talking about the necessity of reaching the masses and bringing the masses together. The cinema would do this for us.[44]

The following month, in March 1914, a lecture entitled "The Camera As Educator" was given at the headquarters of the Co-operative Union, Holyoake House, Manchester. Similar sentiments were expressed, and the ideological dimension of the lecturer's understanding of Co-operative education was apparent when "he threw on the screen illustrations of the CWS factories, at the same time appealing to his audience to support the products of these factories, *and thus aim a decisive blow at the sweatered industries*".[45] The outbreak of the Great War precluded any further progression in the Movement's comparatively sophisticated appreciation of the political potential of the film medium.

The war was a crucial catalyst in bringing into greater prominence across Europe both the position of the national Labour Movements, with particular gains by extreme radical groups, and the awareness on the Left of the oppositional potential offered by film. Accordingly, moves were effected to create a viable "alternative" cinema that offered a radical challenge to the dominant cinema which was perceived as promoting the interests of the capitalist class. In a rather simplistic formulation, the commercial cinema was seen as "doping" the workers into acceptance of the status quo. The emerging "alternative" cinema practices were components of a broader attempt to erect Socialist cultural forms that would bring workers together in comradeship and unity. Most fully developed by the Left parties in Germany, such attempts were represented in Britain by the Clarion Clubs, the Unity Theatre, the British Workers' Sports Federation, the Workers' Music Association, the Left Book Club, and so on,[46] and were important in fostering a sense of class identity and fellowship throughout the interwar period.

The emergent British workers' film Movement was at all times constrained by financial and technical difficulties. Important activities centred on the establishment of workers' film societies; to facilitate that aim, the Federation of Workers' Film Societies was founded in October 1929. In an attempt to provide a viable environment for exhibition, the Co-operative Movement was often a vital partner. Obstructive attitudes by unsympathetic local councils – through the stringent operation of fire regulations, bolstered by the prohibition of screenings on Sundays in licensed cinemas – invariably made progress difficult. Fortunately, suitable venues were sometimes available in the form of the local Co-op hall. For example, the London Workers'

Film Society's inaugural presentation was almost cancelled when the London County Council refused permission for a screening at the Gaiety Cinema, Tottenham Court Road, on Sunday 17 November 1929. The proposed show actually went ahead on the following day in the Co-operative Hall, Tooting, for which the Royal Arsenal Co-operative Society (RACS) had secured a Cinématographe licence in 1925. A second show was held there on 16 December 1929.[47] The Merseyside Workers' Film Society met similar opposition:

> The adventures of the early days are worth recording. After two shows an avalanche descended – the films had been *Two Days* and *Turk-Sib*. The Hall – a theatre run by the University Settlement – refused permission for further performances; the press conducted a campaign against what they called the subversive character of the society, and the secretary was forced to resign by his employers. Then came a show in a cinema closed for a few days while talkies were installed and then an application to the Magistrates for Sunday performances – refused, of course. Permission to use a hall belonging to the city was sought and refused but, at last, fortune, in the shape of the local Co-operative Society, smiled and produced the uncomfortable but fire-proof hall in which present shows are given.[48]

Issues of Left filmmaking practices and aesthetics were debated in Labour journals, and the participation of the Co-operative Movement was included in those discussions. Thus, in April 1929, the film correspondent of *The New Leader* could demand "that the labour, co-operative, and socialist movement sit up and consider the effects that films have on the lives and on the outlook of the workers in general".[49] In 1925, the Labour Movement had to respond to the political film activity of the Conservative Party, which began to utilise mobile daylight cinemas for propaganda work. Film publicity work was consolidated in May 1930, with the establishment of the Conservative & Unionist Films Association.[50]

Two Co-operators who showed a clear determination to advance the position of the workers through the use of film were Alderman Joseph Reeves, Education Secretary of the RACS (1918-38), and F H W Cox, the sponsored filmmaker of the Political Committee of the LCS.[51] Reeves was a towering figure in Co-operative education between the wars, and believed that his work "[would] make bad citizens for capitalism and good citizens for the Commonwealth".[52] He tirelessly promoted the use of film throughout Co-operative educational circles, and was instrumental in introducing the film medium in support of the RACS's educational programme as early as 192o, with a film commissioned of the society's trading and cultural activities. The propaganda activity of the workers' film Movement was crucially facilitated by the advent of "sub-standard" (16mm) film which was both cheaper to use and fell outside the provisions of film censorship. Writing retrospectively, Reeves could declare:

> [W]ith the invention of the 16mm, non-flam film, I was convinced that the time had come for the workers' movement to work out ways and means whereby the film could be used to make known our social aims and for the purpose of counter-acting the subtle propaganda for the existing order of society which comes to us from Hollywood and elsewhere.[53]

However, Reeves's ambition for Labour film went beyond his pioneering educational work at the RACS and the limited potential of amateur filmmaking practices. Ideally, he envisaged a film organisation that embraced the full Labour Movement; his dreams were realised in the summer of 1938 with the formation of the Workers' Film Association, with Reeves appointed as Secretary/Organiser. The new organisation was an outgrowth of the Joint Film Committee of the Trades Union Congress (TUC) and the Labour Party, which had been founded in 1936 for the purpose of promoting film within those two democratic organisations, and the National Association of Co-operative Education Committees, of which Reeves represented the film section. Reeves' desire was to see the direct production of films by Labour groups, and his ambitions were apparent in one of his first pronouncements for the Workers' Film Association:

> I would like to see Railway Unions providing a film on the life of the railwaymen, the Transport and General Workers Union, one on the risks a motor driver takes from day-to-day providing transport for the people and goods, indeed the life of the great army of workers, builders, miners, seamen, printers, electricians should be dramatised because their life and work are the stuff of which life is made.[54]

Much effort was expended to influence the production of workers' films, but, with the outbreak of war in 1939, little progress was made.[55] Of most significance were two films completed in the "Five Year Film Plan" of the metropolitan Co-operative societies. *Advance Democracy* (1938; NCFC 070), directed by Ralph Bond, was arguably the key film produced in Britain advocating a popular front against Fascism. Ambitiously blending fictional domestic scenes illustrating the political awakening of a London docker, and documentary footage of work at the docks and of the annual May Day parade for "Peace, Freedom and Democracy", the film was a considerable advance on previous efforts of Left filmmaking. The second and final film under the Plan was *The Voice of the People* (1939; NCFC 085), a history of the struggle of the workers against the injustices of capitalism. Both films had been budgeted at an impressive £1000 ensuring they attained a polish rare amongst the productions of the workers' film Movement. Unfortunately, production of three further proposed films was never undertaken. Throughout the Second World War, the Workers' Film Association continued its educational and promotional work, making its contribution to the radicalisation of the British electorate through the screening of progressive documentaries that aided in the election of a majority Labour Government in July 1945.[56] In November 1946, the Workers' Film Association was superseded by the National Film Association, which, despite the Socialist euphoria of the time, proved a disappointment. The new-looking and more patriotically-labelled association achieved little in the way of film production, continuing to rely on the provision of film shows and the organisation of film schools, the backbone of the work undertaken by the Workers' Film Association in more trying circumstances. A major film project was undertaken for the Labour Party – *Their Great Adventure* (1948; NCFC 120), produced by the CWS Film Unit. Conceived as "a film of considerable entertainment value which also contains a message of deep social significance",[57] the film was lacking in radical fervour, and was reflective of the consensual approach adopted by the Labour administration at the time. Melodramatic in approach, it focused on an inter-class love-match to which both fathers disapprove. The day is saved by an impassioned speech by the local Labour MP (Cecil Trouncer) who promised the couple a secure and worthwhile future under a Socialist Britain. Audiences were forced to bear 25 minutes of soap opera before the film was brought to life by this piece of oratory. The National Film Association was wound up in 1953, having achieved little.

In the period 1937-45, the film work of Frank Cox for the Political Committee of the LCS was adventurous and relatively prolific. Cox was a pioneer of 16mm sound film technology, and perceived in that cheaper, flexible system the means for workers' groups to produce films for their needs. Like Reeves, he was an able propagandist and communicated his ideas widely within the Co-operative and Labour Movements. He conformed to the conventional viewpoint on the Left that saw the mass media as a soporific, helping to keep the masses satisfied with their lot in life, and angry that "we are content to leave this weapon almost entirely in the hands of our enemies".[58]

Cox's ideal was the establishment of a well-resourced film unit producing for the entire Movement. In the event, tensions between the CWS/Co-operative Union, with their library of publicity and educational films, the National Association of Co-operative Education Committees, who were guided by Reeves, advocating production on the professional 35mm format, and, finally, Cox with his predilection for 16mm direct sound-recording, meant that Cox would ultimately confine his work to the Political Committee of the London Society.[59] The resulting productions were varied in scope and ambition. *Peace Parade* (1937; NCFC 061) was a cogent plea for pacifism in the midst of mounting international tension. The film marks the striking ideological conflict on the Left at that time, when the rise of Fascism, and in particular the Spanish Civil War, caused many Labour people to search their souls for the proper response. *Peace Parade* records the peace demonstration to Hyde Park, which was sponsored by the Political Committee and involved what appears to be a substantial proportion of the society's transport fleet, suitably dressed for the occasion. Only a year later, the LCS would be co-sponsors of *Advance Democracy*, which called for united action against Fascism, but which, it should be noted, did not involve Frank Cox.

Another remarkable film was the record of the 1938 Co-operative Day massed pageant at Wembley Stadium, released as *Towards Tomorrow: Pageant of Co-operation* (1938; NCFC 078). The day-long programme, enjoyed by 60 000 Co-operators, was compressed into a 40-minute film shot by seven cameramen. Further films followed in regular succession, but few appear to have survived. A particular loss is represented by several films produced in the early war years, when the unit was renamed Pioneer Films. Such films appear to have offered a radically different view of the Home Front to the officially-sponsored Ministry of Information documentaries. For instance, *The Home Front* (1940; NCFC 390) depicted "shopkeepers doing a little profiteering on the quiet; rich women shoppers doing a bit of private food hording during the early days of the war".[60]

Such films as *The Home Front* and *Mr Smith Wakes Up* (1940; NCFC 392) appear to have controversially held up for discussion the type of postwar world for which Britain was fighting. In 1942, Pioneer Films was accredited as the 16mm production unit for the Workers' Film Association. I have not been able to ascertain to what extent productions were actually undertaken in this capacity, although a surviving film, *Progress* (1942; NCFC 101), clearly resulted from that unison. The film represents the most complete film record of a local Co-operative society, in that case Coalville Working Men's Industrial Association in Derbyshire.

Finally, a mention of one of the least known and discussed films of the Left. *Song of the People* (1945; NCFC 105) was co-sponsored by the CWS, with creative input from a host of British filmmaking talent: Mischa Spolianski, Sydney Box, Muir Mathieson, and Max Munden as director, amongst others. Contributions from cultural artists on the Left were also impressive: Reg Groves, Bill Owen, Phil Cardew, and so on. The film evoked the emergent progressive consensus of the war years which explained the curious mix of film industry professionals and Labour stalwarts. The film was constructed like a pageant, with its narrative charting the irresistible rise of the workers' Movement presented in music and song. The film's advocation of an "alternative" history of British society stressing conflict and struggle, contrasted strongly with "official" imagery, whereby history was mobilised to advance the notion of progress and the efficacy of Britain's liberal democratic institutions and ideals.

Two major wartime feature productions celebrated Tory prime ministers. Both *The Prime Minister* (1940) (depicting Disraeli) and *The Young Mr Pitt* (1942) mythologised Tory paternalism and disinterest, and drew contemporary parallels with recent events. Such cinematic representations have been judged as a "partisan Tory historiography in the making".[61] In stark contrast was *Song of the People* which traced its historiographical lineage through A L Morton's *A People's History of England* (1938). The film was resplendent with images of Stakhanovite British workers defiantly singing at their workbenches: "We are history's bloodstream,/Stop us if you can./We are many,/We are one,/We are the working-class." It presented a great clarion call to audiences to recognise the persistent struggle of the working classes, and, probably unique among Britain's wartime cinema, criticised the all-important ally, the United States. Soviet Russia comes in for no such approbation. For those reasons and many more, *Song of the People* is one of the most remarkable films in the collection.

Films for education

One of the seven original principles of the Rochdale Pioneers had been the promotion of education. Even as the state began to assume a greater role in the provision of learning, a distinct concern for Co-operative education remained. The Movement was involved in a number of important developments in adult education; for instance, providing the students and tuition fees to help launch the University Extension Movement. In 1903, CWS employee Albert Mansbridge set up the Workers' Education Association, and its first two branches were formed by local Co-operative retail societies at Reading and Rochdale. The wider view on the nature of Co-operative education that had generally prevailed within the Movement was one that embraced the whole of the cultural activities provided for members. It was stressed that such shared activities – whether evening classes, summer schools, choirs, dramatic groups, leisure clubs, and so on – were necessary to develop a sense of unity without which the Movement would disintegrate and lose strength. In arguing a policy, it could be claimed that such an approach had "demonstrated the truth that co-operative educators think of the leisure of co-operative members and of culture as well as of technical education and education for social change".[62]

It was soon appreciated that the moving picture show provided a valuable opportunity to bring members together for the aim of entertainment, instruction and fellowship, and proved a natural progression on the well-established magic lantern lecture. In fact, early Co-op film demonstrations simply supplemented the lantern show, conforming to a pattern recognised by American film historian, Charles Musser, whereby the advent of moving pictures probably came as less of a "shock" to early audiences than has generally been admitted. Rather, it should be accepted that the first films were a further advanced stage in the history of "screen practice", and that Victorian audiences had already developed some familiarity with projected images and visual illusions.[63] David Lazell has suggested that magic lantern lectures met four aims:

> FIRST, to educate members on Co-operative development, the SCWS being especially active in this area of work, to the point that their lecture circuit (including William Maxwell, Keir Hardie etc) was used as a model for later 'organisation' south of the border;
> SECOND, to raise funds and resources for various good works, paralleling some of the work done by church and temperance organisations, thus Mossley Co-op Society – which later had its own cinema – raised funds for the 'poor and deserving of Cornwall', in a lecture presented by someone who had just returned from the West Country. Similarly, Miss C M Mayo, a fine worker for Guild causes, lectured on homelessness – need for affordable housing was a frequent theme in Lantern Lectures in the 1890s and later;
> THIRD, shows mainly for children and young people and allowing for a great deal of experimentation (some audiences were rather restive and a lecturer on the work of place Ruskin Hall at the Chipping Norton Co-op Society was rather put out by the sheer exuberance of a youthful audience);
> FOURTH, what might be called the Members' Jamboree, when slides of Co-op enterprises were accompanied by free samples by the CWS, interludes by local artists, 'glees', affable words from committee members, and in general what might be termed a long night out![64]

The introduction of moving pictures into the programme quite clearly furthered the same objectives of education, promotion of good causes, entertainment and publicity. Indeed, the subject of the first films commissioned by the Movement paralleled existing series of lantern slides used in popular Co-operative lectures: the productive works of the CWS. An illustrated lecture service was provided for societies by both the CWS and the Co-operative Union. The former was promoted in the following manner:

> [W]e are prepared to arrange lectures on the CWS and its various productive works illustrated by a powerful lantern, for any societies who are willing to try this attractive method of propaganda. Our slides include views of the Manchester premises and the various home and foreign branches and depots, complete sets to illustrate the processes and manufactures carried on at Crumpsall Biscuit and Sweets Factory, Irlam Soap and Candle Works, Middleton Jam and Pickle Factory, Batley Woollen Factory, Leeds and Broughton Readymades and Tailoring Factories, Broughton Cabinet Works, Dunston Flour Mill and the Irish Creameries of the CWS.[65]

The educational nature of the programme is clear from the above. Members were having the nature and extent of "their business" shown and explained to them. A presentation to members of the Birmingham Co-operative Society in the winter of 1897 achieved a much broader coverage of Co-operative topics:

> [A] lecture on the aims and immense development of co-operation was given on December 4th by Mr W Cope, illustrated by limelight views on slides kindly lent by the Co-operative Union. The lecturer dwelt upon Rochdale, the original, Oldham the most advanced, Leeds the largest. Twenty-five slides illustrated the buildings, works, and ships of the Wholesale [CWS] all over the world. Productive co-operation was then explained, illustrated by views of the Equity, Sundries, Cutlery and Hebden Bridge works. The indebtness of co-operation to the great departed was indicated by views of Messrs Neale, Hughes and Mitchell; the great living forces by presentments of Messrs Gray, Maxwell, B Jones, and McInnes.[66]

This impressive scope embraced retail Co-operation, wholesale Co-operation, producer Co-operation and intellectual Co-operation.

The cinematograph display was easily incorporated into that pedagogical approach, and was often used in conjunction with a lantern lecture. As late as October 1913, a CWS lecturer was still combining the two technologies:

> Mr F C Crowther (CWS Manchester) in his lecture on 'The CWS and its Works' illustrated by lantern and cinematograph films showed goods manufactured by the CWS from the raw material to the finished article. Mr H Redfern (Chairman of the Educational Committee) impressed upon the members the need for more loyalty to their own Society and to the CWS. At the conclusion of the lecture, samples of CWS productions were distributed free.[67]

The earliest Co-operative film shows were presented in 1898/99, and the first films commissioned by the CWS "showed views of their soap, starch and candleworks at Irlam, their biscuit factory at Crumsall [sic] and the tea warehouses of the English & Scottish Joint Co-operative Wholesale Society in London".[68] It is probable that, for many in the more remote rural areas, this was their first contact with moving pictures. The typical venues for CWS film shows were Co-operative and village halls, churches and chapels, with a number taking place in the open air. By 1914, almost all of the CWS factories had been filmed, and a library of 40 films was compiled. Individual films were now being given their own titles, and some were twenty minutes long.[69]

The CWS film lecture service remained an important provision for informing members of retail Co-operative societies about the history and ideals of the Movement, its trade and its products. As already discussed, the programme of CWS films, which commenced in 1928 with *The Magic Basket* (NCFC 015), was important, at one level, in giving members an insight into the productive operations of the Movement's factories. The mechanism whereby such films were made available to societies was further consolidated in 1938 with the establishment of the CWS National Film Service. The existing library service, providing a two-hour programme of CWS publicity films for 35 shillings, was to continue, supplemented with an additional service which was more educational in nature. A "well-balanced" two-hour display comprised of "1 Travel Talk, 2 Educational, 1 Feature, 1 Comedy, 1 Cartoon and 1 Publicity".[70]

Film as an aid to education was an important consideration for local societies, with constructive activity at Portsmouth, Leicester, Long Eaton, Bolton, Ipswich, Royal Arsenal and Middlesborough, amongst other societies. The breadth of a society's trading and cultural activities was recorded by the cine-camera, and subsequent film shows around the trading district provided an attractive way of spreading awareness about the society. The resourceful Co-operative Publicity Manager, Reginald Denny, emulated a popular commercial form with the commencement of a Co-operative newsreel for both the Portsea Island Mutual Co-operative Society (1935) and Leicester Co-operative Society (1937). His endeavours at Portsmouth were particularly appreciated for their value in informing the new member:

> For this purpose a new film is in course of production, entitled *Behind the Scenes* [1935; NCFC 037] which deals with all the various workshops and services of the Society which are not readily visible to the new member. It is hoped that this will prove an invaluable method of acquainting a new member with the full extent of the Society's services.[71]

Co-operative events covered by the Leicester Co-operative society newsreels included the society's annual Penny Bank galas, the arrival of Father Christmas to open the Xmas Bazaar, the opening of new branch stores, International Co-operative Day demonstrations, and the society's participation in the regional agricultural show. Such film recordings gave promotion to, and a certain validation of, the cultural elements to Co-operation. In addition to the filming by local societies of sports days, children's gatherings, the building of central emporia, the opening of a new model bakery, Co-operative Day celebrations, and the crowning of the Co-operative Carnival Queen, the voluntary associations within the Movement – such as the adult guilds – and youth organisations – such as the Woodcraft Folk (WCF) and the British Federation of Co-operative Youth – made films of their activities. George Durham's colour film of the 1939 Woodcraft Folk Harefield Camp is a fascinating pre-war record of the fellowship and comradeship of that anti-competitive and anti-militaristic organisation. The preparation of films by local societies and voluntary associations continued until the 1970s, when ciné technology began to be replaced by video. The material is now invaluable as evidence of alternative cultural forms and organisation, essential to the wider expression of Co-operation and its ideals.

The most ambitious film ever undertaken by the Movement was the commemorative *Men of Rochdale* (1944; NCFC 104), marking the centenary of the establishment of the Rochdale Equitable Pioneers Society and the opening of their first store on Toad Lane, Rochdale. It was produced by the CWS Film Unit in collaboration with the commercial producer, Sydney Box, whose own career was poised for launch with his huge success, *The Seventh Veil* (1945).[72] A narrative, semi-feature film dramatically detailing the hardships and opposition encountered by the pioneer Co-operators, *Men of Rochdale* was probably the most widely seen Co-operative film. Budgeted at an impressive £15 000, it was undoubtedly the most expensive film produced by the Left in Britain at that time. A consummate history lesson, substantially based on the meticulous research of Co-operative historian and activist, G J Holyoake, the film was a companion to *Out of the Box* (1942; NCFC 100), the story of the emergence of Co-operation in Scotland, commissioned by the

SCWS in 1942. The SCWS supported an impressive scheme of film production and exhibition for member societies, and many titles were prepared that offered valuable educational benefit. Representative titles and subjects included: *How SCWS Cigarettes and Tobacco Are Made* (1938; NCFC 073); *March of Progress* (c.1938; NCFC 079); *Know Your Business* (1947; NCFC 111); *Pride and Progress* (1949; NCFC 124); *Productive Grocery Departments* (1959; NCFC 223). As we have seen, the society put into operation the Movement's first mobile film unit scheme in 1948, bringing the Co-operative message to even the remotest district.

The English CWS, following the establishment of its own film unit in 1940, also extended its provision and options. The unit's first film was a 16mm sound record of the 1940 Co-operative Congress held in Glasgow: "It contains a well-reasoned commentary admirably delivered, and, in addition to a number of interesting views inside Congress Hall, shows 'shots' of many leading personalities".[73] One important new area of activity was the production of films to aid in the training of Co-operative employees. The Joint Committee on Technical Education had made original proposals on the matter in January 1939, stressing that the Movement was falling behind competitors such as the Bacon Marketing Board. The difficulties posed by the war meant that progression in that area had to wait for a period. The first film was *Behind the Counter* (1941, re-released 1946; NCFC 093), which had the training of the counterman and of the future branch manager as its main object. The initiative was welcomed by the North Western General & Grocery Manager's Association: "as a useful aid to the training of employees, and gave the film unit the signal to go ahead and make other films on the same lines."[74]

Subsequent training films included: *Milk Salesmanship* (1947; NCFC 112); *Counter Courtesy* (SCWS, 1947; NCFC 110); *Your Silent Salesman* (SCWS, 1947; NCFC 114); *Meat for the Millions* (1958; NCFC 411); and *What's So Important About a Window Bill?* (1966; NCFC 296). Training films were established as part of the CWS Film Unit's production programme, alongside promotional films and general Co-operative subjects; soon, employees engaged in transport, grocery and foodstuffs, footwear, drapery and outfitting, pharmacy and staff management were benefitting from this new educational technique.

In concluding this examination of Co-operative education and culture, it would be remiss not to discuss a striking example of the breadth of Co-operative provision – Co-operative cinemas. In justifying the expenditure of Co-operative resources on such a venture, a Movement propagandist, W H Brown, advocated the organisation of the "amusements of our members. They come to the stores for their daily fare; why not supply their evening pleasures?".[75] In fact, in the early decades of the cinema, Co-op halls had proved a convenient site for displays of moving pictures, and, following the 1909 Cinematograph Act, numerous Co-operative societies sought a cinema licence for their hall. With the general growth of cinema as a leisure activity into the 1920s and 1930s, some societies developed those premises into impressive cinema auditoria: the Pioneer Cinema, Dewsbury; the Co-operative Cinema, Horbury; the Jubilee Cinema, Scunthorpe; the Co-op Cinema, Billington and Whalley; the Co-operative Picture Hall, Fylde; the Co-operative Cinema, Birtley; the Brookfield Cinema, Poynton; the Jubilee News Theatre, Blackpool; and so on.[76] The commercial industry responded aggressively to such developments; whereas the screening of Co-operative and progressive films non-theatrically had been adjudged the "Free

Show Menace", their opposition to the Movement's cinemas was articulated against the practice of distributing a dividend on ticket purchases, considered an "unfair practice". As we have seen, private interests continually arranged themselves against the efforts of ordinary working people to better their circumstances through mutual action. As should be expected, the commercial cinema industry acted no differently.

Into the early 1960s, the Co-operative Movement was maintaining a well-resourced approach to cinema and film. The Movement's products were promoted through a steady stream of publicity films: *Biscuit Time* (c.1960, NCFC 236); *Seal of Success* (1954, margarine; NCFC 159); *Father Takes the Cake*. Co-operative democracy and ideals were promoted through the centenary film of the CWS, *Symbol of Success* (1963; NCFC 259). The Movement was forced to respond to immense changes in society and the pattern of retailing in the 1960s. A reorganisation of the CWS Publicity Department swept away a central pillar of the Movement's film structure. That policy ensured the rapid disintegration of film work and, eventually, the awareness of the Co-op's remarkable film heritage. Films passed out of the Movement's possession (fortunately, some of them into approved archives!), or lay dormant in society basements or members' lofts. The establishment in 1992 of the National Co-operative Film Archive at the Co-operative College, Stanford Hall, near Loughborough, was a concerted effort to investigate the Movement's use of film and to assess and preserve its film heritage. Immediate and striking results were obtained which justified the mounting of the 1994 Festival of Films on Co-operation, part of the 150th celebrations of the Rochdale Equitable Pioneers Society. This catalogue demonstrates a second phase of the researches of the National Co-operative Film Archive, and provides an indication not only of the success of the project in locating Co-operative film material, but also, more importantly, of the scale and scope of the Movement's film activity. The *British Co-operative Movement Film Catalogue* represents nine decades of innovation and success, whereby a voluntary organisation comprising working people sought to use the film medium to bring about a better, fairer and more just society.

Notes

[1]   Johnston Birchall, *Co-op: the people's business* (Manchester; New York: Manchester University Press, 1994): 124.

[2]   Jayne Southern, "Co-operation in the North West of England, 1919-1939: Stronghold or Stagnation?", *North West Labour History* 19 (1994/95): 106.

[3]   For a discussion of the re-emphasis of Co-operative strength from the North-West to the South, see ibid.

[4]   For example, see A J Davies, *To Build A New Jerusalem: The British Labour Movement from the 1880s to the 1990s* (London: Michael Joseph, 1992). Particularly revealing is a diagram of the "British Labour Movement: Organisation and Parties", which can find space for marginal and momentary bodies such as the National Council of Labour Colleges, the Socialist League and the Left Book Club, whilst completely ignoring the central position and longevity of the Co-operative Movement.

[5]   Raphael Samuel and Gareth Stedman Jones, "The Labour Party and Social Democracy", in Raphael Samuel and Gareth Stedman Jones, *Culture, Ideology and Politics: Essays for Eric Hobsbawm* (London: Routledge & Kegan Paul, 1982): 327-328.

[6]   Quoted in Birchall: 113.

[7]   Stephen Yeo (ed), *New Views of Co-operation* (London; New York: Routledge, 1988): 207.

[8]   *The Economist* 20 May 1933: 1126, quoted in ibid.

[9]   Neil Killingback, "Limits to Mutuality: Economic and Political Attacks on Co-operation during the 1920s and 1930s", in Yeo (ed): 224.

[10]   The Co-operative practice of paying a dividend on purchases was a major bone of contention for private traders. Legislation was passed disallowing the payment of a dividend on Co-operative transport services, and strenuous efforts were made by the Milk Marketing Board to prevent Co-operative societies paying dividend to members on milk purchases. See F Hall and W P Watkins, *Co-operation: A Survey of the History, Principles, and Organisation of the Co-operative Movement in Great Britain and Ireland* (Manchester: Co-operative Union, 1937): 362. Similarly, commercial cinema-owners sought to eliminate the practice of paying dividend on ticket purchases at Co-operative cinemas. See Alan Burton, "The People's Cinemas: The Picture Houses of the Co-operative Movement", *North West Labour History* 19 (1994/95): 42.

[11]   Hall and Watkins: 361.

[12]   Ibid: 358.

[13]   Arnold Bonner, quoted in Birchall: 94.

[14]   Hall and Watkins: 329.

[15]   Peter Gurney, "Heads, Hands and the Co-operative Utopia: An Essay in Historiography", *North West Labour History* 19 (1994/95): 5.

[16]   Ibid: 15-16.

[17]   Hall and Watkins: 330-331.

[18]   Ibid: 357.

[19]   Ibid: 331.

[20]   Ibid.

[21]   For a discussion of the Movement's initial involvement in film, see Alan Burton, "The Emergence of an Alternative Film Culture: The British Consumer Co-operative Movement and Film before 1920" *Film History* 8 (December 1996): 446-456.

[22]   *The Co-operative News* 28 February 1913: 281.

[23]   *The Producer* December 1927: 3.

[24]   *The Co-operative News* 28 January 1928: 11.

[25]   Ibid: 23 November 1929: 3.

[26]   The film in question was *Kitchen Capers* (1937; NCFC 058).

[27]   *The Producer* August 1938: 204.

[28]   Ibid.

[29]   *Merry Mondays* has not yet been located.

[30]   *The Co-operative News* 23 October 1937: 15.

[31]   *The Producer* January 1937: 7. Sadly, none of the Movement's cartoons from the period has so far been located.

[32]   Although the two films were released separately, there is some evidence that they were conceived as a single project. For further thoughts on their interrelation, see their catalogue

entries.

[33] *The Wheatsheaf* January 1941: 3.

[34] *The Co-operative News* 19 August 1950: 1; *The Producer* September 1950: 20.

[35] *The Producer* June 1962: 8-9.

[36] *Co-operative Union Annual Congress Report 1936*: 100.

[37] For more details on the remarkable Horace Masterman and on Co-operative cinemas in general, see Burton (1994/95): 34-37.

[38] *The Co-operative News* 1 August 1914: 984.

[39] Denny would continue to pioneer local Co-operative filmmaking at the Leicester Co-operative Society, where he became publicity manager in 1936.

[40] For an overview of that work, see Jonathan Buchsbaum, "Left Political Filmmaking in the West: The Interwar Years", in Robert Sklar and Charles Musser (eds), *Resisting Images: Essays on Cinema and History* (Philadelphia: Temple University Press, 1990): 126-148.

[41] Ibid: 126.

[42] Studies of the British Labour Movement and film have concentrated on the interwar period (commencing with the "Third Phase", that of the Comintern's policy of "Class Against Class", through to the conclusion of the Popular Front). That is convenient when emphasis is placed on the more radical groups such as Kino and the Workers' Film and Photo League, but ignores progressive groups such as the Workers' Film Association (1938-46) and the National Film Association (1946-53) which had a considerable and crucial Co-op presence. See the bibliography in this volume.

[43] See Bert Hogenkamp, *Deadly Parallels: Film and the Left in Britain 1929-1939* (London: Lawrence and Wishart, 1986).

[44] "The Cinema. Should It be Used for Co-operative Purposes?. How to Reach the Masses", *The Co-operative News* 28 February 1914: 268. The views presented here are all the more remarkable given that they were articulated before the general development of a more sophisticated appreciation of propaganda and the mass media during the First World War. The article is reproduced in Appendix A.

[45] Ibid: 21 March 1914: 358. Emphasis added.

[46] For a discussion of the British Labour Movement and working-class leisure, see Stephen G Jones, *Workers At Play: A Social and Economic History of Leisure 1918-1939* (London: Routledge and Kegan Paul, 1986). It should be noted that considerable friction existed between groups on the Left, whose leadership were capable of showing equal hostility to each other as to their avowed enemy, the capitalist state. In practice, however, the ordinary member was often quite content to enjoy a concert sponsored by his/her trade union, a supper and dance put on by the Co-op, a sports club organised by the Communists, and to send their children to the Labour Party League of Youth.

[47] Hogenkamp: 36-37. For details on the granting of a cinema licence for the Tooting Co-op Hall, see *The Co-operative News* 28 November 1925: 6.

[48] M R Roberts, "Towards a Workers' Cinema in England", *Experimental Cinema* 4 (1932): 28.

[49] Quoted in Don Macpherson (ed), *Traditions of Independence: British Cinema in the Thirties* (London: British Film Institute, 1980): 130. Numerous contemporary articles are collected in this volume.

[50] T J Hollins, "The conservative party and film propaganda between the wars", *The English Historical Review* April 1981: 359-369.

51   For further discussion on these two advocates of a Labour cinema, see Alan Burton, *The People's Cinema: Film and the Co-operative Movement* (London: National Film Theatre, 1994): 52-73. Also for Reeves, see Hogenkamp: 176-191.

52   *The Co-operative News* 12 December 1931: 5.

53   Ibid: 3 September 1938: 7.

54   Joseph Reeves, "Films and Propaganda", *Co-operative Youth* February 1939: 72-74.

55   For a discussion of the Workers' Film Association, see Alan Burton, "Projecting the New Jerusalem: the Workers' Film Association, 1938-1946", in Pat Kirkham and David Thoms (eds), *War Culture: Social Change and Changing Experience in World War Two Britain* (London: Lawrence & Wishart, 1995): 73-84.

56   For the emergence of a progressive documentary form during the war, see Nicholas Pronay, "'The Land of Promise': The Projection of Peace Aims in Britain", in K R M Short (ed), *Film & Radio Propaganda in World War II* (London; Canberra: Croom Helm, 1983): 51-77.

57   *National Film Association Journal* September-October 1948: 13.

58   Frank H W Cox, "A National Co-operative Film Society", *The Millgate* 373 (October 1936): 40.

59   For a history of the Political Committee of the LCS, see Stan Newens, *Working Together: A Short History of the London Co-operative Society Political Committee* (London: CRS, 1988).

60   *The Co-operative News* 9 March 1940: 4.

61   Nigel Mace, "British Historical Epics in the Second World War", in Philip M Taylor (ed), *Britain and the Cinema in the Second World War* (London: Macmillan Press, 1988): 116.

62   Hall and Watkins: 329.

63   Charles Musser, "Toward A History of Screen Practice", *Quarterly Review of Film Studies* 9: 1 (winter 1984): 59-69.

64   Presentation given to "Towards Tomorrow" Co-operative History Workshop, July 1994.

65   *The Wheatsheaf* December 1898: 94.

66   *The Co-operative News* 11 December 1897: 1374.

67   Ibid: 25 October 1913: 1421. The lecture was at Congleton.

68   Sydney Box, "Britain's First Advertising Films Were Shown in 1899", *The Commercial Film* March 1936: 6. The films would have been approximately one minute long.

69   No CWS films from the pre-First World War period have been located.

70   F Churchward, "Movement's Screen Debut", *Co-operative Review* November 1938: 335-6.

71   *The Producer* November 1935: 335. An account of local Co-operative filmmaking in Long Eaton is reprinted in Appendix G.

72   Robert Murphy, *Realism and Tinsel: Cinema and society in Britain 1939-1948* (London: Routledge, 1989): 109-112.

73   *The Co-operative News* 10 August 1940: 5. I have been unable to view a silent print of the 1940 Glasgow Congress held at the SFA. The 1947 Brighton Congress film is so far unlocated. Brief scenes from the Brighton Congress film were included in *Co-operation* (1948).

74   Ibid: 15 June 1946: 6.

75   *The Co-operative Official* 1936: 139.

76   Burton (1994/95).

The British Co-operative Movement
Film Catalogue

NCFC 001
Wishaw Co-operative Society Gala Day
(1909)

b/w · 3m 6s · silent · Scotland · 16mm · SFA

■ A short two-shot film recording a parade of society members and children on their way to the station to begin their Co-op Gala Day out.

I   A long procession files past a static camera: a marching brass band; young girls, many with flags; a Highland pipe band; young boys; some with flags; the Wishaw Co-operative Society banner; some of the society's horse-drawn vehicles dressed with flags and bunting.
II   A group of children files in front of a shop window.

Remarks
The oldest film in this catalogue, its age betrayed by the complete reliance on horse-drawn transport in the parade. It was at about this time that the first motorised vehicles were being brought into service by retail societies, but none was evident at the small Wishaw Society in the Clyde Valley. The Gala Day parade was recorded on 26 June and would probably have been an annual event for the children of society members (adults are largely absent). The film contains an excellent sequence where the society banner is marched down the High Street, one of the best such images caught on film. It is probable that in section II the shop window which the children file past is the Co-op, although the camera angle does not allow for accurate identification. The Wishaw Co-operative Society was founded in 1889, and two decades later its membership had grown to 2334, with annual sales totalling £84 680 derived from four branch stores. A later film of 1939, *Wishaw Co-operative Society Outing*, is held at the Scottish Film Archive, but is currently unavailable for viewing.

NCFC 002
Wrexham Co-operative Society's Procession (1912)

b/w · 3m 30s · silent · Wales · 16mm · WFA
pr Glynn Picture Co

■ A film record of a pre-First World War Co-operative society parade.

I   A busy crowd proceeds down a shop-lined street, towards and past the camera. Near the head of the procession is a brass band, which is followed in orderly file by members and their children, who, wearing overcoats and wielding umbrellas, are braving an inclement July day. As some horse-drawn transport enters the field of vision, the film ends.

Remarks
The film comprises a single static shot. The participants move close to and by the camera, and many of the onlookers are clearly more interested in the moving picture technology than in the events on the street. It is noteworthy that the procession exhibits no visible sign of it being a Co-operative activity, and, in contrast to the filmed records of such activities from the interwar period, lacks flags, banners and placards promoting Co-operation and the local society. Without the title card, there is no evidence to indicate that it is a Co-operative event. The importance and value of the film are that it is one of the few surviving pre-First World War films, and one of only two known examples of Co-operation in Wales recorded on film. The Wrexham Co-operative Society had been founded in 1890, and was a small society, which by 1922 had only 2350 members. It is possible that the majority of the membership are evident here in the parade.

NCFC 003
The Evolution of Modern Bakery (1920)

b/w · 12m 56s · silent · 35mm · NFTVA
pr Gaumont

■ An information film about modern baking methods, centring on the modern machine bakery of the Royal Arsenal Co-operative Society (RACS).

I   Traditional baking methods: the moulding of dough by hand; bread baked in an old-fashioned oven; freshly baked loaves are drawn from an old-fashioned draw plate oven.
II   Modern baking methods: exterior of the RACS's modern bakery; sacks of flour are hoisted up to the flour store; flour is poured into a trough and conveyed to the blending machine; the giant dough-mixing machines, driven by belts; the dough is fed into troughs and left to rise; the diving machines cuts the dough into even portions of 2lbs which are then

shaped and led to the machine room; the dough passes through the proving chamber; wide-angle shot of the machine room; the dough, placed in tins, is fed through a giant oven by conveyor; the freshly baked bread is collected at the other end of the oven, conveyed to the cooling room and stacked.

III Exterior of bakery. Sign reads: "Royal Arsenal Co-operative Society Ltd. Bakeries: Brixton and Woolwich. Awards For Quality 1920. Bread Deliveries Throughout South and South East London."

Remarks

This commercially produced film of the RACS bakery at Brixton was probably the first film project undertaken at the society during the tenure (1918-38) of its innovative and influential Education Secretary, Joseph Reeves. In the 1930s, he became a leading figure in the workers' film Movement. Scenes of the Brixton bakery were reputedly included in a RACS "newsreel" dated 1921 and as yet unlocated. The Brixton bakery was originally planned in 1914 to help ease the pressure on the overworked RACS bakery at Woolwich. Problems in material supply caused by the war meant that the bakery was not officially opened until February 1917. The venture was an immediate success, and one newspaper, *The Daily Sketch*, not normally an advocate of Co-operation, had to concede that "by the use of labour-saving devices, the Royal Arsenal Co-operative Society are able to sell their bread at 10d. per quarter, while other bakers charge a shilling" (quoted in W T Davis and W B Neville [eds], *The History of the Royal Arsenal Co-operative Society Ltd* [Woolwich: Pioneer Press, 1921]: 136). The baking and retailing of bread was a major Co-operative success story in the interwar period, and nationally the Movement attained a leading place in the industry. 1800 sacks of flour were used each week at the Brixton bakery to produce 324 000 loaves for society members.

NCFC 004
[Model Bakery] (1921)

b/w · 17m 47s · silent · 35mm · NFTVA

■ An information film about the model bakery of the Burslem and District Industrial Co-operative Society.

(Introduction missing)

I A wide panning shot of the Burslem Society model bakery.

II Sacks of CWS flour are hoisted from a barge into the bakery's flour store.

III The mixing process – ½ ton in fifteen minutes; the dough is left to ripen; 40 loaves per minute are shaped in the moulding machine; the dough is weighed, divided and proved; the continuous travelling bread-oven, baking 2400 2lb loaves every hour; the freshly baked loaves are removed from their tins; the loaves are stacked in the cooling room; the bread is loaded into the society's delivery vans, each holding 800 2lb loaves.

IV The horse-drawn bread vans set off on their house-to-house deliveries.

V Motorised transport leaves the depot, bound for the society's 30 branch stores distributing 30 tons of foodstuffs daily.

VI Members are requested to invest their savings in the society. Graphic card: "Workers of the Society. Women appreciate the value of Co-operation. It means pure food and honest dealing, and the surpluses come back to them at quarter end."

VII Members of the society and the guilds parade out of the bakery with banners; four men (Directors/Officials?) are shot in portrait.

VIII Graphic card: "Join the stores and *save* by spending. The more you spend the more you *save*."

Remarks

The Burslem and District Industrial Co-operative Society had been formed in 1901, and traded in the Staffordshire area. This rather exceptional film, given the year of production, was thus the occasion of the society's 20th anniversary. No evidence of further filmmaking activities at Burslem has so far come to light, and it is possible that this early documentary experiment was an isolated occurrence. This medium-sized society had almost 24 000 members, and the model bakery was described as the largest and most up-to-date Co-operative bakery in the Midlands. The bakery had been opened on Easter Monday 1910, the event being made the occasion for a public demonstration. The buildings were designed by Mr F Horns of the architects' department of the CWS. It produced 150 000 2lb loaves each week. An interesting aspect of the film is the final sequence, where a parade of members is staged leaving the premises. Females overwhelmingly make up the large group, again indicating the central importance of women as customers/members and auxiliaries (Guildswomen) to a society.

NCFC 005
[Colchester Co-operative Society Jubilee Parade] (c.1921)

b/w · 4m 58s · silent · 16mm · EAFA

▪ A film record of a Co-operative society parade.

I   A procession of horse-drawn vehicles, and a few motor vehicles and bicycles, moves through streets lined with crowds. Several vehicles are decked with Co-operative slogans or are promoting Co-operative trade – for example, Co-operative coal.
II   The procession enters a parkland area and the dressed vehicles drive towards and pass the camera, cheered by the onlookers. The long take allows for the impressive scale of the procession to become apparent.
III A closer side-view of the procession. Vehicles promoting: CWS Devonia Serges; CWS soaps; Colchester Co-op hardware department; CWS down quilts; various tableaux; CWS Solvo cleaner; delivery boys on their bikes; *The Millgate*, monthly Co-operative journal.
IV Final brief shot, possibly of a Co-op store.

Remarks
The film poses an intriguing puzzle for the Co-operative historian. Judging by the grandness of the occasion, the society was celebrating a jubilee. The society was founded in 1861 and, according to the society history, celebrated its 50th (1911) and 75th (1936) anniversaries. From the visual evidence in the film (dress, vehicles, and so on), the procession appears to have been staged in the immediate post-First World War period. It is possible that the society celebrated its Diamond Jubilee in 1921, of which the film provides a record. At present, this assessment remains unsubstantiated.

NCFC 006
[RACS Trading and Cultural Activities] (1922)

b/w · 11m 47s · silent · 35mm · NFTVA

pr Gaumont

▪ A film detailing some of the trading and cultural activities of the Royal Arsenal Co-operative Society.

I   Graphic card: "Works Department. Carpenters' and Joiners' Shop."
II   Two views of the busy shop floor.
III Graphic card: "Wheelwrights and van builders".
IV A slow panning shot of the craftsmen at their various tasks.
V   Graphic card: "Bostall Estate. Upwards of 1,000 houses have been erected by the Society on its own estate. A view of 'Howarth' Road and specimen house."
VI A long-shot looking down Howarth Road; a front view of a substantial Edwardian house.
VII Graphic card: "TAILORING WORKSHOPS. Clothing made under ideal trade conditions."
VIII Two views of the busy shopfloor of female machinists and male operatives ironing garments.
IX Graphic card: "Wear RACS Garments Winter and Summer. Made in your very own workrooms by skilled Tailors."
X   Graphic card: "SPORTS GROUND. Bostall Estate. Cricket Match. RACS Employees v. London Society."
XI Extreme long-shot of the game, broken by jump-cuts.
XII Graphic card: "Everything for SPORTS WEAR. In the Stores' Outfitting Depts."
XIII Graphic card: "Motor Garage and Engineers' Shop. General view."
XIV Exterior of garage. A charabanc leaves and enters the premises; panning shot of the society's motor fleet.
XV Graphic card: "Engineers employed on maintenance work".
XVI A general view of the workshop with engineers busy at their benches.
XVII Graphic card: "The Society's Chars-a-banc. Trips arranged to any part of the country."
XVIII Fully-loaded charabancs drive through a London street.
XIX Graphic card: "SEE THE 37/6 OVERCOATS in our windows".
XX Graphic card: "Bostall Estate Woods. 'The Kiddies Paradise'. RACS Works Department Employees' Day."

Remarks
The RACS first purchased a portable film projector early in 1920, and began screening general educational subjects,

CWS films and humorous shorts. In January 1921, a film depicting the operations of the society was announced, and was available for screening to member groups by the autumn. That film included scenes of the Brixton bakery; the society farm; Shornells, the society education centre; and an employees' football match. Unfortunately, the film has not been located. This film is without doubt a subsequent project expanding on the range of subjects presented in the first film.

The Rochdale Pioneers had stated, as part of their Commonwealth dream, the desirability of erecting houses to improve the domestic and social conditions of the members. In the spirit of that ideal, the RACS acquired the Bostall Estate in January 1899, and building work commenced in the following May. Certain roads were named in commemoration of Co-operative pioneers and landmarks: "Rochdale", "Owenite", "McLeod", "Greening", "Shieldhall", "Howarth", and so on. The adjacent 26 acres of the Bostall Wood were turned over to recreational and leisure activities. The period before the First World War had witnessed many Co-operative societies acquiring motor traction vehicles. In 1911, the RACS had acquired a Foden steam motor for warehouse work and for the delivery of goods to branches. The investment in traction quickly grew, and a garage was provided in Kingsman Street. The society became a pioneer in the excursion business amongst Co-operative societies.

NCFC 007
Children's Gala 1923 (1923)

b/w · 8m 44s · silent · Scotland · 16mm · SFA

■ Events at a children's gala day sponsored by the Cowdenbeath Co-operative Society.

I   Girls parade down a crowd-lined street, waving a variety of British nation flags.
II   A Scottish Highland band marches past the camera.
III   Young boys parade with their flags and banners.
IV   A small group of children in fancy dress forms part of the procession.
V   A marching brass band; further shots of the parade; a fleet of trams makes up the rear of the procession; a panning shot of a section of the crowd.

VI   A large group of children seated on a lawn; children, bandsmen and adults resting on the grass; the fancy dress participants; portrait shots of groups of youngsters and adults; a portrait shot of the committee (?); various shots of fun and relaxation around the park.
VII   Boys' races; two girls in a sprint race; boys' race; girls' race.
VIII   A section of the large crowd.

Remarks
A single item with a Co-operative subject included within a longer newsreel, *Years Ago in Cowdenbeath* (1920-24). Most of the shots are staged for the camera, which tends to lead to a certain lifeless quality for the film as a whole. The absence of explanatory titles also hinders in discerning characters and the significance of events. The Cowdenbeath Co-operative Society had been founded in 1875, and remained a small society, operating only three branch stores by the end of the 1920s.

NCFC 008
The "Kibbo Kift" (1923)

b/w · 53s · silent · 35mm · NFTVA
pr Topical Budget

■ A short newsreel item on the children's organisation, the "Kibbo Kift".

I   Graphic card: "Great Missenden. The 'Kibbo Kift'. Meeting of new Kindred who aim at a race of intellectual barbarians."
II   Graphic card: "Mr H G Wells is a member of this camping fraternity, who combine the ideals of scientists and Red Indians".
III   A male and a female camper prepare a camp meal; a group of children, gathered together and seated in front of their tents.
IV   Graphic card: "Tribe meets Tribe".
V   Two groups greet with a ceremonial salute.
VI   Graphic card: "Council".
VII   Campers are gathered in a large circle; a ceremony is performed in the centre; a herald reads out a proclamation.
VIII   Graphic card: "Handicrafts".
IX   A group of boys carving sticks of wood.
X   Graphic card: "Kibboettes".
XI   Four girls perform a classical dance enjoyed by a large crowd.

Remarks

The Kibbo Kift Kindred was formed in 1920 by John Hargrave as a breakaway group from the Boy Scouts (Hargrave had held the position of Scout Headquarters Commissioner for Woodcraft). The term "Kibbo Kift" was archaic English meaning "proof of great strength", and the disciplined organisation stressed Woodcraft activities with an emphasis on pageantry and ritual, as shown in the film and notably in the costumes. The organisation had great appeal for radical educationalists, and attracted sponsors such as H G Wells and Julian Huxley. The RACS began to sponsor "tribes" early in 1921. Within a few years, the Co-operators became uneasy with the organisation's elitism and the deepening interest in mysticism. At the annual camp – "Althing" – held in Great Missenden in 1924, some of the RACS tribes themselves broke away from the new organisation, led by the 18-year-old Leslie Paul, and formed the Woodcraft Folk, which followed more closely the ideals of democracy and fellowship. On two occasions in this film, Joseph Reeves, Education Secretary of the RACS, and strong promoter of the Kibbo Kift Movement at that time, can be seen participating in the activities. The Topical Budget newsreel functioned between 1911 and 1931, and was an entirely British operation. It is noteworthy, if unsurprising, that the news item should take a patronising attitude towards this unconventional organisation (note, in particular, section X).

NCFC 009
Kirkham, November 1926 (1926)

b/w · 7m 32s · silent · 16mm · NWFA
pr Co-operative Picture House, Kirkham

■ A film record of the official unveiling of the Kirkham War Memorial.

I	Title card: "Unveiling of the Kirkham War Memorial on Sunday, November 7th, 1926, by Lt. General Sir Richard H K Butler KCB KCMG".
II	A long procession through the town to the Garden of Remembrance. Representatives of various civilian and military services are clearly visible.
III	The arrival of the Mayor and officials, followed by the arrival of Lieutenant-General Sir Richard Butler, accompanied by the Reverend Cresswell Strange, Chairman of the Memorial Committee. The General inspects a line of Great War veterans

(?).

IV	The Memorial is unveiled and the last post is sounded.
V	Councillor Wood lays a tribute on behalf of the Council.
VI	Shots of the spectators gathered around the Gardens.
VII	The local people inspect the Memorial.
VIII	Shot of the nearby Wesham Memorial.

Remarks

The connection of this film to the Co-operative Movement is in its production – it was made as a local record of an important civic event by the Co-operative Picture House, Kirkham, for screening to local audiences. Several local Co-operative societies operated a cinema for the benefit of members and the local community. The greatest concentration of those cinemas was to be found in the North and North-West. The Co-operative Picture House was owned and managed by the Fylde Industrial Co-operative Society, and seated 475 people. It had formerly been the Co-operative Hall, and was converted into a cinema during the silent period. It closed in 1962 – like many cinemas, a casualty of changing leisure demands. There is no evidence that the Co-operative Picture House commissioned films of local Co-operative activity, although that remains a distinct possibility.

NCFC 010
Lochgelly Equitable Co-operative Society's Shopping Week (1927)

b/w · 6m 27s · silent · Scotland · 16mm · SFA

■ A film record of a local society promotional campaign.

I	Central premises (exterior), built 1903; store front with banner proclaiming the "Shopping Week".
II	Group portrait of the Management Committee, including the General Manager, John Mitchell, the Branch Manager and Heads of Department.
III	"Views of Exhibits": society transport is dressed for a parade. The various trading departments are represented with their own display.
IV	Competitors in the fancy dress parade. The participants are dressed as popular Co-operative products – Lutona cocoa, CWS tea, CWS jam, Adana cigarettes, Unitas oats, etc.
V	The Grand Parade marching up the

High Street: a brass band, dressed vehicles, Highland pipe band, fancy dress contestants; further shots of the parade off the main shopping district.
VI Ex-Bailie Agnew addressing the crowd in Lochgelly Public Park.

Remarks
This is an excellent early film record of a society's promotional campaign, slightly marred by overexposed photography in some scenes. The "Shopping Week" at Lochgelly ran from 4-9 July 1927, thus incorporating the International Co-operative Day celebrations which were held on the first Sunday of each July. The first "Shopping Weeks" had been organised by local Chambers of Commerce to facilitate trade in a town. In many instances, local traders objected to the participation of the Co-operative society, and the natural response of a local society was to organise its own "Shopping Week". Many of the first Co-op "Shopping Weeks" were mounted during the period of the second International Co-op Day, 1924. It is interesting to note the relatively high incidence of horse-drawn transport even by that date. Lochgelly, a mining centre near Dunfermline, founded its Co-operative society in 1865, and by 1927 had attained a membership of 5506 responsible for annual sales worth £303 3/4. The civic office of Bailie is somewhat akin to that of sheriff in English local government.

NCFC 011
How Bluebell Margarine Is Made (c.1927)

b/w · 10m 11s · silent · Scotland · 16mm · SFA

■ Part of the manufacturing processes involved in the production of SCWS Bluebell margarine.

I Graphic card: "Over 100 tons of this delightful margarine are sent out every week to the homes of the co-operators of Scotland".
II The nearby Bladnoch River.
III General views of the creamery; stoking the boilers; the generating machinery and operatives.
IV Graphic card: "Wigtownshire is the chief dairying country in Scotland. We draw our milk supply from the finest herds."
V Dairy cattle herds; cows entering the milking sheds where they are milked by hand.

VI A lorry loaded with full churns on its way to the creamery; numerous lorries arriving at the creamery; the milk is weighed and samples sent to the laboratory; the pasteurisation process; cooling the milk; the milk ripening room, where the milk is processed in a series of tanks.
VII Barrels of fat are unloaded from a railway wagon and into the creamery; the fat storeroom; fat is fed into the melting tanks; empty barrels returning to the siding.

Remarks
A film similar in approach and structure to the three other surviving industrial films produced for the SCWS at the time. Bluebell was one brand name among several adopted by the SCWS for their margarines, and remained in use at least until the 1960s. The film was probably two reels in length (c.20 minutes), and only the first reel has so far been located, thus making the film considerably more detailed than its companion, *How Guild Margarine Is Made* (c.1928; NCFC 017).

NCFC 012
Bubbles (1928)

b/w · 10m 8s · silent · 16mm · NWFA
pr Publicity Films Ltd

■ A promotional film for CWS soap products.

I A mother plays with her child by blowing bubbles. The child is left to play whilst her mother visits the Co-op.
II "The birthplace of billions of bubbles – the CWS soap works at Irlam, Manchester": exterior view; barrels of fat are melted using steam; the pan-room where the fats are processed; the soap is cooled and forms into large slabs; the slabs are cut into bars and stacked; the bars are cut into individual cakes, stamped and wrapped – CWS Minerva soap.
III The making of flake soap: the soap is shredded and its moisture extracted; packaging the soap flakes and loading into cartons.
IV Soap is passed through a roller mill where perfumes and colours are added for the making of toilet soaps; the tablets are cut and stamped; the making of soap boxes; packing for despatch to Co-operative stores; the boxes are loaded onto transport.

V   A Co-operative store: exterior; interior scene – the mother is served by a counter assistant, who loads her basket.

VI   Back at home, the child is still playing at making bubbles – "Whether for bubbles, toilet or tub, there is a CWS soap for every purpose!": mother in the bathroom; father shaving; mother washing clothes and hanging them out.

VII   A basket of CWS soap products: "Ask at your Co-operative Store for CWS soaps – the best obtainable. Made in your own factories by fellow Co-operators."

Remarks

The CWS Irlam soap works were opened in October 1894 (the same year as the Manchester Ship Canal), replacing an older factory at Durham. Other works soon followed at Silvertown, London, in 1908, and Dunston-on-Tyne in 1909. The two newer factories were timed to make an assault on the Soap Trust headed by Sir William Lever, which was temporarily on the retreat. In 1910, Lever commenced a total of 38 legal actions against 22 retail societies for cutting off the sale of Trust brands and switching over to CWS productions. Lever was resoundingly beaten at the Court of Appeal and mutual trade had won an important victory. The final intertitle of the film hints, perhaps, at the sweet victory over monopoly capitalism in 1912. The film, released in August 1928, was the second in a series commissioned by the CWS from Publicity Films for screening in local cinemas (some of the scenes feature in the inaugural film, *The Magic Basket* [1928; NCFC 015]). Particularly noticeable is the high proportion of female operatives, evidence of the increase in female employment between the wars.
See also: xx

NCFC 013
The Cup That Cheers (1928)

b/w · 5m 52s · silent · 16mm · NWFA
pr Publicity Films Ltd

▪ A promotional film for CWS tea.

I   A brief exposition on the history of tea, both as a refreshing drink and as a medicine: a Chinese man of an earlier century enjoys a reviving cup; in Elizabethan England, an elderly couple makes the mistake of eating the leaves; in Victorian times, tea had assumed its central position within British society as a social pastime.

II   Chests of tea are unloaded at the busy Port of London.

III   The Leman Street tea warehouse of the English and Scottish Joint CWS (exterior): tea-tasting; the tea store; the sifting and curing process; the blending process; mechanical packing; female operatives load packets of tea into cartons.

IV   "The English and Scottish Joint CWS is filling the Nation's teapot" – a housewife pours tea into a giant teapot.

V   Lorries loaded with tea set out from the factory to Co-operative stores.

VI   Co-operative store (exterior). Inside the store, a housewife purchases tea, which is placed in her basket by the counter assistant.

VII   At home, the housewife explains to her friend the value of Co-op tea and the Co-operative dividend, over a cup of Co-op tea.

VIII   Graphic card: "Secure your share of the Dividend. At Your Co-operative Store the Finest Tea Procurable."

Remarks

The third film produced by Publicity Films and sponsored by the CWS as part of a concerted campaign of cinema publicity. Each film was booked in up to 1000 cinemas, and the playing dates were listed each week in *The Co-operative News*, enabling Co-operators to assess this innovative marketing campaign. Tea, of course, was one of the Movement's most celebrated products, and the phrase "Filling the Nation's Teapot" one of its most well-known slogans. The image of the housewife filling a giant pot with tea from atop a set of stepladders was used across various publicity literature, and is spectacularly captured in the film. In 1928, the annual tea sales of the English and Scottish CWS amounted to 77 million lbs, with 1.25 million lbs of tea being despatched from the Leman Street warehouse each week. The Co-operative Movement was clearly of crucial importance in the provision of the "nation's favourite beverage".
See also: NCFC 028

NCFC 014
Ipswich Co-operative Fete, Saturday July 7th, 1928 (1928)

b/w · 55s · silent · 16mm · EAFA

■ A film record of a Co-op gala.

I   The crowd assembles. A marshal attempts to bring order.
II   A young girl presents a bouquet of flowers to an unidentified woman.
III   Youngsters are loaded onto a vehicle decked in the Union Jack and the Japanese flag (!).
IV   A procession of vehicles through a crowded street: motor cycles lead; motor cycles and side-cars; motor cars decked in flags and bunting.

Remarks
A short, crude film consisting of only four shots. However, it does provide a brief record of that important day in the Co-operative calendar, International Co-operative Day – a day for Co-operative propaganda and celebration, aimed at providing a point of rally which would give an identity to Movements scattered around the world. The first Saturday in July was chosen, corresponding in spirit and distinction to the "May Day" of Socialism. The possibility of good weather was an important consideration for European Co-operators wishing to organise outside events. The first Co-op Day was celebrated in 1923. It provided a popular event enjoyed by Co-operators, and was captured for posterity on film on a number of occasions at various societies. The practice of dressing vehicles for procession, often the distributive transport of the society, was widespread, and the activity was considered to be beneficial propaganda for the local Co-op, as well as for the Movement. The Ipswich Industrial Co-operative Society had been founded in 1868, and operated 21 branch stores by 1928, for the benefit of nearly 26 000 members.

NCFC 015
The Magic Basket (1928)

b/w · 6m 42s · silent · 16mm · NWFA
pr Publicity Films Ltd

■ A promotional film for various CWS brand products.

I   An intertitle points out that the housewife's shopping basket is supporting the whole of productive industry and labour.
II   A montage of wheels, cogs and pulleys – modern industry.
III   Exterior of CWS preserves works; operatives load a trolley in the storeroom; an operative checks dials during the cooking process; jars are labelled and packed – CWS strawberry jam.
IV   Exterior of CWS biscuit factory; cream crackers pass on a conveyor; trays of freshly baked crackers are unloaded into boxes; the cream crackers are packaged by hand – Crumpsall cream crackers; tins of cream crackers pass on a conveyor and are stacked.
V   The Irlam soap works: exterior; brief scenes of production processes inside the factory; CWS Minerva soap is packaged.
VI   A Co-operative society store: exterior; a close-up of a shopping basket full of CWS brand products; a busy store interior – a counter assistant loads a shopper's basket. Both agree that the "divi" is very "handy".
VII At the society's offices, a housewife collects her dividend. She intends to treat herself to a new frock to celebrate her wedding anniversary.
VIII At home, she unloads her basket, prepares tea, and tries on her new frock. She explains to her husband that the purchase was possible with the Co-op dividend; besides, she also has a present for him, a new scarf.
IX   Graphic card: "Join The Co-operative Society and fill your shopping basket with CWS products made in your own factories. They are the best of their kind and profits are returned to YOU."

Remarks
An impressive scheme of cinema publicity was begun by the CWS in 1928. A series of promotional films was commissioned from a leading commercial producer, Publicity Films, and bookings secured in 1000 cinemas nationally. *The Magic Basket* was the first in the series, released on 13 February 1928. The film introduced a style that would serve as the basis of the series for the next five years, namely, brief dramatic sequences framing the obligatory documentary sequences of CWS production. It was hoped that "non-co-operators who see the film, if they are wise people, will follow the example of 'Mrs Everett' – they will become loyal purchasing members, of a co-operative society, and either save the dividend or put it to the same good use" (*The Co-operative News* 28 January 1928).
See also: xx, xxx, NCFC 012, NCFC 017

NCFC 016
[SCWS Soap Manufacture] (1928)

b/w · 22m 14s · silent · Scotland · 16mm ·
SFA

▪ An information film detailing the industrial
processes involved in the manufacture of
soap by the SCWS.

I   Exterior view of the SCWS soap works
        at Grangemouth.
II   The storage yard for solid fats. The
        barrels are lifted by crane into
        position.
III   Soap manufacture: the large boiling
        pans; adding salt to separate soap
        from glycerine; the glycerine lye is run
        off; adding the perfumes and
        fragrances to the soap; the soap is run
        into frames for cooling – an impressive
        aerial tracking shot travels over the
        frames; cutting the blocks of soap; the
        bars are stamped and wrapped by
        female operatives; cartons are
        conveyed to the warehouse on the
        "gravity runway".
IV   The manufacture of toilet soap: bars of
        soap are chipped and shredded;
        "French milling" – the mixing of
        perfumes with the soap; cutting soap
        into tablets; the hand-stamping of the
        soap bars – "Palm and Olive Oil
        Soap"; the tablets are trimmed by
        hand; the bars are wrapped and
        sealed.
V   The making of soap flakes: the
        shredded soap is processed into
        diamond-shaped flakes; the flakes are
        boxed by hand and sealed.
VI   Soap powder is boxed and sealed by
        machine; boxes of "Dinna-Fret" are
        packed into cartons; soap powders
        and polishing powders are packed
        into drums.
VII   Candle-making: moulding the wax into
        lengths; cutting and packing the
        cakes.
VIII A lorry is loaded with crates, and
        leaves the factory; a goods wagon is
        loaded with crates – "A truck load of
        soap for Scottish Co-operators"; a train
        pulls out from the factory along the
        siding.
IX   Product-testing in the laboratory.
X   A party of delegates and buyers
·   inspects the goods yard.
XI   The end of the day's work: the
        employees leave the factory.

Remarks
The history of Co-operative soap-making is
a revealing one, since it was a trading
activity where the conflict between
Co-operation and capitalism was particularly
acute. Both the CWS and SCWS operated
their soap works in the face of aggressive
tactics from private interests and trusts. In
the case of the SCWS, they were led into
the manufacture of soap because a private
supplier not only dictated for what price it
could be sold, but also laid down the
ultimatum that no dividend could be paid on
soap purchases. With the necessary
support of retail societies, trade with the firm
ceased, and supplies were temporarily
obtained from the English CWS, which had
opened a factory in 1891. The Grangemouth
soap works of the SCWS were opened in
1897 for the supply of retail societies in
Scotland. That was a fortunate occurrence,
since it ensured that the Movement was in a
position to resist the demands of the
powerful Soap Trust, established in 1906.
As the historian of the SCWS concluded,
writing barely a decade after the events, "the
people outside the Co-operative ranks are
virtually in the hands of a Soap Trust. The
Grangemouth works, therefore, constitute
one of the principal theatres of the war
between Co-operation and capitalism" (J A
Flanagan, *Wholesale Co-operation in
Scotland* [Glasgow: SCWS, 1920]). The
manufacture of candles began in 1927.
    The film offers a detailed record of the
industrial activities undertaken at
Grangemouth; interestingly, the intertitles
make a specific female address, suggesting
that it was aimed at consumers
(conventionally identified as women by the
Movement), rather than at the predominantly
male membership who managed the retail
societies. I have so far been unable to
determine the exhibition arrangements for
the early SCWS industrial films, but this
internal evidence would suggest a general
audience – people who were likely to shop
at the Co-op.

NCFC 017
How Guild Margarine Is Made (c.1928)

b/w · 6m 51s · silent · Scotland · 16mm ·
SFA

▪ An information film about SCWS Guild
margarine.

I   Wigtownshire, the finest dairy county
        in Scotland. A herd of cattle passes
        into the milking sheds; they are milked
        by hand.
II   Lorries of milk churns arrive at the

creamery; an aerial view of the SCWS creamery; samples of the milk are examined in the laboratory; the pasteurisation process; the milk-ripening room; hogsheads of fats are emptied and broken up, ready for mixing with the milk in the emulsifier; the cooling of the margarine and collection into wagons; laboratory testing of the margarine; the kneading of the margarine in huge churns; the kneading tables; the wrapping of Guild margarine into ½lb packets; packing into cartons for despatch.

III   A packet of SCWS Guild margarine: "Take A Packet Home With You NOW".

Remarks
One of four surviving films from the period detailing SCWS industrial activities – [Shieldhall Part Two] (c.1930), preserved at the SFA, is not available as a viewing print and therefore is not included in the catalogue). It is instructive to compare those films with a similar series commissioned by the English CWS, commencing with The Magic Basket (NCFC 015) in 1928. The Scottish films are narrower and more direct in approach, dealing exclusively with the manufacturing processes involved, whereas the more sophisticated English productions include narrative sequences and a more overt ideological message, often spelling out the distinct ownership structure of the Movement and the benefits of the dividend. The Scottish films are content with simple product promotion. It must be remembered that the CWS screened its films in cinemas to general audiences where it could be expected that knowledge about the Movement was not extensive. I have uncovered no evidence that the Scottish films were exhibited in such a manner, and were more likely screened at members' meetings where audience awareness would have been deeper. The Bladnoch creamery and margarine factory in Wigtownshire was established in 1899.
See also: NCFC 011

NCFC 018
A Matter of Form (1929)

b/w · 11m 15s · silent · 16mm · NWFA
pr Publicity Films Ltd

▪ A film promoting CWS Desbeau corsets.

I   The historical development of the corset: in the time of ancient Greece;

in medieval times, the corsetière was an armourer; at the Elizabethan court; the rigorous corsets of the Victorian age.

II   A modern fashion designer at work – blending the skills of artist and scientist.

III   The CWS Desborough corset factory: workers enter the factory; the great shop-floor; various scenes around the factory; testing of the cloth for tensile strength; marking out a pattern; cutting the material with a hand knife; cutting with the guillotine; cutting and winding the strapping; printing the fronts; stitching and inserting the busks; stitching with the four-needle machine; boning; fitting and binding; trimming; making-up and edging the suspender; flossing or fixing the steel ends; eyeletting; attaching the hooks and eyes; pressing; examining and packing; a boxed CWS Desbeau corset.

IV   Various models of Desbeau corsets on display in a Co-op store.

V   Graphic card: "Ask at your Co-operative Store for Desbeau Corsets – the best obtainable and secure YOUR share in the PROFITS. CWS."

Remarks
The fourth in the series of promotional films produced by Publicity Films for the CWS and released into cinemas for general exhibition. That policy was judged a success, a Co-operative trade journal concluding that "[t]he intriguing interest of the Desbeau pictures, with the dramatic featuring of old-time style, has provided a great attraction" (The Producer April 1930). Every effort was taken to gain the maximum trade advantage from the screenings in the 30 to 40 picture houses each week. Co-operative drapery managers were advised in advance of local screenings and prompted to arrange for adequate stocks of Desbeau corsets in anticipation of the demand. In addition, it was recommended that they make special window-displays of Desbeau corsets, and display posters announcing the film in their shops. CWS corset-making began in 1898 in Manchester, re-establishing itself in Northamptonshire in 1905, and quickly expanding due to the generosity of the Desborough Co-operative Society, which made land available. At the time of the film's production, it was claimed that there were a remarkable 400 models of Desbeau corset. By the late-1920s, corset manufacturers were beginning to become

concerned with the downturn in their trade, and to speculate about a "corset revival". It was becoming evident that the "modern woman" was demanding a freedom of Movement beyond that allowed by foundation garments.
See also: NCFC 049

NCFC 019
Seeing Is Believing (1929)

b/w · 11m · silent · 35mm · NFTVA
pr Max-Willmaur Film Service

■ An informational film about the Vauxhall Road dairy operated by the Birmingham Co-operative Society (BCS), and promoting the nutritional value of fresh, clean milk.

I   A doctor checks the health of a young child; the doctor recommends fresh milk for the child, but the parents remain sceptical.

II   Advice from "The Man Who Knows": at the society's farm; the parents witness the clean and hygienic conditions of milking; churns are loaded onto a lorry, which then sets off; lorries arrive at the Vauxhall Road dairy; empty churns are cleaned and sterilised.

III The mother inspects the dairy: the milk-cleaning machines; the pasteurising tanks; the temperature-indicator board; floats return the empties to the dairy; crates are conveyed to the bottle-washing machines; clean empties en route for filling – mother closely inspects the process; filling, measuring and capping 4000 bottles per hour; the bottles are loaded into crates – mother inspects a full bottle; the laboratory; the heating boiler; the giant water cooler; the reception room for visitors – mother enjoys a refreshing glass of milk; mother bids farewell to the plant manager.

IV Mother confirms to her husband the healthiness of pasteurised milk – "BCS milk is the best"; a horse-drawn milk float; young Tony thrives on fresh pasteurised milk – "The Richest, Cleanest and Purest Milk Obtainable".

V   BCS milk floats setting out on their morning deliveries – "Are they calling at your home?".

VI Graphic card: "Place your orders for regular supplies with BCS Dairy Ltd, Vauxhall Road".

VII Close-shot of a bottle of milk.

Remarks
BCS began its dairy operations in a converted grocery warehouse in 1920. From this inauspicious start, second-hand plant was installed, and the milk was delivered in second-hand floats. The business rapidly expanded and the Vauxhall Road site was quickly developed with new buildings and machinery. Throughout the whole Movement, this period was one of tremendous expansion in the dairy trade, whereby the Co-op became the nation's major provider of milk. By the date of this film, the BCS dairy was processing 100 000 gallons of milk per week. At a time when there was considerable distrust of retail milk supplies for health reasons, the purpose of the film becomes evident.
See also: NCFC 210

NCFC 020
The Bright Side of Things (1930)

b/w · 18m 28s · silent · 16mm · NWFA
pr Publicity Films Ltd

■ A film promoting CWS Pelaw polishes.

I   A child at play in a suburban garden. Her mother, Mrs Bright, tends to some flowers. The mother explains that she must leave to do some shopping.

II   Next door, the neighbour struggles over her polishing chores. She is fed up!

III The little girl has fallen over and grazed her knee. The neighbour takes the child into the child's home to dress the wound. She is astounded by the cleanliness and brightness of the kitchen.

IV The mother returns, and the neighbour enquiries of her: "How do you keep everything so bright?". She replies that it is essential to use the right polishes – hers come from her own factory at Pelaw!

V   The CWS Pelaw polish factory (exterior): scenes on the shop-floor; the filling of cans of Grato, CWS grate polish; the packing department; cans of shoe polish are filled and their lids fixed; packing of cartons for despatch; lids are placed on cans of floor polish; the labelling and boxing of CWS furniture polish.

VI The mother explains that other essential household items are produced at the Pelaw factory: the sacking of wholemeal; the canning of baking powder; the boxing of Kako cake-mix; the wrapping of "Snow Buns"; the research laboratory; bottling and packaging cough syrup; packaging cod-liver oil; labelling glycerine; a transport fleet leaves the factory.

VII Back home, the mother shows her neighbour a shelf full of CWS Pelaw products.

VIII The special shilling sample box of CWS Pelaw polishes.

IX Graphic card: "Always buy PELAW PRODUCTS for every purpose at your Co-operative Store and secure your share of the Dividend. CWS."

Remarks

The seventh addition to the series of films produced by Publicity Films for the CWS, and released into cinemas. Pelaw on Tyneside was something of a manufacturing centre for the CWS, modelled on the SCWS's productive group at Shieldhall, Glasgow. A cabinet factory, printing works, quilt factory, leather goods factory and clothing factory were all sited there, in addition to the well-known dry-salt-works. Work at the drugs factory commenced in 1902. One great change in consumer demand met by the factory, and clearly evident in this film, was the desire for articles in sizeable containers, hygienic, handy and attractive in themselves. Product packaging and brand labelling are more evident in this film than in any of its contemporaries, which spend more time demystifying industrial processes. Like all the films in the series, the characters exhibit a middle-class world, and the home occupied by this family existed only in the dreams of most of the Co-op's customers. *See also:* xx

---

NCFC 021
Her Dress Allowance (1930)

b/w · 6m 8s · silent · 16mm · NWFA
pr Publicity Films Ltd

▪ A film promoting CWS hosiery.

I A young married couple is arguing. She demands a larger dress allowance; he insists that he cannot afford it. An invitation to visit her friend, May, is delivered, and the young housewife decides to see her that minute.

II May has just unwrapped a new dress, and her friend is envious. Proudly showing off her wardrobe and fine bed linen, May decides to pass on her "secret".

III It is twelve months later. The husband is astonished by all the new linens and fabrics around the house. His wife tells him her "secret" – she has joined the local Co-operative society.

IV The CWS hosiery factory, Huthwaite, Nottinghamshire: exterior view; the giant mechanised looms; various scenes of the manufacturing processes; the great shop-floor.

V The wife explains the ownership structure of the Co-operative Movement and the benefit of being a member.
(End missing)

Remarks

The eleventh film in the series of promotional shorts commissioned by CWS from Publicity Films, and the first produced in both sound and silent versions. The film was released into 750 talkie cinemas and 250 silent ones. (None of the sound versions in the series has yet been located.) Like its counterparts, the film promotes the ideal of acquisitiveness in its examination of CWS linen and fashions, and embraces at its narrative centre a profoundly middle-class set of characters. Astonishingly, in this film the friend who has discovered the secret of Co-operation has a maid – something not typical of a Co-op society member! The CWS hosiery factory, at Huthwaite, Nottinghamshire, was founded in 1908, and employed approximately 960 people by 1930. Further impressive expansions were achieved later that decade. *See also:* xx

---

NCFC 022
The King and the Cakes (1930)

b/w · 11m 55s · silent · 16mm · NWFA
pr Publicity Films Ltd

▪ A promotional film for CWS flour.

I King Alfred is asked to mind the cakes which his wife has placed by the fire to bake. With other things on his mind, he lets the cakes burn, and is scalded by his wife when she returns.

II CWS flour mill (exterior): the raw wheat is fed by conveyors to giant washing-machines; the drying process; the husk is separated from the grain in large rollers and sifting drums; the grinding of the grain into pure white flour; the flour is loaded into sacks which are manhandled onto lorries; steam traction engines convey the flour to the bakery.

III   The bakery: sacks of flour in storage; the dough-making process; the dough is divided, moulded and proved; baking in large 70-feet ovens; the freshly baked bread is conveyed to cooling racks.

IV   A fleet of horse-drawn bread wagons leaves the bakery on its daily round.

V   Bags of CWS Wheatsheaf self-raising flour are packed into cartons.

VI   Modern-day husband, Alfred, pleases his wife, having kept his eye on the cakes – baked with CWS flour. The couple and their two children tuck into their treat.

Remarks

The CWS was comparatively late in coming to the business of flour milling, due to the opposition from those retail societies that already had established milling concerns. Eventually, the expense of modern technological processes could only be met by a national federal organisation and the first CWS flour mill was opened at Dunston-on-Tyne in 1891. Other mills were soon approved to be built at London (Silvertown), Manchester and Hull. The mill in the film is probably the one at Avonmouth, established in 1910. It was claimed by the Movement that flour milling was essential to stave off the demands of a monopoly interest in flour, and to ensure supplies of materials to Co-op bakeries who might have faced prejudicial handling from private interests. The Movement thus ensured a fair price for consumers.
See also: xviii

NCFC 023
Round the Clock (1930)

b/w · 10m 36s · silent · 16mm · NWFA
pr Publicity Films Ltd

▪ A film promoting CWS biscuits.

I   A child plays whilst the mother dusts the parlour. They break for a snack, and the mother tells the story of the Giant Cream Cracker – which stands at the entrance hall of a great factory.

II   The CWS Crumpsall biscuit factory: exterior views; the Giant Cream Cracker clock; the workers enter the factory gate; sacks of flour line the storage room; the flour is emptied into giant hoppers and weighed; the

mixing of the dough; the rolling machine; the biscuits are stamped out of the dough; the biscuits are baked in giant ovens; trays of freshly baked cream crackers; the packing room – the wrapping of Crumpsall cream crackers; labelling the tins of biscuits; the storage of the tins; loading biscuit tins onto lorries which leave the factory en route to Co-op stores.

III   A tea-table with plates of biscuits and cream crackers. Father has now joined the family and declares: "Yes – and all these good things are made in our own CWS factory at Crumpsall".

IV   Graphic card: "Ask always for Crumpsall Biscuits and Confectionery at your Co-operative Store. CWS."

Remarks

The Crumpsall biscuit factory was known throughout the Movement as "the daddy of all CWS factories" (as quoted in the film), being the society's first venture into production in February 1873. A further biscuit factory was acquired at Cardiff in 1920. It is instructive to note the continued reliance on biscuit tins for packing and distribution. Although the period after the First World War witnessed a determined move to paper wrapping, considerable amounts of biscuits continued to be sold loose, and it appears that tins remained in use for the bulk distribution of packets, surely soon to be replaced by cardboard cartons. The film places emphasis on the "happy and contented" workforce, a recurrent ideological thrust in the industrial films put out by the Movement in that period. The film was the ninth in the series of films commissioned by the CWS from Publicity Films for release into cinemas.

NCFC 024
Work and Play (1930)

b/w · 24m 55s · silent · 16mm · NWFA
pr Publicity Films Ltd

▪ An information film about the recreational and welfare provisions provided for employees of the CWS.

I   Collages of CWS factories. A Commonwealth of Industry where during 1928 no less than £28 million worth of goods were produced.

II   Display of CWS products.

III   Some of the recreational and physical pursuits of CWS employees: swimming; opening of the New

Manchester sports ground at Moston – sprint, sack race, obstacle race, long-distance race, tug-of-war, relay race, walking race, prize-giving ceremony; hockey; tennis; cricket; football – the CWS Cup Final, the big event of the society's sports year; bowls; gymnastics; table-tennis; boxing (including some "analytical" slow-motion, and "comic" sped-up motion sequences).

IV   Fire-drill: the firemen rush to man their equipment; female operatives pour from the workshop to their stations; the firemen demonstrate their hoses.

V   The annual CWS Horticultural Show: large crowds in the main exhibition arena; shots of floral displays.

VI   The CWS employees' magazine, *Ourselves*.

VII   A CWS factory welfare supervisor counsels an employee. In the sickroom, she attends to her patients.

VIII   Employees arrive for work at the CWS corset factory at Desborough; interior of the busy factory; operatives at their sewing machines.

IX   Graphic card: "CWS Products carry the goodwill of those who made them as well as a dividend for those who buy. Buy CWS products at your Co-operative Store – and – secure your share of the Dividend."

Remarks

As an employer, the CWS had provided dining-rooms and lending rooms, and encouraged employees' clubs for recreation when this had been rare. Drama and music were widely sponsored: the CWS Male Voice Choir was founded in 1901, and the CWS Tobacco Factory Prize Band in 1907. Sports received equal patronage: the CWS Longsight (printing works) Swimming Club commenced in 1902; the CWS Crumpsall biscuit factory was the first to provide a sports ground a few years later; the nineteen-acre sports ground at Moston, Manchester, was established in 1928. The first CWS Football Cup competition was held in 1926, when the Bristol depot were the winners. 40 teams entered the draw, and it was claimed as the largest private works sports competition in the country. *Ourselves*, the CWS staff magazine, began in 1925 as a voluntary effort by staff; it was officially adopted by the society in 1927. The CWS volunteer fire-brigades were first established in the 1880s. CWS staff welfare provision expanded during the Great War, largely as a response to the influx of female employees. The first trained welfare superintendent entered CWS service in 1916, appointed at the Irlam soap works.

One of a series of promotional films sponsored from Publicity Films and released into cinemas, "The CWS Welfare Film", as it was promoted at the time of its release, was quite distinct in being concerned more with corporate identity than with brand products. The Movement's image as an employer was quite high and its staff turnover relatively low: the film would have played its part in reinforcing those circumstances.

NCFC 025
[CWS Canning Factory, Lowestoft]
(c.1930)

b/w · 5m 8s · silent · 16mm · EAFA

■ An information film about the CWS canning factory at Lowestoft.

I   A trawler sets out from harbour. Shots of it at sea.

II   Fishing commences: casting nets; drifting; hauling in.

III   The small fleet returns to the harbour and quayside. The catch is unloaded and transferred to salted barrels, where it is treated by women operatives.

IV   The CWS canning factory. Exterior long-shot across a stretch of sea.

V   Inside the factory: women workers take off the heads; the fish are poured into a machine.

VI   The canning process: the fish are placed into the cans manually, and the cans are moved on via a conveyor belt; the loaded cans are put into large ovens; the cans are labelled "CWS 'Jennie' Brand".

VII   "And out to sea the drifters go again!".

Remarks

A film produced to commemorate the establishment of a CWS canning factory at Lowestoft, Suffolk. The first site was acquired from the well-known Maconochie brothers, and opened in September 1929. A further site, extending the productive area to twelve acres, was added in July 1933. By the eve of the Second World War, 700 employees were involved in its operations. It is interesting to note that the film deals with a subject similar to that in Britain's first "documentary" film, John Grierson's *Drifters* (1929). Not surprisingly, the CWS canning factory film is more businesslike and less poetic. The CWS commissioned a film entitled *Harvest of Sea and Field* (1931;

NCFC 334), focussing on the Lowestoft operation, of which this material may have comprised part.

NCFC 026
[Ipswich Co-op and Labour Fete] (c.1930)

b/w · 3m 23s · silent · 16mm · EAFA

▪ A film record of a workers' gala, co-sponsored by the Ipswich Industrial Co-operative Society.

I   Sports and athletics competitions: men's sprint; eating a hanging doughnut without the use of hands; women's skipping; women's stick and balloon races.
II   Various scenes of competitors and crowds. Individuals and groups are singled out, presumably society directors and managers.
III Fancy dress competition. Well-known Co-operative products are the subject of several entries: Pelaw polish; CWS flour; CWS soap; Lustre cigarettes.
IV Men's steeplechase; throwing.

Remarks
A more sophisticated film than its surviving predecessor, which recorded the Co-op Fete of 1928 (see NCFC 014). Essentially, the film is "unedited" and consists of shots of some of the activities; the film simply begins *in media res* and cuts off at its conclusion. A posed group shot within the film is possibly a portrait of the society's managers and/or directors. The "Co-operative" fancy dress parade was a traditional event and widespread activity, and reflective of the extent of "Co-operative Culture", whereby members and their children simultaneously celebrated and promoted well-known Co-operative products.

NCFC 027
[CWS Toffee] (c.1931)

b/w · 5m 23s · silent · 16mm · NWFA

▪ A film about the making of CWS toffee.

I   CWS toffee lollies pass on a conveyor.
II   A vat of glutinous toffee mixture; a roll of brand labels; toffee lollies pass on a conveyor; a close-shot of a CWS Raspberry Lolli; wrapped toffees pass through a machine; toffee is mixed in a large drum; the liquid toffee is

poured into heated trays; trays of light and dark toffee; toffee is rolled by hand and various layers are added; the toffee is further machine-processed using mechanical rollers; a long strip of toffee is exuded from a machine; the toffee is cut and wrapped into individual portions; wrapped toffees are fed down a chute and form a pile.

Remarks
Although clearly an edited sequence, the film lacks any introductory titles or credits, and explanatory narration or intertitles. At times, it is difficult to be precise regarding the actual process being detailed, and consequently the above description is sometimes necessarily speculative. I have been unable to trace any contemporary references to a film on this subject, and therefore secondary sources throw no further light on the film. It is probable that the film was made by Publicity Films, the leading commercial film company of the time, which, beginning in 1928, produced numerous industrial films for the CWS.

NCFC 028
Rose of the Orient (c.1931)

b/w · 40m · sound · England/Scotland · 16mm · NFTVA
pr Publicity Films Ltd *d* M F Cooper/George Wynn *cam* T R Thumwood/J Rogers *sd* L Page *mus* John Reynders *sc* A Coates

▪ An informational film about the manufacture of tea by the English and Scottish Joint CWS, with tea grown on their own plantations in Ceylon.

I   A young man's father tells him of the historical romance of tea.
II   18th century Britain. The board of the East India Tea Company is in consultation, and the company faces crisis unless it can boost the sales of tea. They seek royal approval of their beverage, and soon it becomes a fashionable drink at court.
III 1760. Dr Johnson and his friends, Boswell and Garrick, discuss the merits of tea.
IV Victorian times. A young couple is about to leave to take up a position on a tea plantation in Ceylon. They take afternoon tea with her parents. It was in Victorian times that Ceylon developed into an important producer of tea – various scenes of the beautiful

island of Ceylon.

V   The tea plantations of Ceylon: the workers at breakfast; the muster is sounded; the British managers organise the work parties; the seed-bearing tea plants are tended; the tea flower – the Rose of the Orient; collecting seeds of the tea plant; a nursery of the CWS – tea seeds are planted and tended; transplanting the young tea plants; pruning the tea bushes; the excellent conditions enjoyed by native workers – hospital, school, children performing the stick dance; the tea bushes are plucked; the native foreman checks the crop which is weighed; baskets of tea are transported to the factory by aerial ropeway; Tamil coolies in their leisure time – singing and dancing.

VI   The CWS Westhall factory: exterior view; the leaves are spread in the withering lots; the rolling machines working on the leaves; the tea on the fermenting floor; the drying ovens; grading the tea in the sifting room; the estate manager tasting and testing the tea; mixing the different batches into bulk and loading into tea chests; the full chests are carried to the railway siding by aerial ropeway and loaded into carriages; an English and Scottish Joint CWS administration building.

VII Colombo. The trucks are unloaded and the chests loaded onto ships which set sail.

VIII London: the Leman Street tea warehouse of the CWS; the tea-tasting room; blending the tea – different blends for areas with different water supplies; bulk blending of the tea in huge drums; the tea is fed into large hoppers and transported to the packing room below; the tea is wrapped and packed into cartons; a Co-op store exterior; a Co-op department store exterior; a store exterior of the Leeds Industrial Co-operative Society; a pack of Co-operative tea is placed into a shopping basket.

IX   An older woman demonstrates to a younger friend how to make a good pot of tea. The young man and his father are winding up their conversation about tea when the two women enter with a freshly brewed pot; couples around Britain enjoying a refreshing cup of tea.

Remarks

This film is the full version of this title, with the narrative sequences framing the film and a greatly expanded documentary section in the middle. The shorter version was released in 1935 with the same title (NCFC 041). The film's structure was typical of the style of industrial film produced by Publicity Films for the CWS in this period, with its mixture of narrative and industrial material. This was obviously an expensive film with impressive production values. Much of the photography, especially in the Eastern sequences, is first-rate. The local CWS Westhall factory, which is detailed in the film, was opened in 1914. An earlier film, *The Cup That Cheers* (1928; NCFC 013), had taken the subject of tea, but did not include any footage acquired at the plantations. *Rose of the Orient* was clearly conceived to make up for the omission. It is probable that this was the first film of a Co-operative subject worked on by Publicity Films' producer, George Wynn. Throughout the 1930s, he would work regularly on commissions from the CWS, and in 1940 he was hired to head the newly established CWS Film Unit.

NCFC 029
HRH The Duke of York Visits the CWS Margarine Works at Higher Irlam (1932)

b/w · 7m 45s · silent · 16mm · NWFA

■ A film record of a royal visit to a CWS factory.

I   A cheering crowd awaits the arrival of HRH the Duke of York.
II   The motorcade arrives at the CWS margarine works. HRH greets managers and executives at the main entrance.
III HRH is introduced to members of the factory fire brigade (external) and then tours the outside of the premises.
IV   HRH inspects the interior of the factory and is introduced to the processes of margarine manufacture.
V   The tour party shown walking and conversing in the recreation park adjacent to the factory.
VI   HRH is driven through lines of cheering workers and spectators.
VII Newspaper cutting quoting HRH: "I feel I must heartily congratulate Lancashire on the cheerfulness, energy and enthusiasm I have noticed among its people everywhere I have been".
VIII Managers, executives and directors congregate following the royal visit.

Remarks

An element of mystery surrounds this film. For many years it was in the possession of Bill Crowther, a surviving relative of F C Crowther and T P Crowther, long-time lecturers/projectionists of the CWS. Bill recalls that instructions were issued that under no circumstances should the film be given public exhibition; the film's box is clearly marked "Not To Be Shown". In addition, a handwritten note survives, written by T P Crowther in 1961, which states that "the CWS Directors had decided that it should not be exhibited to the public". However, extracts from the film appear to have been included in a newsreel compilation of CWS activities exhibited in 1934. It can only be surmised that the CWS were being sensitive to the wishes of the royal household in withholding the entire film. The CWS margarine factory was located in a district of Manchester, employed 1200 workpeople, and turned out commodities annually valued at £3.5 million by 1932. The Duke spent a little more than an hour at the factory, and his visit came at the end of a tour of Lancashire industries to observe welfare facilities.

NCFC 030
From Back to Back (1933)

b/w · 28m 21s · silent · 16mm · NWFA
pr Publicity Films *sc* J Haslam

■ An information and promotional film for CWS tailoring and men's outwear.

I   A herd of sheep is brought into a pen; an old shepherd tells his young colleague how the wool of sheep is transformed into cloth – "from sheeps' backs to men's backs".

II   Sheep are sheared of their wool.

III   The young man at his tailor where he selects a pure wool fabric. The tailor tells him how the wool is woven into cloth: a CWS mill (exterior); different grades of wool are combined in the blending machine; the mixture is fed into the carding machine, where the fibres are combed; the wool leaves the machine in a broad downy band and on into the condensing machine which divides it into strips; the wool is further reduced into thinner strands called "slivers", and fed onto giant rollers; the yarn is spun to provide strength.

IV   The tailor explains the weaving process: the various productive processes of weaving are detailed, including the arrangement of the pattern.
(END OF PART ONE)

V   The tailor explains the cleaning and milling process for the cloth which produces a soft texture, and finally the pressing of the material. The requisite manufacturing images are presented.

VI   The tailor's shop: the young man is measured for an overcoat.

VII   The tailoring department of a CWS menswear factory: a pattern is marked out on the cloth and then cut; wide view of the machine finishing department where the pieces of cloth are stitched together; an overcoat is packed.

VIII   The ready-to-wear tailoring department: the cloth, laid out in layers, is marked with chalk; garments are cut to standardised patterns by machinery; cutting by hand; the various machines and processes used in making-up the garments; packing for despatch.

IX   The young man is fitted with his overcoat, with which he is very pleased. He also admires the ready-to-wear suits produced by the CWS.

X   Co-operative store (exterior) – passers-by admire the tailoring display in the window.

XI   Graphic card: a collage of various menswear factories of the CWS – "Upward of 3,500 workers are employed at CWS Men's Wear Factories. CWS Men's Wear is obtainable only from Co-operative stores."

Remarks

The film was made in both sound and silent versions, although only the latter survives. It was the 13th edition in the series of promotional films by Publicity Films for the CWS which commenced in 1928. The film was scripted by the head of the CWS Publicity Department. Menswear was the first Co-operative clothing manufacture, commencing in 1888. After considerable reorganisation in 1934, the CWS operated seven men's and boys' clothing factories, meeting an annual output of three million garments. The scenes presented here of clothing manufacture were probably taken at the CWS Batley mill. Other factories specialised in shirts, overalls, and so on. A companion film was made in 1933, detailing such manufactures and entitled *Song of the Shirt*, but so far it has not been traced. A later film, similarly titled *Back To Back* (NCFC 246), was produced in 1961,

bringing up to date the story of CWS clothing manufacture. In that version, both male and female attire was dealt with.
See also: NCFC 246

NCFC 031
Opening of Tower House, Lewisham (1933)

b/w · 5m 30s · silent · 16mm · ETV

■ The opening ceremony of the Royal Arsenal Co-operative Society's flagship department store.

I   Exterior Tower House, RACS's new department store.
II Employees of the works department putting the finishing touches to Tower House.
III Co-operative and civic dignitaries in discussion outside the store: Alderman W H Green JP, LCC, the Right Hon. C W Bowerman, Alderman Joseph Reeves.
IV RACS coaches arrive with invited guests, including J J Worley, Secretary of the Co-operative Productive Federation. Other guests arrive by car.
V   Large crowds gather outside the store to witness the opening ceremony.
VI The Clock Tower, Lewisham, opposite the store and from which it takes its name.
VII Exterior shots of the store, now with its neon lights on, and the gathered crowds.
VIII At the declaration of the opening of the store, the Rainbow Flag of International Co-operation is raised.

Remarks
The Tower House store was opened by Mr W B Neville, General Secretary of the society, on Tuesday, 7 November 1933. At that time, the RACS had a membership of 385 000. It cost £100 000 to build and equip the new flagship store, which was reputed to be the largest Co-operative store in the south of England. It is disappointing that the film contains only exterior views of Tower House; indeed, it is curious that a respectful distance from the proceedings is maintained throughout. Considerable information is conveyed through title cards, and the viewer is given little more than distant views of the building itself. Tower House contained between 70 and 80 departments, with innovations such as a travel bureau and a ladies' hairdressing salon expensively finished in marble.

NCFC 032
Partners (1933)

b/w · 28m 18s · silent · 16mm · NWFA
pr Publicity Films *cast* Kate Connor, Charles Paton, Sid Crossley

■ A narrative film in which a member of the Co-operative Movement impresses on his friend the great commercial undertakings of the Co-operative enterprise. With the aid of the "magic" camera of a passing newsreel cameraman, they "visit" the Movement's various business operations.

PART I
I   London. Views of the docks and some of the capital's historic landmarks.
II The Leman Street tea warehouse of the English and Scottish Joint CWS: exterior shot; the tea-tasting rooms; the warehouse and packing rooms; the milling process – the huge hoppers and the blending drums; the packing machines and wrapping procedure; the loading of cartons for despatch on lorries.
PART II
III Manchester. Views of the city from the Manchester Ship Canal.
IV The English and Scottish Joint CWS Manchester tea warehouse: exterior views; unloading cargo from the dockside and into the warehouse.
V   The two friends return to London by aeroplane.
VI The Co-operator's wife shopping in a London Co-operative store. Her basket is loaded with Co-operative brand goods, with tea prominently placed. She quotes her share number so that her purchase can be recorded for dividend purposes. The group meet up again in the store, and the wife hears of the two men's "adventures". The wife demonstrates a further advantage of Co-operation when she draws her "divi". The friend is persuaded into becoming a "partner" in the great Co-operative enterprise.
VII Graphic card: "The English and Scottish Joint Co-operative Wholesale Society. The largest Growers, Blenders, Packers and Distributors of Tea in the World."

Remarks
The film was released in both sound and silent versions, but apparently only the latter survives. It was part of a series of productions undertaken for the CWS by Publicity Films, which were released into

cinemas for general promotional purposes. The big tea-packing warehouse at Leman Street, London, dated from 1891. Various activities took place at that site – the London branch of the CWS first operated there in January 1881. The Manchester tea-packing factory, situated on the Ship Canal, opened on 10 December 1930.

NCFC 033
[Co-op Festival, Crystal Palace] (1934)

b/w · 18m 58s · silent · 16mm · ETV

■ A film record of the impressive Festival of Co-operation held at the Crystal Palace.

I   Graphic cards: "Organised by the London Co-operative Societies' Joint Education Committee"/"Entertainment for many Thousands of Visitors to the Great Co-operative Exhibition".

II   Panning shot of the visitors milling about in the gardens and pathways in front of the great Crystal Palace.

III   Graphic card: "British and Foreign Delegates".

IV   Group shot of dignitaries viewing the crowds from a balcony.

V   Graphic card: "Mr Vaino Tanner, President, International Co-operative Alliance. Mr R. A. Palmer, Secretary, British Co-operative Union. Professor F. Hall and Mr C. E. Wood, Education Department."

VI   Several shots of the gathered dignitaries.

VII   Graphic card: "Children of the Enfield Highway Co-operative Society's Junior Organisations".

VIII   The SCWS brass band leads a march along the Grand Parade by numerous children and youngsters carrying banners and the flags of the 40 countries of the ICA; wide-shots of the impressive parade; the dignitaries wave to the marchers; high-angle shots of the procession; close-shots of the children as they file past the camera; a marching brass band.

IX   Graphic card: "The Woodcraft Folk".

X   Contingents of the Woodcraft Folk march towards and past the camera. WCF banners.

XI   Graphic cards: "Children of the R.A.C.S. Woolwich Junior Circle formed in 1884"/"They are dressed in costumes of the years 1884 and 1934 and are led by Miss Phyllis Lawrenson Granddaughter of the founder Mrs Mary Lawrenson".

XII   The RACS Junior Circle anniversary banner presented by children in costume; the banner is paraded by members of the RACS Junior Circle; several close-shots of Circle banners; the magnificent backdrop of the Crystal Palace; various Circle groups parading with their banners and in costumes.

XIII   Graphic card: "Press!! Mr Flanagan. Editor in Chief of the Co-operative Publishing Society. T. W. Mercer Assistant Editor."

XIV   The two gentlemen, in a group of four, cheer the parading youngsters.

XV   Entertainment and displays on the Palace sports ground: the crowded viewing gallery; a display of ballet dancing by younger girls.

XVI   Graphic card: "Folk Dancing by the London Co-operative Society. See the Circassian Circle."

XVII   Distant shots of young girls and boys folk dancing; crowded grandstands; further views of children's folk dancing; closer shots of the galleries; Circle dances and children skipping in file.

XVIII   Graphic card: "Members of the Margaret Morris Dancing Classes, Royal Arsenal Co-operative Society".

XIX   Young girls give a display of eurhythmics; a display of individual Greek dancing; a young boy and girl perform a sketch – Pan and a Nymph; four girls dance a routine.

XX   Graphic card: "A Tableau of all Nations by the Children of the South Suburban Co-operative Society".

XXI   A parade of flags and costumes; Scottish dancing; distant views of the busy arena.

Remarks
Between 29 August and 8 September 1934, the Crystal Palace hosted an exhibition of Co-operative effort organised by the Co-operative Union. On the final day, a great Festival of Co-operation "proclaimed to the world that co-operation [was] unrestrained", and demonstrated "the co-operative movement of leisure" (*The Producer* September 1934). The festival, attended by over 20 000 spectators, involved various societies from the metropolitan area, and would have been organised by the London Co-operative Societies Joint Education Committee (LJEC), which had been established in 1926 by the RACS, London, South Suburban and Enfield Highway societies. The LJEC had been staging festivals at the Crystal Palace since 1929. The film is valuable for the

snapshots it provides of noted Co-operators and officials who, helpfully, are clearly introduced by the text.

Dancing had long been valued as a natural social activity and supported by Labour groups. Joseph Reeves, Education Secretary of the RACS (who can be briefly glimpsed in the film) freely sponsored folk-dancing, which he supported as "purely co-operative, because it is a form of collective activity" (quoted in John Attfield, *With Light of Knowledge: A Hundred Years of Education in the Royal Arsenal Co-operative Society, 1877-1977* [London; West Nyack: RACS/Journeyman Press, 1981]). Classes in morris dancing were instituted at the RACS in 1926, and displays were a regular feature of festivals, galas and gatherings. The film failed to capture the festival's evening activities: the ritual lighting of the WCF camp situated on a Palace slope, and two massed choral concerts within the Palace which concluded with a rousing rendition of "Jerusalem" by over 1000 voices.

NCFC 034
Co-operative Milk (1934)

b/w · 11m 24s · silent · 16mm · PC
pr J H Poyser and L Plackett

▪ "A film showing the progress of milk from the cows grazing on the society's farm, through the dairy processes and distribution, to the members' tea-table" (J H Poyser, "Local Co-operative Films", *The Producer* August 1935).

I   The film's two co-producers, J H Poyser and L Plackett, enjoy a refreshing glass of Long Eaton Co-operative Society (LECS) milk.
II   The society's farm at Meadow Lane: the dairy herd at pasture; the cows are led into the milking sheds; a milk maid arrives with her pale; a cow is milked; calves enjoy a drink of fresh milk; cows are milked in their stalls.
III   A truck loaded with milk churns draws into the LECS dairy; the full churns are unloaded and their contents enter the pasteurisation process; the bottling procedure; the milk is tested in the laboratory; the boiler room; a party of schoolchildren enjoy a glass of milk; the churns are sterilised using steam; machinery is cleaned with a steam hose; the giant vats and other equipment are scrubbed clean; crates of bottles are sterilised.

IV   A young girl is scalded for nearly throwing out the empty milk bottles. She is led inside to wash them, and waits to return them to the milk roundsman.
V   Horse-drawn wagons are loaded with crates of milk; a roundsman loads his hand-drawn truck; a motorised van is loaded with crates.
VI   A milkman out on his rounds makes his delivery and collects the empties from the young girl; the girl and her mother brew up a pot of tea.

Remarks
J H Poyser was a key figure in the promotion of local Co-operative society filmmaking, producing several films on his society's trading and cultural activities, as well as numerous films on Long Eaton itself. This was his first production on a Co-operative subject, the ever popular topic of Co-op milk, a product whose entire chain of production and supply was controlled by the society. This film is particularly interesting for its opening shot, introducing the filmmakers Poyser and his assistant, Plackett, the Education Secretary of the society. The amateur films of the LECS were particularly innovative for including dramatic sequences, a technique developed further in later films.

NCFC 035
[The Crystal Palace Exhibition 1934] (1934)

b/w · 4m · silent · 16mm · ETV, IAC

▪ A film record of a Co-op exhibition held at the Crystal Palace.

       (Introduction missing)
I   "Receiving Mr Väinö Tanner and Mr Harry May", representatives of the International Co-operative Alliance at the Co-operative Exhibition, Crystal Palace, 1934.
II   "The Massed Junior Choirs Nearly One Thousand Strong" – long shot.
III   "The Great Co-operative Exhibition Attended by 140,000 People". Various scenes of the exhibition inside the Crystal Palace. Crowds of visitors inspect the stands and exhibits mounted by societies and trading departments.
IV   The Rainbow Flag is hoisted and 8000 children sing "The Internationale" (the words to the first verse and the chorus are presented).

Remarks

The Crystal Palace had a long association with the Co-operative Movement, the annual National Co-operative Festival being first held there in 1888 (the final event being staged in 1910). Although pre-eminently a cultural festival – perhaps best remembered for the massed singing of the 10 000 strong United Choir – an exhibition of Co-operative production was an important feature. The Co-operative Exhibition of 1934 had been largely stripped of its cultural dimension, and most obviously existed as a showcase for CWS/Co-operative products. At the time, the purpose of the exhibition was seen as "Educating the Public in Co-operation and Persuading Co-operators to Support the Workshops they have Established" (*The Producer* September 1934). The exhibition ran from 29 August to 8 September, the final day being devoted to a Festival of Co-operation, represented in section IV of the film. Väinö Tanner (previously prime minister of Finland [1926-27]) was the President of the International Co-operative Alliance, and Harry May was the Secretary – the exhibition being timed to coincide with the International Co-operative Congress. Those historians critical of the Movement's political radicalism should note the choice of song for choral presentation. Could any other division of the British Labour Movement stage such an impressive performance? The festivities organised as part of a children's day at the Crystal Palace are recorded in another film (see NCFC 062). Various productive exhibits were presented by the CWS and the Co-operative Productive Federation: soap-making, boot-making, the making of spectacles, Co-op cycles and prams, SCWS linoleum, displays by the CWS shopfitting department and building department, including a life-size bungalow fitted out with CWS furniture. Each day the Crystal Palace Cinema Theatre screened Co-operative films. It is possible that the two Crystal Palace films were produced by Frank Cox for the London Co-operative Society.

NCFC 036
Workers' Newsreel No. 1 [incomplete] (1934)

b/w · 8m 40s · silent · 16mm · NFTVA
pr Kino

▪ The inaugural newsreel of the workers' film Movement.

I   The "Daily Worker" 1934 Gala, Co-op Woods, Plumstead. A large crowd enjoys the following: a children's race; boxing; netball; wrestling; men's wheelbarrow race; ladies' egg and spoon race; men's sack race; political caricatures.

II   "The Workers Create". The building of a London Co-operative Society departmental store; provisions; outfitting; drapery; millinery (all exterior).

III   "Whilst Capitalism Destroys". Scenes at the Hendon Air Pageant: air bombing display; protest demonstration for peace; flying displays.

IV   Youth Anti-War Congress, Sheffield.

V   Young Communist League (Bradford Local) march.

VI   Anti-war demonstration, Hyde Park, August 1934.

Remarks

The workers' newsreel was a widely adopted device for agitational filmmaking in the 1930s. They sought to present images of Left activity excluded in the commercial newsreels, and, in doing so, raise the class-consciousness of the worker audiences who would be made aware of the various struggles confronted by their comrades. The *Workers' Newsreels* 1-4 (1934-35) were made and distributed by Kino/Workers' Film and Photo League, radical organisations to the left of the Labour Movement. The inclusion of Co-operative activity in issue 1 is important evidence of the acceptance of the Co-operative Movement in radical political activity in the interwar period. The sequence depicts the building of a LCS departmental store, and is organised in a manner described by Bert Hogenkamp as a "deadly parallel": the construction of the store – "The Workers Create" – is contrasted with militaristic displays – "Whilst Capitalism Destroys".

NCFC 037
Behind the Scenes (1935)

b/w · 24m 51s · silent · 16mm · WFSA
pr PIMCO Publicity Department
prod Reginald Denny

▪ A film recording the various trading departments of the Portsea Island Mutual Co-operative Society (PIMCO).

I   The Committee of Management in session.

II   The administration office – clerks and

typists busy at their jobs.
- III The PIMCO butchery department – a consignment of cattle arrives, a mincing machine (?).
- IV The grocery warehouse – the loading bay, a PIMCO truck is loaded with provisions, the packing of raisins (?).
- V The furnishing workshops – an armchair is re-upholstered; renovation of settees and mattresses.
- VI The hairdressing salon – the barbers at work; the beauty salon.
- VII The works department – a PIMCO delivery truck sets off down the street; the joinery workshop; constructing milk floats in the body shop.
- VIII PIMCO coal depot – a consignment of coal arrives in CWS wagons and is loaded onto motorised lorries; the PIMCO coal yard.
- IX The garage and engineering shops – vehicle maintenance.
- X The milk depot – crates of milk are loaded onto floats; a doorstep delivery.
- XI A man and woman enjoy a smoke (?). *(End missing)*

Remarks

An excellent film record of the multitude of services provided by a local Co-operative society in the interwar period. Such a film would have served as an efficient method of informing members about the business of their society, and it is evident that this project was conceived in such terms: "*Behind The Scenes* deals with all the various workshops and services of the Society which are not readily visible to the new member. It is hoped that this will prove an invaluable method of acquainting a new member with the full extent of the Society's services" (*The Producer* November 1935). A series of PIMCO newsreels, which began in 1935, attended to the various cultural activities of the society, making for a detailed film record of a local society at work and at play on the eve of the Second World War.
See also: NCFC 044

NCFC 038
Blackpool Co-operative Society Stone-Laying Ceremony (1935)

b/w · 4m 16s · silent · 35mm · NWFA

■ The commencement ceremony for the building of Blackpool Society's new central premises.

- I A large gathering of people attend the stone-laying ceremony. Mr W Shackleton, President of the Blackpool Co-operative Society, opens the proceedings and addresses the crowd.
- II Golden Jubilee stone-laying ceremony: James Leach and James Horne, the two surviving founder-members, lay a stone dedicated to the first Board of Management; Mr R Baldwin, a former President, lays a stone on behalf of the present board; Mr R Cattle speaks on behalf of past members of the board; Mr B Rushworth JP, Vice-President, moves a vote of thanks, seconded by Mr A Fielding JP.

Remarks

Although this event, commemorating the Blackpool Co-operative Society's Golden Jubilee, 1885-1935, was of undoubted historic importance, it makes for tiresome viewing today. A silent film recording a procession of speeches could hardly be anything else! The official stone-laying ceremony of 12 October 1935 was the first stage in the construction of a new emporium by the society. The impressive departmental store was completed in 1938, and its official opening is captured in the film, *New Emporium for Blackpool Co-operative Society* (1938; NCFC 077). *See also:* NCFC 077

NCFC 039
Bread Film (1935)

b/w · 12m 30s · silent · 16mm · PC
pr J H Poyser

■ An information film detailing the provision of bread and confectionery by the Long Eaton Co-operative Society.

- I A horse-drawn plough at work in a field. Other horse-drawn implements are briefly presented.
- II A mature field of wheat: the wheat is harvested by horse-drawn machinery; the cut wheat is stacked into bales; the wheatsheafs are manhandled onto carts and into threshing machines; corn is loaded into sacks.
- III A CWS flour mill (exterior): grain is loaded onto chutes and conveyed into the mill; the grain passes through various milling processes; CWS flour is loaded into sacks.
- IV The Long Eaton Co-operative Society

bakery (exterior): the sacks of CWS flour arrive by barge and are winched up to the flour store; sacks of flour are poured down a chute to the bakery floor; the mixing of the dough; portions of the dough are rolled by machine and conveyed to the oven; various types of loaf pass by the camera on a conveyor belt.

V   Examples of the bakery's cakes; various processes in making the society's cakes and confectionery – pastry-making, baking, icing a wedding cake.

VI   A horse-drawn delivery van is backed into the bakery; motorised vans leave the bakery; a bread van making its rounds in Long Eaton; a bag of cakes is filled from the trays at the back of the van.

VII   Consumers: a bride and groom admire their wedding cake; a lad tucks into a slice of bread and jam; a girl enjoys a sandwich; a fat boy eats a slice of bread and jam, and a cake!

Remarks

The society's modern bakery was brought into operation in February 1908. It has been reported that "[t]he new building occasioned nationwide interest for it was said to be one of the finest and largest bakeries in the country" (G Kingscott, *Long Eaton Co-operative Society Ltd: A Centenary History*, 1968). The retailing of bread was a major success story for the Movement in the first half of the 20th century. Unusually for local Co-operative society films, this example includes specially taken footage of CWS productive activities, the source of the flour for the LECS bakery. It is worth noting that Poyser obtained his scenes at the CWS Avonmouth flour mill at Bristol, yet the flour used at the bakery is marked as that of the CWS Sun Mill, Manchester – a minor continuity error!

NCFC 040
Building the Long Eaton Co-operative Emporium (1935)

b/w · 12m 45s · silent · 16mm · PC
pr J H Poyser

■ A film record of the building of Long Eaton Co-operative Society's new central store.

I   General scenes of the demolition of the original central premises: walls are knocked down; timber is cut; steel frames are dismantled; and so on.

II   General scenes of the construction of the new premises: scaffolding is erected; floors are laid; masonry is dropped into place; shots of the town from the roof; a stone mason at work; plumber and electricians at work in the interior.

III   Exterior views of the completed emporium.

IV   The official opening ceremony: the gathering dignitaries; the waiting crowds; a speech by the Chairman, Mr J A Ward; crowds jostle to enter the newly opened emporium.

V   A parade of dressed vehicles passes through the crowd-lined streets of the town; various tableaux are picked out – the Co-operative Insurance Society; Empire fruit; the society's Toton Farm; "Co-op, Chef to the Nation"; the local Co-operative Queen; CWS Wheatsheaf brand products; CWS biscuits; Co-op milk; and so on.

Remarks

The original Long Eaton Co-operative Society "Old Central Premises", which at the beginning of the film are seen being demolished by the CWS building department, were erected in 1877. The new Emporium, at 40 650 square feet, was Long Eaton's biggest shop, costing £40 000 to build, and opening on 21 September 1935. The new store conformed to the contemporary taste for open-plan modern department stores, replacing the traditional scheme of trading in separate compartments each behind its own front door. It is a disappointment that the interior of the store was not filmed.

NCFC 041
Rose of the Orient (1935)

b/w · 5m 40s · sound · England/Scotland · 16mm · NWFA, SFA
pr Publicity Films Ltd *comm* Henry Ainley

■ An information film about the tea plantations of the CWS and the SCWS.

I   Scenes of Ceylon: daily life, leisure, industry and agriculture. In Ceylon grows a pretty rose-like flower – the tea plant.

II   Work on the tea estates of the English and Scottish Joint CWS: the tea-pickers muster; British managers and native foremen organise the work team; a school class of workers' children; picking tea and the expanse

of a plantation.
III   The local factory: the raw product
       arrives; drying the leaves; the rolling
       and fermenting process; drying in
       ovens; packing in tea chests.
IV   Loading onto ships.
V   Shots of the estates and premises of
       the tea operations of the English and
       Scottish Joint CWS, including the
       factory in the Anamallai hills, South
       India.

Remarks
In 1882, the CWS had joined the SCWS in a
tea department that was to become one of
the world's greatest tea dealers. Eventually,
tea, coffee, cocoa and chocolate were
articles handled only in association by the
two national federals, which in 1923 joined
as a society – the English and Scottish Joint
CWS. Tea-growing estates were purchased
in Ceylon in 1902, and added to in 1913,
eventually expanding into southern India in
1916. By 1939, the Joint Society operated
29 841 acres in India, and 5408 acres in
Ceylon; annual tea sales amounted to
£7.5m. It is always instructive to compare
the more workmanlike documentaries of the
Co-op (and other commercial sponsors)
with the more famous films of the celebrated
British documentary film Movement – in this
instance, with Basil Wright's poetic *Song of
Ceylon* (1934), which, interestingly, was
criticised for its romantic view of the island,
and its myths, culture and traditions. The
trade journal, *The Commercial Film* (June
1935), considered the Co-op's more prosaic
Rose of the Orient "an admirable example of
a short industrial film, calculated to stimulate
the interest of Co-op tea drinkers in the
source of their supply".
See also: NCFC 028, NCFC 097

NCFC 042
Safety First (1935)

b/w · 21m 19s · silent · 16mm · WFSA
pr PIMCO Publicity Department
prod Reginald Denny

▪ A promotional film for the production and
distribution of milk by the Portsea Island
Mutual Co-operative Society.

I   A bottle of PIMCO milk on a mock-up
       zebra crossing – Safety First!
II   Scenes at a Hampshire dairy farm: the
       cattle are led in from the field; the
       modern hygienic methods employed
       in the milking sheds; the PIMCO
       Co-operative dairy (exterior); the milk

churns are emptied into a large vat
and weighed; the empty churns are
scolded and sterilised; the dairy
analyst tests samples of the milk; used
milk bottles are stacked into the huge
bottle washing machines, and
sterilised; clean bottles are delivered
from the machine; further procedures
and testing in the laboratory; the milk
bottles are automatically filled and
capped; milk token discs are sorted
and counted; milk crates are stacked
onto a float; the busy despatch
department; loaded floats draw away
from the dairy.
III   A large lorry loaded with milk pulls in
       front of a Co-operative store; the lorry
       pulls into a depot, and the crates are
       transferred to hand-pulled carts; the
       carts are wheeled out of the depot; a
       milkman making deliveries from his
       cart on a suburban street – he chats
       with one of his customers; relaxing in
       the back garden, a mother and young
       daughter enjoy a glass of milk.
IV   Graphic card: "PIMCO MILK is safe,
       pure and fresh, and is excellent for
       children and grown ups too. The
       dividend on two pints of PIMCO milk
       daily for a year is equal to 47 pints of
       free milk."
V   A display of 47 pints of PIMCO milk –
       "The Dividend Equals This Amount of
       Milk Free".
VI   A close-shot of a glass of milk and two
       milk bottles. A hand takes the glass,
       and offscreen it is drunk. When
       returned, the straw is animated into
       movement.
VII   Butter-making at the PIMCO dairy: a
       barrel of milk is spun rapidly; butter is
       kneaded by machine and patted by
       hand; butter is weighed and patted
       into blocks.
VIII   It is the end of the day. The power
       switches are turned off and the
       generator comes to a halt.
IX   Graphic card: "Shopping at 'PIMCO'
       Pays. £1,000,000 already returned to
       members."

Remarks
The Publicity Department of Portsea Island
Mutual Co-operative Society, trading in the
Portsmouth area, purchased a 16mm ciné-
camera and projector in September 1935.
The first project was a newsreel of society
activities, which was quickly followed by this
film on the society's modern processing
dairy at Copner. The PIMCO Society was
founded in 1873, and, by the mid-1930s,
had a membership in excess of 41 000 and

an annual trade of over £1.1 million. The 1930s saw experimentation with film by a number of local Co-operative societies – Long Eaton, Leicester, Bolton, PIMCO, and so on. This example of early film work at PIMCO is amongst the most competent and detailed, with some excellent camerawork, fluid editing and innovative inclusion of animation techniques.

NCFC 043
[Twenty-Fifth Membership Gala] (1935)

b/w · 8m · silent · 16mm · ETV

■ 10 000 people celebrate 25 years of membership of the Royal Arsenal Co-operative Society.

I   Shots of the gathering crowds.
II   Entertainment is provided by the Morley College Military Band.
III   Preparations are under way inside the enormous tea tent.
IV   The crowds wait patiently at the specially erected gates, where a ticket system is in operation to move each member efficiently to their place of refreshment.
V   Inside the tea tent, luncheon is taken.
VI   Those members with over 50 years' standing enjoy tea and refreshments inside the Federation Hall.
VII   Portrait shot of an unidentified group.
VIII   The stations for dispensing the gift parcels are made ready.
IX   Presentations to the oldest/longest standing members. Amongst them is Mrs S A Eves, aged 91, a member for over 60 years.
X   Collection of the gift parcels.
XI   Entertainment: folk-dancing; variety performers Alec Gill and Gwen Vaughan; quick-sketch artist Rupert Harvey; comedian Leonard Henry; violinist Mabel Fairhurst; speech by Lord Snell and others, interspersed with shots of the large crowds.

Remarks
A film record of the great garden party sponsored by the RACS for members of 25 years' standing. 8000 members were eligible and 5000 able to attend. A further 5000 members of the general public were admitted to the Co-op Woods to participate in the event. The free celebration, a generous act on behalf of the society, consumed the following: 720 loaves of bread, 224 lbs of butter, 525 lbs of fruit cake, 5000 fancy pastries, 50 lbs of tea, 50 gallons of milk, and 1200 large bowls of fruit salad. The gift parcel comprised of a 4lb Dundee cake and a cake knife, and either a plated cake basket or an oak biscuit barrel. The knife, basket and barrel were inscribed: "Twenty-five years' RACS membership". Lord Snell of Plumstead, a former member of the Society Education Committee, was then-Chairman of the presumably London County Council.

NCFC 044
PIMCO Newsreel (c.1935)

b/w and col · 41m 26s · silent · 16mm · WFSA
pr PIMCO Publicity Department
prod Reginald Denny

■ A collection of "newsworthy" events in the trading and cultural life of the Portsea Island Mutual Co-operative Society.

I   Exterior of impressive civic building – Portsmouth town hall (?); inside a crowded hall, people listen to presentations from the platform – AGM (?); rear exterior of the hall.
II   The Junior Circle fancy dress competition – several entrants are dressed as popular Co-op brand products.
III   Scenes at the Children's Guilds rally and annual outing to Hayling, September 1935 *(one scene in colour)*.
IV   The CWS tableaux vans visit Portsmouth – dressed vehicles parade through the city; exterior of the PIMCO Central Store; crowds gather outside the PIMCO Radio Exhibition.
V   Scenes at a gala event – sports, dressed vehicles, sideshows, etc.
VI   Further scenes at the Children's Guilds' rally and annual outing to Hayling, 1935: departure at Portsmouth Station; the arrival of the huge crowd of children at Hayling Station.
VII   PIMCO Employees' Sports Olympiad: a parade of dressed vehicles; fancy dress parade led by a marching band; scenes around the gala event; sports activities – athletics, tug-of-war, slow cycle race, obstacle race, awards ceremony, and so on *(some scenes in colour)*.
VIII   A large body of staff awaits the arrival of the motor coaches for their annual outing to Hampton Court; the coaches out on the road.

IX   Gala event: historical pageant –
dressed vehicles, fancy dress, etc.
X   Annual sports of the PIMCO dairy at
Alexandra Park – various sports and
athletics events; presentation of prizes.
XI   PIMCO cricket team, champions of the
Southern Co-operative League, take
on the best from the rest of the league
in a game at Eastleigh; Mr J H Mihell
presents the cup to the PIMCO team.
XII   Scenes at a bowls match.
(End missing)

Remarks

PIMCO produced a number of local
Co-operative newsreels: this film is possibly
a collection of those original newsreel items
in a single film. (Note how the children's
outing to Hayling is split into two sections,
III and VI) It is significant that the newsreels
were resolutely popular in concentrating on
cultural activities such as galas, outings and
sports days, leaving the more mundane
matter of Co-operative business and trade
to separate films such as *Behind the Scenes*
(1935; NCFC 037) and *The Key* (c.1936;
NCFC 051). It was the inaugural meeting of
the large-scale Co-operative sports event,
the Olympiad, and 44 coaches were used
for the employees' outing to Hampton
Court! Commencing in the 1920s, the CWS
made available four tableaux vehicles to
augment local Co-op parades and galas.
Each year, the theme of Co-operative
productive industry represented on each
vehicle was changed, and the quartet
carried the message of Co-operation before
millions of people.
See also: NCFC 055

NCFC 045
Madame Decides (1936)

b/w · 13m 50s · silent · 16mm · WFSA
pr PIMCO Publicity Department *d* C E
Barlow

▪ A promotional film for fashions stocked by
the Portsea Island Mutual Co-operative
Society.

I   Models parade on a stage and
catwalk, as at a fashion show. A
variety of dresses, coats, furs, jackets
and evening wear are paraded for the
camera by three models.
(End missing)

Remarks

One of two surviving fashion parade (or, as
they were referred to at the time,

"mannequin parade") films produced by the
Publicity Department of PIMCO. Local
Co-operative Society filmmaking had been
pioneered at PIMCO by their Publicity
Manager, Reginald Denny, who had left
early in 1936; film work was continued by
his successor, Charles Barlow. A surviving
production still of this film shows a film crew
of four, the action being staged in one of
the society's halls. The purpose of the film
would have been to make known and
promote the fashions offered by the society
around the trading district of PIMCO in
Hampshire, especially for the benefit of
those members without easy access to
Portsmouth to visit the fashion department
themselves. Co-operative mannequin
displays were regularly promoted by local
societies. Some were held on stage at the
local cinema house, and, in many instances,
the models were drawn from the counter
staff of the local stores.
See also: NCFC 049

NCFC 046
[RACS Cultural Activities] (1936)

b/w · 9m 55s · silent · 16mm · ETV

▪ Various activities sponsored by the Royal
Arsenal Co-operative Society.

I   Exterior views of Shornells, the RACS's
residential centre.
II   Former students arrive for the Reunion
Garden Party, 27 June 1936. Old
acquaintances meet on the lawn.
III   The New Malden Junior Choir with
their trophies.
IV   Some tutors and members of the
Education Committee (legendary
Education Secretary, Joseph Reeves,
is clearly visible smoking a cigarette).
V   The Shornells orchestra entertains in
the outdoor arena and is presented
with a trophy.
VI   Luncheon in the marquee.
VII Queries are dealt with at the
information kiosk. Education Secretary
Anthony Bingham is orchestrating
activities.
VIII A choir entertains in the outdoor
arena.
IX   Presenting shields to successful
choirs.
X   A portrait shot of Joseph Reeves.
XI   Co-operative Day celebrations at
Summerstown: the gathered crowds
enjoy a sports display; fancy dress
competitors; children's entertainers.
XII "Dr Brook and the prize babies" – a

bonny baby competition (?).

XIII The fancy dress parade, with many of the participants dressed as well-known Co-operative products.

XIV Address by the Chairman of the Education Committee, Mr J Dickinson, followed by Alderman W H Green MP.

XV Membership campaign, 1936. New members visit society establishments by coach.

XVI New members enjoy a stroll in the Co-operative woods, land owned by the society.

XVII The procession of coaches parade through the Progress Estate, south London, owned and managed by the RACS.

XVIII A drive past a society department store.

XIX A walk through a Woolwich laundry. *(End missing)*

Remarks

This film is incomplete and an end sequence is missing. In 1919, as part of the previous year's Jubilee commemoration (50th), the society purchased Shornells, a country house near the society's Bostall Estate, Abbey Wood, as an education centre for its members: "the whole arrangement of the house is eminently suitable for the expression of the Co-operative Summer School idea...the surroundings are such as to give the visitor the impression of a real summer holiday!" (*Comradeship* September 1919). The centre was used for weekend and summer schools for RACS students, as a venue for overseas visitors as part of a scheme of international contacts, and as a social centre. For many members, a residential course at Shornells was their only holiday, year after year, and this provided a crucial service. The students' reunion was an annual event for the 3000 students who attended classes offered by the RACS education department. The 1936 reunion on 27 June included the Shornells and Bexley Heath Co-operative orchestras, the Malden Junior Co-operative Choir, and a performance of the wedding feast from *Hiawatha* by the society's massed senior mixed choirs and orchestras conducted by Michael Tippett.

NCFC 047
The Travel Picture (1936)

b/w · 16m 24s · silent · 16mm · PC
pr J H Poyser *cast* Ken Hollingsworth

- A "day in the life" of the mobile hardware shop of the Long Eaton Co-operative Society.

I The mobile shop takes on stock, standing outside the central premises. It is loaded by its driver, Ken Hollingsworth. The shop sets off on its rounds of the trading district of the society.

II En route to Castle Donnington, over the River Trent. Visiting the branch store at Castle Donnington.

III En route to Diseworth, passing the old windmill. At Diseworth, several customers inspect the merchandise within the van.

IV At Long Whatton, a lady purchases some paraffin. A visit to the branch store is made, and some wire fencing collected.

V Driving through Zouch and over the River Soar.

VI En route to Sutton Bonington. At the village, a clothes-horse is sold. A woman inspects the stock lined along the side of the vehicle. Ken visits the branch store.

VII En route to West Leake. At the Pit House pub, Ken enjoys a drink with customers. In the village, he sells the local sweep some brushes. The gamekeeper buys some paraffin.

VIII En route to Kingston on Soar. A village without a store, it therefore has a great reliance on travelling shops.

IX Visiting the branch store at East Leake.

X En route to Gotham. Visiting the village branch store.

XI The van passes in front of the picturesque thatched cottages of Barton in Fabis.

XII The historic hall at Thrumpton.

XIII Driving through the ford at Ratcliffe on Soar and on into the village.

XIV Approaching Kegworth over the River Soar. Ken sells a clothes-horse to Mrs Cook and enjoys a cup of tea.

XV The old ruined church at Hemington.

XVI The mobile shop returns to Long Eaton and is driven into the society garage in Fletcher Street.

Remarks

J H Poyser was a member of the Education Committee of the Long Eaton Co-operative Society in Derbyshire. He had commenced experiments with 16mm silent filmmaking in 1934, and each autumn/winter a film programme toured the society's trading district which, according to the activists, "proved convincingly that the sub-standard film is a popular and most fruitful medium of co-operative propaganda, education, and entertainment" (J H Poyser, "Local Co-operative Films", *The Producer* August 1935). Both factual and fictional filmmaking were undertaken. *The Travel Picture* was particularly innovative in style, incorporating a "subjective camera technique", whereby the audience were placed in the position of the mobile van – a result attained by the cameraman valiantly strapping himself onto the moving vehicle. An amateur filmmaking group has continued to be supported by the local Co-operative society, and recently they traced the van driver, Ken Hollingsworth, and recorded his observations on the film. He has also been able to provide details unavailable to the modern viewer, thus allowing for an accurate interpretation of events. This is truly a remarkable instance of oral history and its benefits. Most Co-operative societies operated mobile shops – grocery, hardware, butchery, and so on – providing an important service in rural districts and, after the war, on the new housing estates where businesses were often not established until after the residents had moved in. This is the only Co-operative film to deal substantially with the service. A video viewing copy of this film is currently being screened with the title *Hardware To Your Door*.

NCFC 048
[CPF Factories and Workers] (c.1936)

b/w · 7m 20s · sound · 16mm · EAFA

- An information film about Co-operative Co-Partnership Productive societies.

(Introduction missing)
I   General view of the factory floor at a hosiery factory, close-shots of machinists and cutters.
II   Finished garments are paraded in a salon and the fashions and materials are explained – casual wear, evening dresses and coats.
III   Workers enjoying the rest room facilities – first aid, sun lamps, gymnastics.
IV   A view of Kettering from the top of a factory; a busy city street; a small village Co-Partnership factory.
V   A map of Great Britain, indicating the different sites of Co-Partnership businesses and industries.
VI   Graphic card: "Co-operative Productive Federation Ltd. Producer with Consumer. Their common interests.

Equity in Industry. Ask For Co-operative Co-Partnership Goods At Your Co-operative Stores."

Remarks
The Co-operative Productive Federation (CPF) was established in 1882 as a federal organisation promoting the interests of Co-operative Co-Partnership enterprises which offered the workers a share in the results and control of their industry. The South Midlands became an important centre of businesses based on industrial democracy, with a particular concentration of Co-Partnerships in Kettering – notable examples being the Kettering Clothing Manufacturing Co-operative Society, the Holyoake Boot Society, the Union Boot Society, and the Kettering Corset Society. The CPF was represented on the Central Executive of the Co-operative Union, although there had long been tension between the producer and consumer Co-operative Movements following the CWS's decision to deny its employees a direct share of the profits, preferring instead to return the surplus to members in the form of a dividend on purchases. The surviving film is a DIN print, made for rear projection purposes.

NCFC 049
The Foundation of Beauty (c.1936)

b/w · 11m 23s · silent · 16mm · WFSA
pr PIMCO Publicity Department *d* Reginald Denny/C E Barlow

- A promotional film for CWS Desbeau corsets stocked by the Portsea Island Mutual Co-operative Society.

I   A fashion salon where CWS Desbeau corsets are being modelled.
II   "Loraine" for the junior, 3s 11½d; "Rhoda" for the heavier figure, 10s 6d; "Donna", the latest model, 6s 11d; the "Uplift" for the large figure, 12s 6d; "Vionnet", with self-supporting brassiere, corset 11s 6d, brassiere 3s 11d; "Nymph", ideal for summer wear, 5s 11d; "Milan" for the heavier figure, 14s 11d; "Esther", 10s 11d; "Helen", for the slim figure, 6s 11d; "Model S.D. 38", 31s 6d; "Angela", 6s 11d; "Jaunty", for the slim figure, 8s 11d; "Model 39/8" popular model for the junior, 4s 11d; "S.D. 36", a "Super Desbeau Style", 23s 6d; "Dawn", for the average figure, 9s 11d.
III   Graphic card: "Remember ladies, you

can see any of these models at Co-operative House, Fratton Road, Portsmouth – 'The Super Store of the South'."

Remarks
A second "mannequin parade" film from the PIMCO Society. This is altogether a more assured production than *Madame Decides* (1936; NCFC 045), especially in its use of explanatory intertitles, and was presumably a later film. Its punning title provides some indication of its subject-matter; historically, the film makes an interesting comparison with the CWS's *A Matter of Form* (1929; NCFC 018), which dealt with the manufacture of Desbeau corsets at the CWS factory at Desborough, Northamptonshire. With its parade of female models in their underwear, the film would presumably have been somewhat risqué.

NCFC 050
[Historic Portsmouth] (c.1936)

b/w and col · 19m 50s · silent · 16mm · WFSA
pr PIMCO Publicity Department
prod Reginald Denny

▪ A collection of scenes of historic Portsmouth.

I   Numerous picturesque and historic scenes of Portsmouth are presented, including: the sea front gardens and recreational facilities; holiday-makers on the beach; a major civic building – the town hall (?); the war memorial, amongst the beach huts *(colour)*; the harbour *(colour)*; museum and gallery; a medieval church; the house where the Duke of Buckingham was assassinated in the 17th century; unidentified gateway; the docks; Charles Dickens's birthplace; the George Hotel, where Nelson spent his last night in England; HMS *Victory*; the 'Old Sally' Port of Portsmouth.

Remarks
A film of limited Co-operative interest. Produced by PIMCO, it includes only one brief image of a Co-operative subject, a trolley bus prominently carrying the advertising logo, "Shop At The Co-op". A civic film, entirely of local interest, it would have been screened within a programme of Co-operative society subjects to provide some variety.

NCFC 051
The Key (c.1936)

b/w · 10m 7s · silent · 16mm · WFSA
pr PIMCO Publicity Department

▪ A promotional film for a hire purchase scheme and savings club offered to members of the Portsea Island Mutual Co-operative Society.

I   Newly-wed Mrs Wise is at home playing the piano. Her friend calls and is impressed by the beautifully furnished house. Mrs Wise shows her friend around: the living room; the bedroom – she proudly shows off her wardrobe of dresses; the box-room; the kitchen – Mrs Wise shows off her wringer; the parlour.

II   Mrs Wise tells her friend how she has managed to make such a beautiful home – the "key" to her secret is the PIMCO Easy Payment System and the PIMCO Mutuality Club: shots of the membership cards and repayment books.

III Graphic card: "The PIMCO Easy Payment System and the PIMCO Mutuality Club are open to all PIMCO Members. Membership of the Co-operative Society is FREE – you can join at any PIMCO Branch. JOIN NOW – and share in the benefits of Co-operative Trading."

Remarks
Between 1935 and 1936, Reginald Denny, the Publicity Manager of PIMCO, pioneered a remarkable period of local Co-operative society filmmaking, undertaking a broad and imaginative range of subjects and styles which incorporated newsreels, documentaries, promotional films and narrative shorts such as this one. In 1936, he joined the Leicester Co-operative Society, where his innovation continued with experiments in sound filmmaking. It is not clear whether this film is from Denny's period at PIMCO. The subject of this film, the society's savings and repayments schemes, is of particular historical interest within the context of the Co-operative Movement. An original Rochdale principle had been cash trading only; however, changed economic and social circumstances had ensured a reconsideration of the ideal, and numerous societies began to offer club schemes and hire purchase (HP) arrangements in the 20th century. Official statistics show that in 1953 Co-operative societies had £13 358

882 outstanding in debts on HP, and, as the "affluent society" of the 1950s became more entrenched, the demands on HP arrangements intensified.
See also: NCFC 044

NCFC 052
[PIMCO Bakery] (c.1936)

b/w and col · 28m · silent · 16mm · WFSA
pr PIMCO Publicity Department
prod Reginald Denny/C E Barlow

▪ An information film about the bakery of the Portsea Island Mutual Co-operative Society.

I   Shots of wheat being harvested in the Hampshire countryside.
II Sacks of CWS flour are loaded onto PIMCO lorries at Fratton Station, near Portsmouth.
III The PIMCO bakery (interior): sacks of flour are lifted to the flour room store and weighed; a panning shot of the huge flour store – just one day's supply of flour for the bakery; the blending of the flour; a measured quantity of flour is dropped into the giant mixer, water is added, and the dough-making commences; the dough is cut into blocks and placed into the dividing machine; the proving of the dough samples; the dough is conveyed to the "umbrella" machine which rolls the dough into soft balls; the spindle-moulding machine for sandwich loaves; making Exhibition loaves, Cottage loaves and Coburg loaves; baking the bread in giant "travelling" ovens.
IV The pastry and confectionery department: the mixing of pastry; the pastry-roller; the making of pies; cake-making – sandwich-splitting; mixing and rolling the bun-mixture; preparing fondant icing; cake decoration by a professional – a completed wedding cake; trays of cakes are placed into the oven.
V   Bread and rolls are taken from the oven and stacked for cooling; sample loaves are weighed and placed onto trays for delivery.
VI A display of breads from the PIMCO bakery; a display of cakes from the bakery; a tray of PIMCO confectionery is displayed by a young woman *(colour)*.
VII Graphic card: "You have seen glimpses of the ideal conditions under which PIMCO Bread and

Confectionery is produced ... <u>Do We Supply You?</u> or may we take your instructions? A representative is waiting in this hall to attend to your requests."

Remarks
One of several surviving films made by Reginald Denny, Publicity Manager of PIMCO, and coming after a successful film project on PIMCO milk. Bread and milk were typical subjects for local Co-op society filmmakers, as the chain of manufacture of those products was often entirely in the control of the society – the produce was derived from the society's farms, distributed by its transport fleet, processed in its factories, and retailed in its shops. The Co-op's proud boast of universalism was no more evident than in those two products – the Movement claimed a huge market share for bread and milk in the interwar period – and hence a film detailing the trades made a telling propaganda point, as well as informing audiences about the manufacturing processes involved. Bread-making was one of the earliest productive activities at PIMCO and, although it is not possible to date exactly, commenced before 1878. It is interesting to note the manner in which the film was presented as a direct marketing opportunity, with canvassers attendant at screenings to facilitate trade.

NCFC 053
[A V Alexander at Leicester] (1937)

b/w · 2m 11s · sound · 16mm · EAFA
pr LCS Film Unit *prod* Reginald Denny

▪ An International Co-operative Day address by A V Alexander MP to the Leicester Co-operative Society.

I   The bandstand platform and gathered spectators at De Montfort Gardens, Leicester.
II Society President, Mr Hall, makes a welcoming address, and introduces the guest speaker, A V Alexander, who makes his presentation on the importance of Co-operative spirit, in addition to Co-operative trading.
III Brief panning shot of the large audience.
    (End missing)

Remarks
Commencing in 1936, Reginald Denny, the Publicity Manager of the Leicester Co-operative Society, began making

newsreels of local society activities. Editions from 1937 and 1938 survive. It is probable that this brief film record of Co-operative MP, A V Alexander, making an address at the ICD celebrations sponsored by LCS, was intended for inclusion in the 1937 LCS newsreel. It is clear from the staging that the actual presentation we see was for the special benefit of the camera. No doubt the crude recording equipment had failed for the address proper, and a restaging of the speech had been necessary. Alexander, a senior political figure in the Movement, appears in several surviving Co-operative films, most notably *Advance Democracy* (1938; NCFC 070).
See also: NCFC 059

NCFC 054
Brighton Children International Camp. 1937 (1937)

b/w · 11m 43s · silent · 16mm · EAFA

▪ A film record of an international youth camp hosted by the Woodcraft Folk (WCF).

I Arrival of the London WCF groups to the camp.
II The marching band of the Czech contingent.
III Close-shot of some leaders and teachers and some younger members.
IV Some formal and informal camp activities: erecting tents; throwing and catching bodies in a blanket; chasing games; some members on the beach; marching with drums and makeshift percussion; mealtime.
V Entertainment: an accordion group; folk-dancing; the marching band of the Czech contingent; two young girls amuse onlookers with a display of "pat-a-cake"; folk-dancing/dramatic performance.
VI Demonstrations of peace and solidarity: a simple tableau; speeches from the "Peace Tower"; a march past with flags and banners; the marching band; a pageant depicting issues of peace and war, 1918-37; further shots of the gathered congregation around the "Peace Tower".
VII Open Day. Visit by parents and Co-operative society representatives.
VIII The Rainbow Flag of International Co-operation.
IX Folk musicians and dancers marching with banners. The banner of the WCF London Kin.

Remarks
The WCF, founded in 1925, had immediately sought contacts with overseas Socialist youth Movements. In the 1930s, it had become recognised as the English representative of the Red Falcons, the youth wing of the Socialist Educational International. The Brighton Camp of 1937 (in fact at Ovingdean, near Brighton) was the Folk's second international camp, involving 3000 campers, which included 1000 overseas visitors from ten countries. The event attracted concerted opposition from the British Union of Fascists, and sympathisers of the Right had not been amused when the Czech contingent and their marching band had struck up "The Internationale" upon disembarking at Brighton Station, and proceeded to march noisily through the town, down to the sea front and onto the camp. There were many comments in the local press complaining that a children's camp was an improper use of the downs. The camp lasted for three weeks, and the provisions bill came to £1500 with the CWS, and £600 with the local Co-operative society.

NCFC 055
[Building Works] (1937)

b/w and col · 18m 48s · silent · 16mm · WFSA
pr PIMCO Publicity Department
prod Reginald Denny

▪ A film record of the building of the new Portsea Island Mutual Co-operative Society central premises, 1936.

I A long-shot of the newly erected steel frame of the building; steel girders are lowered into place by crane; general scenes of workmen around the site; tarring the roof; various distant shots of the site with the building in various stages of construction; a team of bricklayers at work; the nearly completed exterior looking onto a busy city street; plumbing-in the large boiler; portrait shots of the numerous builders who contributed to the construction; masons at work on the Portland stone, putting finishing details to the façade of the building; the iron casing for the huge clock is eased into place.
II The exterior of the store is dressed with bunting in preparation for the grand opening.
III Crowds gather outside the store;

Father Xmas arrives, creating a stir; a march past by a parade – Father Xmas, brass band, dressed vehicles; the huge crowds lining the street outside the store *(colour)*.

IV A huge mass of people clogs the streets outside the store.

V The official opening of PIMCO Grocery Branch No. 43 at Lee-on-the-Solent, August 1935; a crowd gathers in front of the branch store; a speech is made by Mr R White, who is flanked by other representatives of the Board of Management; the store is officially opened and the eager crowd moves in.

Remarks
On 20 July 1934, PIMCO central premises burst into flames and the building was totally destroyed. Modern replacement premises were immediately planned with designs furnished by the society's own architect, Mr H C Wilding. The main contractor used in the construction of the store was the society's own Co-operative works department, employing over 200 operatives. The store, Co-operative House, was opened on the 4 September 1937 and included new departments, such as pharmacy, a luxury top-floor restaurant, extensive jewelry and sports departments, air-conditioning and a studio for the PIMCO Publicity Department Film Unit. During the war years, PIMCO suffered severe losses to its property, with perhaps one third of all property destroyed during 1941 and 1942. The biggest blow came on 10 January 1941, when Co-operative House was completely demolished by a severe incendiary and high-explosive attack. Item V seems to be unrelated to the main film, and was probably a newsreel item for the original *PIMCO Newsreel* (c.1935; NCFC 044). Furthermore, item III, including the presence of Father Xmas, may have been a later event unconnected with the official opening of the store – an event probably captured in item IV – and again a PIMCO Newsreel item that subsequently became incorporated in this print.

NCFC 056
The Co-operative Co-Partnership Reunion
(1937)

b/w · 6m · sound · 16mm · EAFA
pr Leicester Co-operative Society Publicity Department *prod, comm* Reginald Denny

■ A film record of the annual Co-operative

Co-Partnership Propaganda Committee (CCPC) sports gala.

I Scenes at a cricket match – a brass band is in the middle of performance; J J Worley, Secretary of the Co-operative Productive Federation makes an address from the clubhouse balcony. He endorses the method of Co-operative Co-Partnership production as a solution to the world's ills.

II The final of the cricket competition for the CCPC Cup, played for by teams from Kettering and Wellingborough.

III A display of dancing by female Co-Partnership employees.

IV The final of the tennis competition for the CCPC Cup between Leicester Co-operative Printers and Kettering Hosiers.

V A display of tap dancing by a young woman; a waltz from the play, *Careless Rapture*.

VI A long queue forms for tea and refreshments; further scenes of the tennis competition, won by Kettering Hosiers.

VII The bowls competition at Rockingham Park between Walsall Lock and the Union of Co-operative Boots Society.

VIII The prize-giving ceremony, with cups presented by J J Worley.

IX The crowds leave at the end of the day.

Remarks
The Co-operative Co-Partnership Propaganda Committee was a tripartite committee representing the Co-operative Productive Federation, the productive societies and the retail societies. The objects of the CCPC were stated to be "to further the principles of Industrial Democracy and accordingly organise educational and propaganda work" (*Co-operative Co-partnership Production in Great Britain* pamphlet [n.d]). The film was made by the Leicester Co-operative Society Publicity Department under the supervision of the Publicity Manager, Reginald Denny. It is their only known film of a subject not directly part of the LCS trading and cultural activities. Co-operative Co-Partnership production was particularly well represented in the East and South Midlands.

NCFC 057
Coronation Celebrations May 12th 1937
(1937)

b/w · 9m 2s · sound · 16mm · EAFA
pr Leicester Co-operative Society Film Unit
prod, comm Reginald Denny

▪ Representatives of the Leicester
Co-operative Society participate in the
Coronation celebrations of George VI.

I	Members of the LCS Grocery
	Managers Committee and the Board of
	Management ready to embark on their
	trip for the Coronation celebrations in
	London.
II	The trippers, onboard a bus, tour the
	route of the Coronation which is
	dressed with impressive decorations:
	Cheapside and the Bank of England;
	Tower of London; over Tower Bridge;
	the riverboats on the Embankment;
	busy Whitehall – the Cenotaph;
	Westminster Abbey – scene of the
	Coronation ceremony; Big Ben; the
	view down Pall Mall; Park Lane;
	Oxford Street; the magnificently
	dressed exterior of a London
	Co-operative Society department
	store, depicting the "Empire homage
	to the Crown"; Piccadilly Circus.
III	The Leicester Coronation celebrations:
	the Clock Tower, Leicester town
	centre, the LCS Central Store, the
	great procession representing the
	City's industries and civic life – the
	men of the British Legion, the city's
	first steam fire engine, various dressed
	floats for the city's industries and
	businesses, Leicester's first public
	vehicle, scenes from Leicester's
	history, the seven pioneers who
	founded the LCS, the LCS dairy, Walt
	Disney cartoon characters sponsored
	by LCS, the huge crowds milling in the
	city's streets.

Remarks
One of the first short subject films made by
the Publicity Department of the Leicester
Co-operative Society, which commenced in
the autumn of 1936 with a LCS newsreel
(see NCFC 355). In the spring of 1938, over
twenty films shows were mounted by the
Department, which attained audiences of
4500 adults and 5000 children, thus proving
a valuable propaganda and publicity
exercise. This film provides an interesting
contrast between the capital's extensive
Coronation celebrations (George VI) and a
provincial town's still impressive turnout.

NCFC 058
[Kitchen Capers] (1937)

b/w · 11m 25s · sound · 16mm · ETV
pr Publicity Films

▪ A promotional film for CWS canned foods.

(Introduction missing)
I	A married couple is having an
	argument about a dinner party. The
	wife refuses to cook for her husband's
	business friends, and he storms out
	after smashing the dinner service.
II	A "Voice of God" tells the wife not to
	worry, her pantry is magically filled
	with excellent CWS Waveney tinned
	products.
III	"Miss Waveney" demonstrates how to
	prepare a superb meal with CWS
	Waveney products: hors d'œuvres;
	soup; fish course; steak and kidney
	pudding; vegetables – peas and new
	potatoes; the desert – strawberries
	and cream; the cheese course.
IV	The husband sheepishly returns, and
	is impressed by the spread that is now
	available.
V	Peas are gathered on a CWS farm in
	Suffolk; the shelling of the pods; the
	canning process at the CWS Lowestoft
	canning factory; the herring fleet sets
	sail; a day's fishing and the fleet
	returns; a view of the CWS canning
	factory across the harbour; the
	wrapping of spreading cheese; the
	staff dining-hall; the staff playing-field;
	exterior view of the factory with a
	goods train leaving.
(End missing)

Remarks
The film is almost certainly that listed as
Kitchen Capers in the *CWS National Film
Service Catalogue* (1938), and rather tersely
described there as an "insight into the
canning industry". It would have been made
by Publicity Films, the long-time film
producers for the CWS. Such films were
screened at cinema lectures organised by
the CWS Publicity Department. The lecture
series for 1937-38 was devoted to the trade
of the CWS Lowestoft pure food factories
and *Kitchen Capers* was specifically
produced for that purpose. It was
subsequently claimed that 237 000 people
attended the 1196 cinema lectures that
season. Each audience member received a
coupon for Waveney cheese, redeemable at
the local society store. Furthermore, the
screenings were closely allied to the trading
activities of the retail societies; in addition to

the money-off coupons, special window displays were made available, of which 4000 were claimed by societies.
See also: xxxivn26, NCFC 191, NCFC 257

NCFC 059
LCS Newsreel [1] (1937)

b/w · 9m 19s · sound · 16mm · EAFA
pr LCS Film Unit *prod* Reginald Denny

■ A newsreel of important events in the calendar of Leicester Co-operative Society (LCS), 1937.

I   LCS Penny Bank Children's Gala, held at the Agricultural Showground, Aylestone, 27 August 1937: the young members of the Penny Bank, smiling and waving at the camera from the grandstand; a Punch and Judy show; shots across the showground; acrobats entertain the young spectators; the youngsters collecting their cups of tea and cakes; sitting and enjoying their refreshments; the children sing a chorus of "It's a long way to Tipperary".

II   Opening of the branch shops at Bannerman Road and Leicester Forest East: long shots of the new premises at Bannerman Road with a waiting crowd; Councillor Adams, President of LCS, makes an address in front of the store; Councillor Adams, in medium close-up, addresses the camera, and appeals to the audience to become members if they are not already so; long shots of the new premises at Leicester Forest East with a waiting crowd; exterior of the former premises, a temporary wooden structure; the official opening of the butchery department; portrait shot of society dignitaries; view of the pleasant surroundings seen from the store.

III   Large crowds watch as Santa Claus and Disney characters mount their sledge on their way to the official opening of the Xmas Bazaar at the LCS central premises; the horse-drawn procession, ready for the off – Mickey and Minnie Mouse, the Three Little Pigs, the LCS brass band; the procession moving through busy city centre streets to the music of the brass band.

Remarks
The Leicester Co-operative Society film unit was the brainchild of its publicity manager, Reginald Denny. He had previously pioneered Co-operative filmmaking at the Portsea Island Mutual Co-operative Society. In August 1936, it was announced that the "Leicester Society has acquired a complete 'talkie' film apparatus and projector, with which to record and show pictures of the many activities of the Society" (*The Co-operative News* 22 August 1936). Leicester was amongst the first Co-operative societies to experiment with sound, the narration being provided by Denny himself. The popular newsreel form lent itself to local society filmmaking whereby the various trading and cultural activities could be recorded and subsequently screened for members around the trading district. The annual children's Penny Bank, a savings club, was filmed for both the completed newsreels (1937 and 1938). The gala event was enjoyed by over 4000 youngsters, and the refreshments provided by the society amounted to 5000 bars of chocolate, 20 000 cakes and 300 gallons of milk. The opening of a new branch store was an important occasion for a local society, indicating the improved trading strength and vibrancy of the business. The scenes of Santa and his friends being paraded through packed city-centre streets are thrilling, and illustrate the interest that could be generated by the local Co-op, in this instance, bringing the city's trams to a standstill. It is possible that the LCS newsreels have been re-edited since their original production. A contemporary report on the 1937 LCS newsreel listed the following items: the arrival of Father Noah and Father Xmas to open the society's Xmas Bazaar; children's gala day; the De Montfort Hall International Co-operative Day celebration, with address by A V Alexander; and the opening of the dairy garage (*The Co-operative News* 4 December 1937). The item featuring A V Alexander at the International Co-op Day has survived as a separate item, and is listed as NCFC 053.

NCFC 060
Meat for the Millions (1937)

b/w · 8m 50s · sound · 16mm · IWM
pr Publicity Films

■ An informational film about the CWS trade in meat.

I   Scenes of busy industry and the working day coming to an end. Streams of workers leave a factory.

II   Several pairs of workers discuss their intentions for the evening, but decide

to stay in to enjoy a meat dinner.
III A mother and her son at a Co-op butcher's shop. The butcher describes the trade and the source of his supplies: a piggery; sheep out at pasture on the South Downs; a herd of cattle and CWS buyers examining them; sheep grazing on the Welsh hills; sheep and cattle at market; parading beasts at a cattle show; at the abattoir carcasses are inspected and weighed; foreign supplies – Canadian beef, Australian mutton, New Zealand lamb, Argentinian beef, and Argentinian cattle show; cargo ships at the London docks – carcasses are unloaded; the CWS Distributing Centre, Smithfield, London; Co-operative butchery stores (exterior).
IV The several groups of workers at home enjoying their dinner of CWS meat: "I prefer CWS meat because it comes from the best animals, carefully selected by expert buyers, whose motto is 'Only the best is good enough for the CWS'".

Remarks
For a considerable period, the Co-operative meat trade remained retail and local. The CWS experimented for the first time in imported meat in 1914, a period when 40% of all meat consumed in the UK was imported meat. An expansion in trade led to the opening of CWS meat departments in Manchester, Newcastle and London in 1925. A CWS presence at Smithfield was established in 1927. By the early 1930s, the CWS had purchasing offices in the Dominions, and participated substantially in the Argentine beef market. The subject was tackled again in the 1958 CWS production, *Meat for the Millions* (NCFC 411), a film that has not yet been located. In the tradition of Publicity Films' productions, the young boy has a upper-middle class accent, and had probably never in his life set foot in a Co-op shop!

NCFC 061
Peace Parade (1937)

b/w · 10m 43s · sound · 16mm · EAFA, IWM
pr LCS/Pelly and Healy Ltd *prod* F H W Cox

■ A "newsreel" record of the peace demonstration organised by the Political Committee of the London Co-operative Society on Sunday, 19 September 1937.

I Preparations for the "Peace Parade": a "peace tableau" arranged by the Cann Hall Women's Guild; vehicles of the LCS are dressed for the parade; the line of transport across the Embankment before the off; shots of various trucks decorated with peace slogans and banners.
II The great procession commences: various sections of the parade are viewed; the procession passes the Houses of Parliament; en route at Hyde Park Corner; spectators line the streets; demonstrators split from the vehicles and head for a rally in Hyde Park.
III The peace rally: a large gathering within Hyde Park; Alfred Barnes MP addresses the crowd; followed by Mr Reginald Gosling, President of LCS; the resolution for peace is put to the assembly by Percy Holman; "England Arise" is sung.
IV Graphic card: "Arise O England, For the Day Is Here".

Remarks
The first production in a three-film programme sponsored by the Political Committee of the LCS. Cox was an important propagandist for Co-operative film production, calling for the formation of a National Co-operative Film Society in 1936. His intention was for production on the substandard 16mm film, and he claimed important advances in direct sound-recording on that format. *Peace Parade* was the first experimental production in that technique (witness the "live" recordings at Hyde Park), and was sufficiently deemed a success to proceed to further productions. Cox's ideal for a national Co-op film unit, working on 16mm, never materialised, since other bodies such as the WFA and the CWS preferred production on "professional" 35mm, with subsequent reduction to substandard 16mm for local use. The film is a remarkable record of an interwar Left-political demonstration, and especially striking is the support, in terms of transport provision, from the LCS trading division.
See also: xxvii, NCFC 062, NCFC 102

NCFC 062
The People Who Count (1937)

b/w · 18m 37s · sound · 16mm · NFTVA
pr Pelly and Healy Ltd/LCS *d* Geoffrey Collyer *prod* F H W Cox *comm* A V Alexander MP

- A detailed presentation on the history, aims, ideals and activities of the Co-operative Movement.

I   Who are the people that count? – the workers, the wives and the mothers. Shots of busy streets; crowds at sporting events; interior of a London Co-operative Society store; and so on.

II   "Practical Co-operation", where the work of one benefits many. Shots of various work processes, trades and activities: man at a lathe; a milk-bottling plant; Co-operation in nature – honey bees; teamwork – relay races and football; the failure of Co-operation, trusted leaders co-operate with their opponents – shots of the MacDonald Cabinet, 1931.

III   The birth of the Co-operative Movement: Victorian Britain, an unscrupulous storekeeper cheats his customers; workers co-operate and establish their own corn mills; the ideas and influence of Robert Owen; the Rochdale Pioneers – shot of the Toad Lane store (exterior); T W Mercer, author of *Towards the Co-operative Commonwealth*.

IV   Co-operation in London: exterior shots of Co-op department stores, including East Ham (LCS), Tower House (RACS), a store of the South Suburban Co-operative Society; store interiors (LCS Hammersmith) – drapery department, ladies fashions, shoe department, chemist's department; assistant Miss Holly talks about the benefits of being a Co-op employee – the store's roof garden for staff and members.

V   The Movement's democratic and cultural activities: a branch meeting of the WCG; a Co-operative rally; children's sporting events; a Co-operative Party political rally; Alfred Barnes MP, addressing the crowd; Barnes of the Political Committee in discussion with a colleague.

VI   A discussion about the need for Co-operative political activity. The conflict between Co-operation and capitalism is stressed: shots of competitors' stores – Sainsbury's, International Stores, Home and Colonial, MacFisheries, Maypole, Woolworths, British Home Stores.

VII   The democratic structure of the Movement: the Management Committee of the LCS.

VIII   Poverty and misery in the 1930s: unemployment and slums are contrasted with the easy life of the idle rich.

IX   Scenes of war and destruction: taxes for warships and guns, yet little for poor families who rely on charity.

X   Scenes at a large International Co-operative gala at the Crystal Palace. International Co-operation is the hope of the world.

Remarks

The second film produced by Frank Cox for the Political Committee of the LCS under a three-film scheme commenced in September 1937 with a grant of £1500. Following the "newsreel", *Peace Parade* (1937; NCFC 061), came this documentary portrait of the Co-operative Movement and the work of the Political Committee of the LCS. On these two films, Cox, with the assistance of producers Pelly and Healy, pioneered the use of 16mm direct sound-recording techniques. Experiments in this process are most evident in sequence IV, where employee Miss Holly talks directly to the camera, and, judging by the results here, the team still had some way to go before perfection could be claimed. The third film in the programme, the narrative film, *Utopia* (1938; NCFC 372), does not appear to have survived. The late-1930s were a rich period of Co-operative filmmaking, with Frank Cox pioneering 16mm film work north of the Thames for the LCS, and Joseph Reeves exploring the potential of 35mm film production south of the river with the RACS. Their films of that period represent important records of the tense and difficult times, and articulated a progressive view of world and domestic events. Scenes of the International Co-op Gala Day at the Crystal Palace were recorded earlier in the decade by Cox, and it was on the strength of those that he gained the commission from the Political Committee for the three-film programme. *See also:* NCFC 102

NCFC 063
"Postman's Knock" (1937)

b/w · 5m · 16mm · PC
pr Publicity Films

- An entertaining promotional film for CWS soap products.

I   Four women perform a song-and-dance routine in a large kitchen. Various lodgers intrude and demand that the girls get on with their laundry

duties.
II The postman arrives with a large sack of dirty washing. He is pleased to announce that the Mayor has sent the girls four tickets for the ball.
III A man in a bath preparing to go to the ball.
IV The fancy dress ball: the grand parade; the Mayor and Mayoress observe from the stage; the postman arrives on stage and performs a song-and-dance routine – "I've got them in the bag".
V He announces "the real winners" – the four girls enter the stage in their costumes: CWS Crysella soap flakes; CWS Green Olive toilet soap; CWS Congress washing soap; and Paddy soap powder.
VI The four girls perform a dance routine with the postman.
VII Graphic card: "And the real winners: Crysella Soap Flakes, Green Olive Toilet Soap, Congress Washing Soap, Paddy Soap Powder. Obtainable only at Co-operative Stores."

Remarks
The print of this film is of poor condition with sections clearly missing. The film's address is presented in a highly entertaining style, and represents possibly the earliest of a series of musical presentations promoting CWS products. By the mid-1930s the CWS was operating a successful Cinema Lecture Service whereby publicity films were an integral part of periodic product campaigns. In 1938 the product featured was soap, and "*Postman's Knock*" undoubtedly contributed to the push to sell more CWS soap products. A further soap film, *Merry Mondays* (1936; NCFC 356), which would have served the campaign, remains unlocated.
See also: xxi

NCFC 064
Saint Monday (1937)

b/w · 12m 20s · silent · 16mm · PC
pr J H Poyser *cast* Wynn Davis

▪ A dramatic film promoting the advantages of CWS labour-saving products.

I It is Monday 31 June, and a working-class housewife prepares for the day's chores. A large tub of water is heated and dirty linen is sorted. A large cake of soap is cut and laborious hand-washing begins.

II After the vigorous manual agitation of the garments, the various items are fed through a mangle. Stubborn stains are attacked with a brush and soap.
III 11.05 am. Preparations for the daily meal begin; potatoes are peeled.
IV The washing is carried outside and hung up to dry. At 3.45 pm it is collected.
V Inside, it is folded and passed dry through the mangle, then it is ironed.
VI In the evening, the housewife completes the £100 prize crossword in *The Reynold's News*.
VII Awaiting the postman, she eagerly accepts her delivery – she has won the prize crossword.
VIII With her cheque from the CWS, she sets off to the local Co-operative store, where she purchases large quantities of CWS cleaning products.
IX In the hard goods department, various labour-saving devices are demonstrated for her: washing-machine, water-boiler, oven.
X It is Monday 31 September. Before commencing her all-electric washday, the laundress enjoys toast from her new electric toaster, and a cup of tea with water boiled in her new electric kettle.
XI With the new CWS cleaning products and labour-saving devices, washday is no longer a grind; each stage is demonstrated.

Remarks
The film was clearly intended to promote to members the virtues of modern CWS electrical gadgets, available at the local society store (the retailing sequences were shot at the Co-op branch store, Derby Road, and the Co-op store, Station Road, Long Eaton). Judging by contemporary accounts, a final sequence is missing, in which the housewife, now with leisure time resulting from the easy electric washday, visits a local cinema. However, the moral of the story remains clear. The popular Sunday newspaper, *The Reynold's News*, had been acquired by the Co-operative Movement in 1929.

NCFC 065
[Co-op Day at Grays] (c.1937)

b/w · 5m 12s · silent · 16mm · EAFA

▪ A film record of cultural activities at the Grays Co-operative Society in the late-1930s.

I   The Rainbow Flag of Co-operation.
II A Co-operative parade through a residential area, with children in fancy dress and dressed vehicles.
III The parade reaches a recreational ground; marching band; the Woodcraft Folk with a banner; fancy dress contestants.
IV Festivities and events: a children's race; a family relay race; a dancing display.
V   A costume parade with participants dressed in the national costumes of the member nations of the International Co-operative Alliance, and carrying flags; a dramatic presentation of swordplay (symbolic of the suppression of armed conflict?); the participants gather round a huge globe – Co-operation circles the world!, "Peace, Freedom, Democracy".
VI The Rainbow Flag of Co-operation.

Remarks
Grays Co-operative Society (GCS) was founded in 1867, and therefore it is possible (although it is not stated) that the activities recorded in the film were part of a 70th Jubilee celebration. GCS had a membership approaching 40 000 by that date. The dramatic presentation in section V is reflective of the international tensions of the late-1930s, and Co-operators' fears of war and conflict, and hopes for international peace through unity and a brotherhood of nations. The slogan, "Peace, Freedom, Democracy" belonged to the People's Front, a loose affiliation of Left organisations determined to resist Fascism. This is one of three films recording scenes of propaganda activities staged by the society.

NCFC 066
[Grays Co-op Exhibition] (c.1937)

b/w · 4m 4s · silent · 16mm · EAFA

■ A film record of a local propaganda event staged by the Grays Co-operative Society.

I   A clown on stilts attracts the attention of shoppers for the "Great Co-operative Exhibition".
II Speeches are made from a platform to a large crowd – official opening of the "Great Co-operative Exhibition".
III The crowds queue to gain admittance to the exhibition, whilst the clown amuses them.
IV Inside the exhibition: brief shots of some of the stalls and demonstrations

(poorly lit).
V   A parade of dressed vehicles promoting the trading and cultural activities of the society and the CWS.
VI Celebration banquet (poorly lit).
VII Further brief shots around the exhibition (poorly lit).

Remarks
This is one of three films recording local Co-operative propaganda activities mounted by the Grays Society, Essex. It includes typical events intended to engage the local population and inform them about their society: crowd entertainers, exhibition, parades and processions. Note the placard exhorting "Join Now"; such events were important opportunities to attract new members. The exhibition was mounted in the autumn of the Grays Society's 70th anniversary year, and involved substantial participation by the CWS which contributed regularly in this manner to aid local societies in propaganda work.

NCFC 067
[Grays Co-op Propaganda Activities]
(c.1937)

b/w · 4m 4s · silent · 16mm · EAFA

■ Brief scenes of a Co-operative propaganda event and exhibition staged by the Grays Co-operative Society.

I   Models parade various fashions on a catwalk. The sequence ends with a special display of bridalwear.
II An operator prepares a propaganda vehicle/outside-broadcast van. He tests the public address system and drives away. The van is promoting a "Great Co-operative Exhibition"; brief shot of the CWS "tea demonstration van".
III Inside the Co-op exhibition: cloth-making machinery (poorly lit); a potter at work; a hosiery machine, making stockings.

Remarks
An interesting overview of a typical interwar propaganda event managed by a local Co-operative society and supported by the CWS. Numerous Co-operative exhibitions were staged annually, drawing large crowds to witness Co-operative productive techniques and sample the latest CWS products. Such events were typically combined with membership drives. The "tea demonstration van" was made available for

propaganda work by the English and Scottish Joint CWS, and comprised the following: "The interior of the van is fitted with stock cupboards, kitchenette, portable talkie film projector and public-address equipment with a working range of one mile" (*The Producer* August 1935). It was designed and built by the CWS motor body and wheelwright's department, and became operative in 1935.

NCFC 068
Les Pioneers A Charade (c.1937)

b/w · 9m 8s · silent · France · 16mm · EAFA

▪ A film record of a French youth camp of the Red Falcons.

I A vista shot of a picturesque valley; the flag of the Faucons Rouges (Red Falcons).
II Young campers file through a wood and make a clenched fist – the salute of the workers!; two young girls look out over a valley; a young girl reads a Faucons Rouges' pamphlet; a young couple plays with a mouse; a cart is wheeled up a hill; a party collects firewood and load the cart, eventually returning to camp; the logs are cut; preparing a meal in a large cauldron.
III Activities around the camp: a small group relaxes, reading or playing music; another group improvises a camera and mocks the antics of the filmmaker; young men playing a ball game; a group sweeps the camp; a game of volleyball – a section in slow-motion; a ball-game enjoyed by a large group; a horn is blown and the crowds rush down the hillside for mealtime.
IV On a hike through the forests.
V A boy is tossed in the air and captured on a blanket (slow motion); dancing around a night-time bonfire.
VI Marching through woodland and into a town behind the banner of the Faucons Rouges; in a square, the group joins hands and sings.

Remarks
The Faucons Rouges (Red Falcons) were the French Socialist youth Movement affiliated to the international Falcon Movement. The group would have come into contact with the Woodcraft Folk, a Co-operative youth organisation, through international work and camps. This print, and *République des Faucons Rouge*

(c.1937; NCFC 069) also in the collection, come from a collection of films held by the former LCS, and no doubt had been acquired in an exchange of materials between the two organisations. The film is very similar to surviving WCF films of the 1930s, but is distinguished by its well-chosen and well-executed slow-motion sequences.

NCFC 069
République des Faucons Rouges (c.1937)

b/w · 7m 9s · silent · France · 16mm · EAFA

▪ A film record of a French youth camp of the Red Falcons.

I General scenes at a Falcon camp: pitching tents, wooded glades, etc.
II Children's folk-dancing; groups relaxing; strolling around camp; playing on a beach; morning keep-fit exercises.
III A large sign for "Pioneers, Frente Popular"; young adults gather round for discussion; general activities and tidying around the tents; boys' washing facilities in use; a marching game on the beach.
IV A large group of children files past the camera in uniform; mealtime.
V "La Fête" – a large crowd watches a march past by the young Falcons, with banners and flags; a display of keep fit and acrobatics; a circle game; a display of folk-dancing; a musical dance skit; a comedy bull-fight with a theatrical bull; a dramatic presentation (work and toil?).
VI "Les Huiles" (The "High-Ups") – speeches by adults.

Remarks
A second film in the collection recording a camp of the French Socialist youth organisation, the Faucons Rouges. Of particular note is the reference to the "Popular Front", France's great political experiment of the mid-1930s, and demonstrably supported here by the youth group from Spain. Within only a few years, following the wartime occupation, many of the young people in this film would have been persecuted for their political beliefs. *See also:* NCFC 068

NCFC 070
Advance Democracy (1938)

b/w · 16m 42s · sound · 35mm: NFTVA /
16mm: ETV
pr Realist Film Unit *d, sc* Ralph Bond
cam Gerald Gibb/A Jeakins *cast* Fred Baker,
Kathleen Gibbons *mus* Benjamin Britten

■ A propaganda film calling for workers to
join the Popular Front against Fascism in
the late-1930s.

I Scenes around London. The well-off
   are contrasted with working people –
   for example, a woman orders luxury
   foods from Fortnum and Masons,
   while workers eat at a cheap café.
II We are introduced to Bert, a
   craneman at the London docks.
   Various scenes around the docks are
   presented. He talks with his mates
   about the prospects of war, but his
   ideas do not appear well-informed.
III At home, his wife May has his tea
   ready. She also has been discussing
   the possibility of war at a meeting of
   the Women's Co-operative Guild, yet
   Bert remains unconvinced of the
   virtues of the Co-operative Movement.
   May suggests that he tune into a
   programme about the Co-op on the
   wireless.
IV In a studio at the BBC, Co-op MP, A V
   Alexander, commences his broadcast
   on "Democracy and the Co-operative
   Movement": the Tolpuddle Martyrs; the
   Rochdale Pioneers; the growth of the
   Rochdale Society; various store fronts
   of premises in the London area –
   South Suburban Co-operative Society,
   Royal Arsenal, London Co-operative
   Society; wheatfields in Canada; tea
   plantations on the subcontinent;
   democracy in danger, the rise of
   Fascism – Hitler, SA troops, war in
   Spain.
V Bert has been converted to the cause
   of peace and anti-Fascism. He makes
   a speech to his workmates, and his
   resolution to march in the May Day
   parade is accepted.
VI Scenes at the huge march for "Peace,
   Freedom and Democracy" across
   London. Numerous Labour banners
   are visible, and the whole sequence is
   cut to Socialist songs – "The
   Internationale", "Keep the Red Flag
   Flying", the battle hymn of the Spanish
   Republic, etc.

Remarks
In November 1937, the London Joint
Education Committee of the metropolitan
Co-operative societies announced their
intention to spend £1000 a year on the
production of films – known as the "Five
Year Film Plan". The London, Royal Arsenal,
South Suburban and Enfield Highway
Societies contributed to the funding of the
first film, *Advance Democracy*. The driving
force behind the plan was Joseph Reeves,
who provided the draft scenario for the film,
and whose Workers' Film Association,
formed in 1938, distributed the film
throughout the Labour Movement. The two
principal actors were regulars with Unity
Theatre, the Socialist collective, whilst Ralph
Bond, the film's director, was a key figure in
the interwar workers' film Movement, and
later became prominent in the Association
of Cinema Technicians.

The film manages a gloss and
professionalism beyond the typical workers'
film of the period, due to the comparatively
high level of funding from the Co-operative
Movement, the experience and drive of
Reeves, who was determined that
production should proceed on the
professional 35mm format, and the skills of
contributors such as Bond and Benjamin
Britten. The film is a revealing document on
the Popular Front campaign. The film clearly
calls for a united front against Fascism,
something the official Co-operative
Movement and Labour Party did not support
(although the Co-op newspaper, *The
Reynold's News*, was a most consistent
supporter of the Front). Ralph Bond, a
Communist, would evidently be supportive
of the call, and Reeves was also outspoken
in his demands for what he called a
"People's Front", despite his society's firm
opposition. More surprising is the
participation of Co-op MP, A V Alexander,
who opposed a resolution calling for a
United Peace Alliance at the Co-operative
Party Conference in 1938. It can only be
concluded that the film activists were
allowed considerable autonomy on the
project, and that certain participants were
hoodwinked into making their contributions.

The final sequence of the film
marvellously captures the breadth and
sweep of the 1938 London May Day parade.
Excitingly cut to a montage of workers'
songs orchestrated by Benjamin Britten, it
represents one of the most stirring
sequences of interwar Labour film.
Surprisingly, a contemporary critic
considered the climax "the film's one
weakness"! (Frank Churchward, *The
Co-operative Review* November 1938).
See also: xxvi, xxvii, NCFC 053, NCFC 085,
NCFC 090

NCFC 071
Co-operette (1938)

col · 14m 19s · sound · 35mm · NFTVA
pr Publicity Films d Montgomery Tully
sd Charles Poulton ed C Beaumont
cam Harry Waxman cast Stanley Holloway,
Hal Walters, Debroy Somers and His Band,
the six Co-operettes sc H V Purcell/Terence
Egan

▪ A comedy musical promoting shopping at
the Co-op.

I   Sam Small arrives at a film studio to
        take part in a film. Whilst waiting,
        some of the musical numbers are
        performed for the camera.
II   Debroy Somers and His Band perform
        "There is a Co-op in the Town", cut
        with scenes of a housewife unloading
        her shopping basket of CWS brand
        goods.
III   Sam Small is getting into trouble,
        making too much noise at the studio.
IV   Debroy Somers and His Band perform
        another musical number, cut with
        appropriate scenes of Co-op
        shopping.
V   More comic business with Sam Small
        and a rope.
VI   A dance routine with the six
        Co-operettes; two of the Co-operettes
        perform the "Carrot and Onion Dance"
        against a backdrop of giant cans of
        Co-op canned goods; a tap-dance
        routine by the six Co-operettes.
VII   Sam Small is called onto the set for
        his role *(section missing)*.
VIII   A final musical number from Debroy
        Somers and His Band.
IX   Graphic card: "All the goods featured
        in this film are CWS products.
        Obtainable at CO-OPERATIVE
        STORES only."

Remarks
An extravagant musical comedy film,
utilising expensive talent and shot in the
innovative Dufaycolor process, a supposed
British rival to the American Technicolor
process. The first CWS film to use the
process had been *Homes of Britain* (1938;
NCFC 072), which, probably due to the
system's demand for high light levels (three
times that required for black and white), was
shot entirely on location. Much better colour
results were obtained on *Co-operette*, a
studio-based film – apparently, a new faster
emulsion had been developed. Only one
feature film was shot in Dufaycolor – *Sons of
the Sea* (1939), directed by veteran Maurice

Elvey. *Co-operette* was released into
cinemas, and it was claimed that five million
people saw it during the first week of
release.
    Of primary interest today are the
recreated scenes within a 1930s film studio
featuring celebrated filmmakers and
technicians – Montgomery Tully, later a
competent director of "B" films, and
cinematographer Harry Waxman, whose
later credits included *Brighton Rock* (1947)
and *The Family Way* (1966) – going about
their craft. Stanley Holloway made several
contributions to Co-operative films, first
making an appearance in a c.1937
production for the English and Scottish Joint
CWS tea department, alongside the
Houston Sisters, a film now believed to be
lost, and finally with the 1949 puppet film, *A
Change For the Better* (NCFC 121), which
he narrated. The six Co-operettes were
West End chorus girls under contract to the
theatrical impresario, C B Cochran. Debroy
Somers and His Band were a successful
dance orchestra regularly featured in
Publicity Films productions. There is a
sequence missing (section VII), which now
exists as a separate print, and released as
Sam Goes Shopping in 1939 (NCFC 084).
See also: xxi, NCFC 084, NCFC 121

NCFC 072
Homes of Britain (1938)

col · 5m 11s · sound · 16mm · NWFA
pr Merton Park Studios Production
d George Wynn cam Harry Waxman
sd Charles Poulton ed C Beaumont
mus John Reynders comm Ivan Samson
sc H V Purcell

▪ A picturesque tour around the "Homes of
Britain".

I   Shots of various contemporary
        dwellings – houses and flats.
II   Homes of Scotland: Loch Lomond;
        Edinburgh Castle; Holyrood Palace,
        Edinburgh; Abbotsford, home of Sir
        Walter Scott.
III   Homes of Yorkshire: street scene at
        Haworth; the Brontës' home.
IV   Homes of the industrial north: a family
        potter around their terraced house.
V   Homes of Surrey: old-world Tudor
        houses and village scenes.
VI   Homes of Somerset: an old-world
        village and agricultural scenes.
VII   Homes of Cornwall: homes of the
        fishermen atop a rocky headland; on
        the beach, a fisherman attends to his

lobster pots, observed by a young girl; the winding streets and narrow lanes of the port.

VIII   In the garden of a suburban home, a family enjoys afternoon tea made with CWS Prescription tea.

IX   Graphic card: "Drink Prescription Tea and Lutona Co-op Cocoa obtainable at all Co-operative Societies – and use the coupons either separately or collectively to secure valuable Free Gifts or Free Railway Travel!".

Remarks
One of three surviving films commissioned by the CWS from the Merton Park Studio in the late-1930s, and shot in the innovative Dufaycolor process. The core of the Merton Park production team was hired in 1940 by the CWS to staff its recently established film unit, with George Wynn becoming its producer, Harry Waxman its cinematographer, and C Beaumont its editor. Waxman was quickly lost to the RAF Film Unit, and eventually moved into the feature film industry, becoming a celebrated lighting cameraman, being replaced by Bert Hampson. The film is an uneasy mix of travelogue and publicity, the link apparently being two great English traditions – the Englishman's home and the English cup of tea. The relevance of CWS Lutona cocoa in this scheme can only be guessed at! It is interesting to note the promotional tie-in with the railway companies.
See also: NCFC 071

NCFC 073
How SCWS Cigarettes and Tobaccos Are Made (1938)

b/w · 13m 43s · silent · Scotland · 16mm · SFA
pr Jay's Film Service *d* Ronald L Jay

■ An information film about the production of SCWS cigarettes.

I   Workers gathering leaves on a tobacco plantation.

II   Aerial view of the SCWS tobacco factory, Shieldhall, Glasgow.

III   Hogsheads of tobacco are opened and their contents weighed; the leaves are selected and blended; overall view of the busy factory floor; female operatives select and prepare leaves; the leaves are spun into long ropes, known as the Thick Black; view of the busy cigarette-making department; stalks are removed from the leaves;

leaves are fed into the cutting machine; the cigarette-making machines – 1200 per minute; made-up cigarettes pass on a conveyor and are inspected for quality; the cigarettes are packed and wrapped.

IV   SCWS brand cigarettes: Turkish No. 1, Adana, Virginia, Cogent, Regale, Straight Cut Virginia, Special Straight Cut Virginia, Gold Flake, Pearl, Sunbeam, Shipmate Navy Cut.

V   Graphic card: "Keep your own factories busy by smoking only SCWS brands of tobaccos and cigarettes".

Remarks
Not content to sell the products of other manufacturers, a tobacco factory was established by the SCWS at its Shieldhall site in 1891. Until 1916, cigarettes were made by hand, but the introduction of mechanisation allowed for a 56% increase in production. The tobacco industry was yet another trade where the Movement was active in opposing a trust for the benefit of the consumer, the direct link to a large national profile of retail outlets affording it a measure of independence. The large range of brand cigarettes produced by the SCWS comes as a surprise to many. On the eve of the war, the SCWS marketed 39 brands of tobacco, 10 "Empire" blends, and 13 brands of cigarette. It was reckoned that the Scottish Movement produced 95% of the tobacco products sold in its stores – a trade in 1936 of £525 972. The scenes of production reveal once again the high proportion of female employment in the interwar period. The SCWS employed a workforce totalling approximately 8000 at that time, and, within the packing, assembly and food-processing trades, the proportion of women would have been high.
See also: xxxii

NCFC 074
Introducing Rogerson Hall (1938)

b/w · 2m 30s · sound · intertitles · 35mm: NFTVA / 16mm: EAFA

■ A promotional film for the recently opened workers' holiday camp.

I   Distant shots of Rogerson Hall holiday camp near Lowestoft.

II   Holiday-making workers stroll on the promenade of the complex. Families relax in the sun lounge, and letters are written home.

III   Camp-site accommodation and

facilities.

IV "First-class chefs prepare first-rate food". Mealtime.

V Sporting facilities, including table-tennis, swimming in the sea, children's play areas and the beach.

VI Torchlight procession and bonfire, "reviving the spirit of comradeship".

Remarks

Rogerson Hall holiday camp was a joint venture between the CWS and the Workers' Travel Association (WTA), and opened in the summer of 1938 at Corton near Lowestoft. It was named after the pioneer secretary of the WTA, Cecil Rogerson. Opening onto a large stretch of sandy beach, the camp covered 36 acres and offered accommodation for 360 workers and their families at rates appreciably below those demanded by the commercial camps. There is evidence that the film was originally narrated; however, the surviving print has only a musical track. The combination of the CWS and WTA was widely applauded "for developing a democratic non-profit making holiday service" (*The Co-operative News* July 1938). The camp was host to 1300 guests in the seven weeks of the 1938 season during which it was open. The CWS and the WTA established a travel organisation, Travco Camps, to develop a number of workers' holiday camps, an action that derived from the stimulus for cheap holidays created by the 1938 "Holidays With Pay" legislation. Unfortunately, the outbreak of war ensured that the plans came to little, and further camps planned for Kent and the South Coast came to nothing. A commercial holiday camp still operates on the site, which, I believe, is run by the Rank Organisation.

NCFC 075
LCS Newsreel [2] (1938)

b/w · 12m 25s · sound · 16mm · EAFA
pr LCS Film Unit *prod* Reginald Denny

■ A newsreel film of important events in the calendar of the Leicester Co-operative Society, 1938.

I An aerial view of the Clock Tower, town centre, Leicester; the LCS central premises (exterior); a switchboard operator of the LCS; a letter is typed on LCS headed paper.

II International Co-operative Day celebrations, De Montfort Hall and gardens: general scenes at the park; the large crowd enjoys a talent contest in the bandstand enclosure; Mr Mayer, board directors and Mr Mann, ex-President; a panning shot of the huge crowd; stalls and sideshows – skittles, hammering the nail, ski-bowls, coconut shy, the great turkey hunt; Mr Adams, President, introduces the guest speaker, Alfred Barnes, Chairman of the Co-operative Party; Barnes with officials of the society.

III Children's Gala Day: general scenes of the showground; the children are led in community singing; 4500 children queue up for tea and are served with a drink and cakes; "Miss LCS" is crowned and paraded around the showground in a horse and carriage, led by a brass band; a portrait of "Miss LCS" and her matrons; a large group of children smile and wave goodbye to the camera.

IV Bandleader Roy Fox visits LCS central premises. Fox and vocalists Mary Lee and Doreen Ward pose for the camera – some of the spectators are asked for comments.

V The Leicestershire Agricultural Show: dray-horses draw carts; the three horses and wagons of the CWS, Stoughton Farm, Leicestershire; the judging ceremony; CWS entries "highly commended"; show-jumping; long shot of the CWS stall; a display of horsemanship set to music; award-winning LCS horse, Dick, with his dairy cart.

Remarks

The second of two newsreels produced by the Leicester Co-operative Society in the late-1930s. The four "newsworthy" items included in this edition provide a representative sample of local society activities: the important members' celebration centring on International Co-operative Day with the presence of important figures in the Movement; an annual children's gala with its attendant fun and jovialities; a celebrity from the entertainment world participating in an in-store promotion (Roy Fox's signature tune was "Whispering"); and the Co-op's involvement in a prestigious regional trading event and show. The guest speaker at the ICD celebrations, Alfred Barnes MP, was a leading political figure in the Movement. He was the first President of the new London Co-operative Society when it was formed in 1920, and first entered Parliament in 1922 as a Co-operative MP for East Ham South.

He was Chairman of the Co-operative Party (1924-45). In a number of sections, the soundtrack is damaged and virtually inaudible.

NCFC 076
The Mitcham Exhibition (1938)

b/w and col · 13m 30s · silent · 16mm · ETV
cam, ed Thomas Barnes *titles* Joseph Reeves

▪ The RACS and the CWS stage a great celebration exhibition at the Mitcham Stadium.

I	A hoarding announcing the Co-operative Exhibition, 2-16 April 1938, organised under the joint auspices of the CWS/RACS *(colour)*.
II	London red double-decker buses and RAC coaches deliver the visitors *(colour)*.
III	A man on stilts, advertising the exhibition, greets visitors.
IV	The RACS membership booth.
V	Crowds enter the Grand Pavilion.
VI	A WCG branch on a visit.
VII	Foden's Prize Band entertains.
VIII	The exhibits displaying RACS and CWS goods: ladies at work on CWS corsetry and lingerie; a potter; a painter of ceramics amidst a display of china; textile work; butchery.
IX	Co-operative officials.
X	Daily prize draw.
XI	Troise and his Mandoliers entertain.
XII	Cricket coaching by Andy Ducat; table-tennis demonstration.
XIII	Long queues for the fashion parade; inside the fashion show; Scruffy, the canine film star; fashion through the ages; CWS Desbeau corsets sported by the "Desbeau Four" *(colour)*.
XIV	The crowds leave the exhibition *(colour)*.

Remarks
A large-scale exhibition featuring over 100 stands mounted by the RACS/CWS partnership. The society had organised a hugely successful exhibition at Woolwich in 1927, which provided a model for the event staged at the Mitcham Stadium a decade later. Numerous celebrities were contracted for the impressive proceedings: in the fashion theatre, Miss Diana Mannering, Britain's Best Bathing Belle for 1937, led the charge; and the table-tennis demonstration was conducted by B Vana, the world men's singles champion. It was claimed that the largest marquee ever used for a trade exhibition, providing 40 000 square feet under canvas, housed the trade show.

NCFC 077
New Emporium for Blackpool Co-operative Society (1938)

b/w · 7m 20s · sound · 16mm · NWFA

▪ A promotional film for the New Jubilee Emporium of the Blackpool Co-operative Society.

I	Exterior of Blackpool Co-operative Society bakery. A procession of society vans herald the official opening of the new Emporium.
II	Exteriors of the New Jubilee Emporium; arrival of members of the Board of Management.
III	Scenes of the inaugural meeting at the Jubilee Theatre which occupied the top floor of the building.
IV	Various window displays of the Emporium and store interiors: the chemists department; the drapery department; the millinery department; the clothing departments; the hairdressing salon; the furniture department; and the home furnishings department (fireplaces and bathrooms).
V	A brief tour of the Emporium is offered: the general office; executive offices and administration; the dividend check office; staff canteen; the making of show-cards and publicity; ladies footwear; café. *(End missing)*

Remarks
An earlier film, *Blackpool Co-operative Society Stone-Laying Ceremony* (1935; NCFC 038), had recorded the laying of the foundation stone of Blackpool Co-operative Society's new Emporium. The later film, providing a record of the new store which was modelled on the lines of Regent Street, London, was produced in the popular newsreel style and incorporated some innovative "roving-camera" techniques. The Jubilee News Theatre was an interesting addition to the store, and, although a number of Co-operative societies operated cinemas, the 900-seat Jubilee would remain the only newsreel theatre within the Movement. The first show began on 26 July 1938, and the venture was immediately attacked by the North-Western Branch of the Cinematograph Exhibitors' Association,

who, protective of private interests, declared against the society's practice of attracting customers to the shows with the offer of free seats in the News Theatre for those making purchases in the store in excess of five shillings. This was an inducement which the commercial cinema trade could not match.
See also: NCFC 038

NCFC 078
Towards Tomorrow: Pageant of Co-operation (1938)

b/w · 40m · sound · 16mm · NFTVA
pr LCS *prod* F H W Cox

▪ A film record of the International Co-operative Day Pageant at Wembley Stadium, July 1938.

I Various scenes around the stadium: the eager spectators; a brass band entertains in the arena; clowns entertain the crowds; the Dagenham Girl Pipers; the Pageant Master.
II Merrie England – a happy time before the people were driven from the soil: the heralds enter the arena on horseback; a village fair – Punch and Judy, dancing around a maypole, morris dancing, a dancing bear, etc.
III The arrival of the machines. Merrie Englanders are driven to the centre of the arena: an effigy of a capitalist boss is paraded into the stadium; smoking chimneys belch amidst the machines; the regime of the factory and workhouse begins; voices of protest are raised; Luddites smash machinery; the population is fired upon; Thomas Paine makes an address from the platform; ragged children are forced to work by the cruellest of systems; an address by William Cobbett, radical writer and publisher; the father of Co-operation, Robert Owen, accompanied by bright and cheerful children, makes an address; the work children of Owen's New Lanark dance around the arena, but are chased away by capitalism's thugs.
IV The 28 Rochdale Pioneers of Co-operation take centre-stage; groups representative of the workers parade around the arena – Chartists, Christian Socialists, Co-operators, SCWS, CWS.
V The Socialists have to contend with that great scourge of imperial capitalism – war: great explosions erupt amidst the combat in the arena; the people flee in horror; the angels of death claim the centre of the arena.
VI The voice of women – those who gave birth to all the fighters in the war and whose daughters filled the shells.
VII The praises of Soviet Communism and world Co-operation are sung: a vast international procession of the 39 countries, members of the International Co-operative Alliance, take to the arena. Only in unity is there hope for mankind. The world's Co-operators parade the arena in their national dress.
VIII Reginald Gosling, President of the LCS, presents the 16th International Co-operative Day Resolution. His speech is cut with impressive tableaux as the figures of Peace and Democracy ascend the Wembley stage.
IX The release of pigeons carrying messages of greeting to Co-operators in all parts of the country.

Remarks
Another advance in film technique was claimed by the film unit of the LCS for their production of the Wembley Pageant film. It was their first all-colour film photographed on 16mm with direct sound-recording (unfortunately, only a monochrome copy appears to have survived). The film cost only £500, against an estimated £5000 using traditional production methods. Fourteen technicians worked on the production, the action being captured on several cameras. As well as numerous screenings around Britain, the film also played to Co-operators in the United States, Finland, Canada and Australia.

The two-hour Pageant of Co-operation involved over 3000 artistes and was months in preparation. The music was specially scored by Alan Bush, founder of the Workers' Music Association. The scenario was provided by Montague Slater, and it was dramatically staged by André van Gyseghem. The entire seven-hour festival – which also included massed folk-dancing featuring 1200 members of Children's Circles, a display of massed tent-pitching by 600 members of the Woodcraft Folk, sheepdog trials, and comedy from Tommy Handley amongst others items – was sponsored by the London, South Suburban and Watford Societies at a cost of £15 000, and was enjoyed by an audience of over 60 000. The film records a truly remarkable dramatic presentation, which was undoubtedly beyond the means of any other

Labour organisation in Britain. A further impressive workers' pageant was staged by the Manchester and Salford Co-operative Society at the Belle Vue Stadium in 1939. The colour film record of that event has so far not been located.
See also: xxvii, NCFC 102

NCFC 079
The March of Progress (c.1938)

b/w · 10m 23s · sound · Scotland · 16mm · SFA
pr Jay's Film Service d Ronald L Jay

■ An information film about the manufacture of furniture by the SCWS.

I   A story of Shieldhall furniture: illustrations of furniture designs and manufacturing premises, 1884-1931, operated by the SCWS, Glasgow.
II   The various stages in the preparation of the timber are explained and presented: sawing the timber; storage in the timber shed; preparatory treatment in the machine shop; the planing machine; the cross-cut saw; the sandpapering machine; fixing and pressing the veneers; achieving the final high-quality finish.
III The various stages in the manufacture of furniture are explained and presented: machine-cutting dovetail joints and fitting the panels together; machine-turning the legs; cutting more complicated designs by hand; finishing on the turning-lathe; boring the dowel holes; finishing on the drum-sander; the sawdust extraction and furnace system.
IV   Interior of the assembly workshop: various procedures of carpentry and furniture construction are shown; the work of the polishing shop and of the upholstery shop.
V   The finished articles are presented: furniture for the living-room, bedroom and dining-room.

Remarks
The film presents a detailed examination of the SCWS cabinet factory, part of the giant Shieldhall complex on the outskirts of Glasgow. A twelve-acre site had been acquired at Shieldhall in 1887, and manufacturing began of boots and shoes, brushes, jam and confectionery, tobacco, coffee, chemicals and so on. That development of consolidated production was in contrast to the English CWS, which

had found it necessary to disperse its productive activity to satisfy the claims of the societies attached to its various branches. The original SCWS furniture department had commenced in June 1884 in Houston Street, Glasgow, and transferred to Shieldhall in 1888. A new building for the cabinet factory, covering four acres and making it the largest in Scotland, was erected in April 1931. All furniture made at Shieldhall was produced to plans executed by SCWS furniture designers. By 1937, the annual trade of the department had exceeded £1 million. Glasgow filmmaker Ronald Jay had set up in business in the early 1930s, having left his previous occupation of furrier through occupational illness. A celebrated amateur filmmaker, he developed a successful trade in the sponsored film sector before moving to Paramount in the early wartime period, where he was engaged as a newsreel cameraman.
See also: xxxii

NCFC 080
Out of the Depths (c.1938)

b/w · 9m 11s · sound · 16mm · EAFA
pr Leicester Co-operative Society Film Unit
prod Reginald Denny

■ "The Story of Leicester Co-operative Society Coal".

I   Exterior of Whitwick colliery; the winding engine which raises and lowers the lifts; miners enter the lift cage and descend into the pit; the winding gears; descending in the lift.
II   The cage arrives in the pit shaft and the miners leave the lift; a miner tests for gas with a Davy lamp; the electrically-driven coal-cutter; coal is conveyed from the face using a belt; a pit pony and handler; wagons of coal are brought up from the shaft and rolled along trackways.
III A Leicester Co-operative Society (LCS) coal wagon; fully-loaded LCS coal wagons in transit drawn by a steam engine; the cargo is unloaded into 100 cwt bags and placed on a LCS coal lorry; motorised and horse-drawn trucks leave the rail yard.
IV   A LCS coal lorry on its rounds; a delivery of coal is made to a suburban house; an elderly lady warms herself in front of a coal fire whilst knitting.
V   Graphic cards: "L.C.S. Coal Fires for Comfort". "L.C.S. Coal the best you

can buy with the extra saving of Full Dividend Too!". "Order at any L.C.S. Branch."

Remarks
One of several surviving films of the LCS from the mid-1930s, and amongst the most competent with convincing "live sound" sequences and imaginative construction telling the story of Co-op coal from pit to fireplace. It is interesting to note the coal wagons marked as belonging to the LCS, indicating the substantial business for the society in coal. The CWS manufactured railway wagons at its works at Peterborough, and presumably the Leicester Society stock were sourced from that supply. The voice-over is by a Welshman, presumably to provide a regional authenticity to the subject – unlike all the other LCS sound films, which were narrated by the filmmaker himself, Reginald Denny.

NCFC 081
Co-operation in Middlesborough (1939)

b/w · 11m 7s · silent · 16mm · NFTVA
pr The Film Unit (Middlesborough) *d* R Ayres *prod* W Shaw *cam* W Maxwell

■ A film record of the trading activities of the Middlesborough Co-operative Society (MCS).

I   Early morning scenes at a dairy farm.
II   Churns of milk are loaded onto a lorry. The lorry makes its way through country lanes.
III   The full churns are unloaded at the dairy: the milk is poured into vats; it is tested in the laboratory; the milk is pasteurised and filtered; the bottling process; stacked in crates, the bottled milk is cooled; home delivery by a milk float.
IV   The bakery at South Bank: dough-making; baking bread in large ovens; pie-making and confectionery-making.
V   The loading of coal sacks onto a horse-drawn cart; the full wagon leaves the MCS central coal depot.
VI   Shots of MCS store exteriors; exterior of a recently opened "pantry" shop.
VII Head office: clerks sort and add members' dividend checks; the board of directors in session.
VIII At the construction site for the new Emporium of the MCS at Linthorpe Road. Various work processes are detailed: laying girders, cementing, and so on. Progress in the

construction until virtual completion is presented.
(End missing)

Remarks
The MCS had been founded in 1867. At the time of the making of this film, it operated 130 stores in the district. The film is a competent record of the undertakings of the society, and particularly valuable for the scenes of the coal business, a Co-operative activity rarely caught on film. It is possible that the milk sequence was shot at the Co-op model dairy at Grovehill, which served the society. It is surprising that no store interiors are featured, nor any of the cultural and educational activities which would have been supported by the society. The final scenes of the film are missing. The new Linthorpe Road Emporium was destroyed in the Second World War, a victim of the Luftwaffe attack on Middlesborough.

NCFC 082
Manchester and Salford Educational Activities, Children's Gala Day (1939)

col · 6m 8s · 217' · silent · 16mm · EAFA
pr Bolton Co-operative Society Film Unit *prod* Alfred Booth

■ A film record of a local society's children's event.

I   A gala procession: a girls' dancing troupe marches down the road, followed by a marching brass band; horse-drawn tableaux promoting Co-op milk, food and the local Manchester and Salford Society; and so on.
II   The procession enters a park; large numbers of spectators follow behind a Highland pipe band; the girls' dance troupe, the marching brass band; the dressed transport, including two large promotional displays for the Manchester and Salford Children's Gala.
III   General scenes in the park.
IV   The crowning of the Co-operative Queen: the Queen and her entourage enter the showground and take up their positions on the platform; a display of classical and Highland dancing; the Queen and her party make their exit.
V   The large crowds break for refreshments, and enjoy their tea and cakes.

VI   A display of Highland dancing; modern show-type dancing; toddlers' race; boys' sack race; women's egg and spoon race.

Remarks
One of two surviving films, both in colour, produced by Alfred Booth of the Ciné Department of the Bolton Co-operative Society for the Manchester and Salford Co-operative Society. Unfortunately, a more renowned film of the Manchester and Salford Pageant, held at Belle Vue Stadium and involving over 2000 participants, is now believed to be lost. Booth made several films for his own society, a film of the 1938 Co-operative Union Congress, and films of local community events such as the 1937 Coronation celebrations, and football games involving Bolton Wanderers. One of these films has been located, *Display By the National Fire Service* (NCFC 096), a 1942 record of a display by the Bolton division of the National Fire Service.

NCFC 083
People With a Purpose (1939)

b/w · 15m 40s · sound · 16mm · ETV, IAC
pr Realist Film Unit *d* Ralph Bond
cam Gerald Gibb/Eric Wilbur *sd* H G
Halstead *cast* Joseph Reeves, Michael
Tippett, members of the RACS *comm* John
Morgan MP

■ A promotional film for the educational work of the RACS.

I   Woolwich in the 1880s. A meeting of the Education Committee of the RACS is historically re-enacted. Its first act is to provide assistance to the distressed miners of South Wales.
II   Long-shots of the Woolwich area and a brief exposition of its industrial history. The RACS developed rapidly, and by the 1930s its trading area extended over 80 square miles of South London.
III   Education Secretary, Alderman Joseph Reeves, addresses the camera, and introduces the educational aims and work of the society over the accompanying scenes: lecture courses for members and staff; the mobile film unit; music and drama groups; children's groups – classroom discussion and choir.
IV   In 1925, the Education Committee began an experiment: the children's organisation, the Woodcraft Folk

(WCF), was launched; scenes at a camp-site.
V   Summer school scenes at Shornells, the society's residential centre: gymnastics; swimming; lectures; discussion groups; outdoor theatre.

Remarks
The film was made to commemorate the Jubilee (70th anniversary) of the society. Sponsored by the Education Committee, it specifically illustrated the work of the Education Department. The RACS was innovative in many areas of Co-operative education, not least film. Of particular interest is the presentation by RACS Education Secretary (1918-38), Joseph Reeves, whose advocation of "Education for Social Change" made him an influential figure in the Movement. He had begun experiments with film work immediately upon taking up his post. In 1938, he was instrumental in organising the Workers' Film Association, a film body with responsibility to the entire Labour Movement; the WFA had responsibility for distributing the film to Co-operative and progressive organisations. It is possible that the surviving print is a version re-edited after the war by George Durham, then newly appointed as the Education Secretary of the society. An original running time of 30 minutes is listed. The musical conductor in section III is possibly Michael Tippett, who was a tutor to several of the society's musical groups in that period. The RACS – largely through the enthusiasm of Reeves – played an important role in helping to establish the WCF in 1925. The Folk has always been an autonomous, democratic national organisation, but the RACS was a key early supporter. Reeves's Folk name was the apt "Silver Tongue".
See also: NCFC 090

NCFC 084
Sam Goes Shopping (1939)

col · 5m 40s · sound · 35mm · NFTVA
pr Publicity Films *d* H V Purcell *cam* Harry
Waxman *cast* Stanley Holloway, Hal
Walters, Terry Thomas

■ A comic monologue about shopping at the Co-op.

I   Medium close-shot of Stanley Holloway who begins his monologue direct to the camera.
II   Shot of a busy High Street.
III   Interior of a Co-operative store. Customer Sam enters as the staff are

covering counters at the end of the day's trading.

IV   In the food hall, Sam explains to a young female counter assistant that he has forgotten what he came to purchase at the store, but he remembers that it began with a "d". The assistant suggests numerous items without success.

V   The boyfriend of the young girl assistant, waiting impatiently for her outside the store, is in trouble with the law over a parking offence.

VI   The senior saleswoman takes Sam into the ladies' outfitting department and alights on various "d" items, all without success.

VII   A large party of staff has now gathered to assist in the dilemma. The furniture salesman leads the party into his department and runs through the "d" things, still without success.

VIII   Outside, the increasingly impatient boyfriend is again in trouble with the police for further parking offences.

IX   Finally, the manager arrives and proceeds to detail all items beginning with "d" in the toy department. It is now 10.23 pm, but still Sam has not been able to identify what it is he is after.

X   Sam finally suggests calling the proprietor. The manager laughs and informs Sam that *he* is one of the proprietors – this is the Co-op! Sam chuckles as he remembers his wife had sent him to collect the "divi"!

XI   The staff rush out to catch the last bus. The young lady assistant finally meets up with her boyfriend, who has some words of his own beginning with "d"!

XII   Medium close-shot of Stanley Holloway who completes his monologue.

XIII   Graphic card: "All of the goods featured in this film are CWS products, obtainable at Co-operative Stores only".

Remarks

In the form in which this film survives, it is completely distinct and separate from the previous year's *Co-operette* (NCFC 071). However, it is apparent that *Sam Goes Shopping* originally constituted a part of *Co-operette*, as the film within a film. Indeed, a contemporary still appearing in *The Co-operative News* publicising *Co-operette* is in fact of Sam in the department store, and therefore from the *Sam Goes Shopping* sequence. One

remaining confusion, however, is in regard to the directorial credits: whilst *Co-operette* is credited to Montgomery Tully, *Sam Goes Shopping* bears the credit "Directed by H V Purcell". It is probable that Stanley Holloway's monologue of Sam shopping at the Co-op was considered so successful that it was released on its own with a title and credit sequence. Of particular note to contemporary audiences would have been the presence of the popular Holloway reciting one of his famous monologues. Modern audiences are more likely to be struck by an early screen performance from Terry Thomas, everyone's idea of the fool. Shot at Merton Park Studios in south London, the provisions for the store were genuine CWS productions provided by the London branch of the CWS. The film was shot in the innovative British colour process, Dufaycolor.

See also: xviii, xxi, NCFC 71, NCFC 121

NCFC 085
The Voice of the People (1939)

b/w · 17m · sound · 16mm · ETV, NFTVA
pr Realist Film Unit *d* Frank Sainsbury *prod* Ralph Bond *cam* A Jeakins *sd* H G Halstead *mus* Lennox Berkeley *sc* Ritchie Calder *comm* Ted Willis/Lewis Casson

■ A film detailing the progress made, through struggle, by the common people.

I   "England At The Beginning Of The Last Century". A sequence of 19th century engravings followed by shots of smoking mills, over which is played the hymn, "Jerusalem".

II   "The Struggle of the Common People in the Nineteenth Century": a ragged worker and his young son, Thomas, set off for work at 4.00 am; the boy enduring the hardships of industrial labour; a group of workers meet secretly to discuss their aspirations – they are arrested and jailed; a group of workers listen to a speech by Robert Owen, model factory owner at New Lanark; the trial of the Tolpuddle Martyrs; a Chartist meeting is broken up by soldiers; the Rochdale Pioneers and their Toad Lane store (exterior); working men studying in a Mechanics Institute library.

III   An animated sequence outlining the "March of Progress", including: 1863 – CWS formed; 1867 – town workers win vote; 1871 – legal recognition of trade unions; 1880 – Workmen's

Compensation Act; 1892 – Keir Hardie elected to Parliament; 1900 – Labour Party formed; 1918 – women over 30 win vote; 1924 – first Labour Government; 1934 – London puts Labour in charge.

IV   Today: a father carries his young son, Thomas, to school; scenes at a nursery school; the family health centre at Peckham; scenes at a modern, well-constructed school; children enjoying recreation in the open air and sunshine; the improved housing of the workers; training in technical schools; a workers' educational class.

V   "The Continuing Struggle": shots of closed mills and the Labour Exchange – the problems of the Depression and unemployment; the evils of the Means Test; wasted resources – uncultivated land when nine million remain undernourished.

VI   The Future – scenes of Co-operative production: a dairy (interior); factories (exterior and interior); farms; a store of the London Co-operative Society (exterior); agricultural workers gathering wheat; and so on.

VII   Scenes of derelict 19th century Britain are contrasted with the improved conditions of workers in the 1930s.

Remarks

The second film in the "Five Year Film Plan" of the London Joint Education Committee of the metropolitan Co-operative societies, following *Advance Democracy* (1938; NCFC 070). (This time Grays Co-operative Society contributed to the film's funding, in addition to the four instigating societies of Royal Arsenal, London, South Suburban and Enfield Highway.) No further films were forthcoming under the plan, due to the outbreak of war in September 1939. The two films, in terms of production values and professionalism, represent the pinnacle of Left political filmmaking in Britain in the interwar period. *The Voice of the People* boasts some impressive and interesting credits: commentary written by Socialist actor, Lewis Casson, and future scriptwriter, Ted Willis (then active in the Labour League of Youth); script outline by the Labour journalist, Ritchie Calder of *The Daily Herald*; and music by the noted composer, Lennox Berkeley: all evidence of the political commitment of artists and intellectuals in the late-1930s. The film's approach parallels the emerging revisionist social history of the period, apparent in such classics as A L Morton's *A People's History of England*,

published by the Left Book Club in 1938, and Cole and Postgate's *The Common People* (1938), which saw history in terms of class struggle, rather than liberal democratic progress. The film lists the formation of the Labour Party as 1900, although that was the Labour Representation Committee; the Labour Party proper emerged in 1906. The film was listed in some contemporary sources as *Achievement*, but is not to be confused with the 1948 film of this name, produced for the SCWS (see NCFC 116). *See also:* xxvi, NCFC 105

NCFC 086
Women's Co-operative Guild Congress Hull (1939)

b/w · 22m 45s · silent · intertitles · 16mm · NWFA
pr CWS

▪ A film record of the 1939 Women's Co-operative Guild Congress at Hull.

I   Street scenes of Hull town centre. Close-shot of a war memorial. Delegates arriving at Paragon Station. Exterior shots of the City Hall, Congress venue, with delegates queuing to gain access.

II   Inside the hall. Delegates register and settle their accommodation arrangements at the "lodgings office".

III   Standing Orders Committee in session.

IV   The Central Committee in session – President Mrs Edith Williams and Vice-President Mrs Dodsworth.

V   Delegates tour the historic city and are seen boarding a local omnibus.

VI   The Lord Mayor addresses the delegates. Shots of the gathered audience and of the main platform. The Lady Mayoress is presented with a copy of the book, *The Lady with the Basket* – the story of the WCG. The President gives her address.

VII   The General Secretary welcomes the international delegates. Official guests, including Mr J Peddie, CWS director, join the group.

VIII   The official opening of Congress. Shots of 2000 gathered delegates. Presentation of Standing Orders, followed by the Annual Report. Various addresses from the platform, including the Secretary's. Shots of the Visitors' Gallery dressed with banners. Vote by ballot.

IX   Delegates leave for lunch. Visit to the

CWS exhibition and Hull Co-operative Society Central Store. Shots of the Co-operative Insurance Society exhibition stand and other CWS exhibits.

X   Shots of WCG banners, including the famous "Women with the Basket" national banner.

Remarks
The WCG Congress was known as the "Mothers' Parliament" within the Movement. This film was produced by the CWS National Film Service, inaugurated in 1938, and followed an innovative film of that year's Co-operative Union Congress held at Scarborough. A Guild Congress was first filmed in 1938 at Southampton, and produced independently by Mr H Niendorf. The 1939 film represents an important historical document, providing the only known film footage of Co-operation in Hull, as well as the first of only two surviving records of one of the premier annual events in the Co-operative calender, the WCG Congress.
See also: NCFC 261

NCFC 087
Woodcraft Festival Camp (1939)

col · 10m 58s · silent · 16mm · EAFA
cam George Durham

▪ A film record of a Woodcraft Folk camp, sponsored by the London Co-operative Society.

I   Views of tents and Woodcraft Folk campers in green pastures.
II   WCF totems and banners.
III Boys constructing tents.
IV Two groups march past the camera; close-shots of young campers; kinsfolk leaders and teachers; an adult refugee from Czechoslovakia; "Little Otter", founder of the WCF (Leslie Paul) in conversation with "Rowan", London Co-operative Society and "Swift Canoe", Headman of London Kin.
V   Preparations for meals: pits are dug; wood is gathered; pots are put to the boil; food is served and eaten.
VI Organised pastimes are enjoyed by an enthusiastic audience: boys' race; high-jump; folk-dancing; choir; drama presentation; children at play; first aid to an injured girl; reading; play wrestling.
VII The council fire.

Remarks
A film record of the Park Lodge Farm Camp, Harefield, Whitsun 1939. An annual event, in 1939 the camp was attended by 500 participants. The film is a remarkable colour record of Woodcraft Folk ceremonies and activities, superbly shot by George Durham on the eve of the Second World War. Also notable is the presence of Leslie Paul, founder of the organisation in 1925, when it split from the Kibbo Kift, itself a splinter group from the Scout Movement. Members were given Folk names, as indicated in section IV. The original idea was that, like a North American Indian, people should earn their name; other Indian ceremonies – totems, fire-building, woodcraft skills – are evident in the film. The building of the council fire was an important ceremony and, as shown, the fire is constructed like a pagoda, for which birch bark was an important fuel.

NCFC 088
Divi Day at Manchester and Salford (c.1939)

col · 6m 52s · silent · 16mm · NWFA
pr Bolton Co-operative Society Film Unit
prod Alfred Booth

▪ A film detailing some of the membership, trading and cultural activities of the Manchester and Salford Co-operative Society.

I   Members queue to draw their dividend; the cashier at work; cash transactions are made.
II   Busy scenes inside a Co-operative store during a sale: the bakery department; women customers search through a pile of hats; bargains to be had in the mantles department; corsets and lingerie; the shoe department; china and glass; clocks; furniture; grocery and provisions; menswear.
III Employees' sports day: the announcer, Alfred Robins, at the microphone; the judges and officials getting ready; men's sprint race; women's egg and spoon race; bicycle race; scenes around the stadium; the schools' relay race; men's relay; women's skipping race; men's sprint race; start of a bicycle race; women's sprint race; women's sack race; walking race; men's sprint race; the St John's Ambulance crew treating an injured athlete and posing for a

portrait; scenes around the track; men's middle-distance race; a tug-of-war; men's obstacle race.

IV   The President, J H H Codd, makes an address; Mrs Codd presenting the awards at the prize-giving ceremony.

Remarks
In June 1935, the Bolton Co-operative Society established a Ciné Department at its Market Street premises. Its manager, Alfred Booth, encouraged the use of 16mm film for educational and propaganda purposes, and received some commissions from the Manchester and Salford Co-operative Society. Booth's work was distinguished by the quality of his colour photography (it was claimed that his 1938 colour film of a Bolton Wanderers football match was the first of its kind), evident here with the brief scenes of "Divi Day" – the only such occurrence recorded in colour before the war. The Manchester and Salford Society was founded in 1859, and by 1939 had over 90 000 members.

NCFC 089
This Milk Business! (c.1939)

b/w · 11m 45s · silent · 16mm · NFTVA
pr Loris Hill

■ A film record of the London Co-operative Society's dairy operations.

I   The dairy herd at the LCS farm, Ongar, Essex. The cows are washed, scrubbed and fed before milking.
II   Milking of the cattle by hand. The milk is stored and cooled. Tuberculin-tested milk is bottled immediately.
III Loading of churns of milk onto a LCS van, which sets off through country lanes to the society's Manor Park pasteurising depot.
IV   At the depot, the churns are unloaded and the milk is poured into the pasteurising plant. A CWS milk tanker is also seen unloading.
V   The churns are sterilised before their return to the farm.
VI   The milk is pasteurised inside the plant at 145-150°F. Various shots of the process: refrigeration; sterilisation of bottles; stamping of bottle caps; bottling and crating.
VII Crates are loaded onto LCS lorries.
VIII A hand-drawn milk float delivers several crates to a school. At 11.00 am the primary schoolgirls enjoy their ⅓ pint of school milk. A mixed infant

class does likewise.
IX   End title card: "Have you had your LCS milk today?".

Remarks
The retailing of bread and milk were important staples of Co-operative trade by the interwar period. Both were popular subjects for Co-operative films, as each provided a productive cycle completely within Co-operative control: a society owned the farms and handled production, distribution and retail operations. In 1926, the LCS produced 1 365 349 gallons of unpasteurised milk, and claimed that its power in the London market was such as to be able to keep the price of the capital's milk down, thus substantially helping "the mothers and children to a further supply of milk" (W H Brown, *A Century of London Co-operation* [London: London Co-operative Society, 1928]). The Ongar farm was also used for holiday camping by members' children.

NCFC 090
[Work of Education Committee] (c.1939)

b/w · 11m 50s · sound · 16mm · ETV

■ An information film about the work of the Education Committee of the RACS.

I   A general introduction to the Royal Arsenal Co-operative Society (RACS), the second largest society in Britain, accompanies shots of a RACS bakery van leaving a depot and the Tower House department store (exterior).
II   Former Education Secretary, Alderman Joseph Reeves, outlines the work of the Education Department.
III A RACS lecture in a Co-op meeting room. Mr R Sorensen MP discusses the unstable world situation and the Movement's required response.
IV   A RACS film display of *Advance Democracy* (1938; NCFC 070); the society magazine, *Comradeship* (scene set in RACS store).
V   Joseph Reeves introduces the new Education Secretary, Anthony Bingham, who provides details of *Comradeship*.
VI   The cultural work of the department: Junior Circle on an outing at the coast; international visits; canvassing for educational classes; the Education Committee.
VII Preparations for war and the Co-operators' resistance to Fascism.

The hopes for social democracy.
(End missing)

Remarks
The film was probably released as *Workers' Education* (aka *Educate and Liberate*). Hogenkamp and Attfield give the year of such a title as 1937, while Ryan suggests 1939. As Reeves vacated his post with the RACS in November 1938, the latter is undoubtedly more accurate. Anthony William Bingham had previously been Education Secretary of the Derby Co-operative Society, for which he had helped in the production of several films of the society's activities, all now believed lost. Certain shots and material are also found in *People With a Purpose* (1939; NCFC 083), produced by the Realist Film Unit (RFU) for RACS. Similar in structure and style, this film could equally be a RFU production. Some initial scenes of the film are missing, as is some material from the end.

NCFC 091
Co-operation Wins (c.1940)

b/w · 28s · silent · 16mm · NWFA

▪ A brief cinema advertising film.

I   Graphic card: "Co-operation Wins. Pull together and win the peace!".
II   Scene at a milk-bottling plant: "Co-op Milk, like all other Co-op products, is Purest and Best!".
III "Tens of Thousands of Pounds in DIVIDEND Every Quarter. Shop at the Co-op!!" Also full Educational Activities! Wigan and District Equitable Co-operative Society Ltd."

Remarks
A further cinema advertisement promoting local businesses, retrieved from the Lyric Cinema in Upholland, Lancashire. Two of the films relate to the local Co-operative society (see also *"I've Joined the Co-op Dear!"* [c.1940; NCFC 092]), the Wigan and District Equitable, promoting those staples of Co-operative production and distribution, milk and bread. This example contains interesting contemporary references to the war, and is already commenting on the need for workers to "win the peace".
See also: NCFC 092

NCFC 092
"I've Joined the Co-op Dear!" (c.1940)

b/w · 9s · silent · 16mm · NWFA

▪ A brief cinema advertising film.

I   A still of a young couple: "I've Joined the Co-op dear!", "Good Work!".
II   Interior scenes at a bakery.
III Graphic card: "Yes, Everyone says the CO-OPERATIVE BAKERY is easily the best!".
(End missing)

Remarks
One of a collection of cinema advertisements, promoting local businesses, and retrieved from the Lyric Cinema, Upholland, Lancashire. Two of the films relate to the local Co-operative society (see also *Co-operation Wins* [c.1940; NCFC 092]), the Wigan and District Equitable, promoting those staples of Co-operative production and distribution, bread and milk. The society had been formed in 1889, and by the beginning of the war had grown to a membership of 11 100, operating 29 branch stores. The society had its own bakery and dairy. These silent films would probably have been accompanied by a cinema organist or some sort of musical track provided. An end title, designating the Wigan and District Equitable Co-operative Society, is missing.
See also: NCFC 091

NCFC 093
Behind the Counter (1941)

b/w · 25m 12s · sound · 16mm · NWFA
pr CWS Film Unit *d* George Wynn *sd* L Page *ed* C Beaumont *cam* T R Thumwood *cast* Elliott Makeham, Max Adrian *ad* Harold Watson

▪ A training film for branch managers of Co-operative stores.

I   A customer complains about poor service to the owner of a private store. Another customer is lost by the incompetence of the two young counter assistants.
II   George, the nephew of the store owner and a successful Co-op branch manager, explains to his uncle where he is going wrong.
III The importance of stock organisation and tidy shelves; the basics of salesmanship; window displays – the "deadly sins" of window-dressing: drabness; avoid "pushing" old unwanted stock; overcrowding; lack of

design; being out-of-date; and monotony.

IV The uncle visits George at his Co-op store, and receives a demonstration of efficient management and salesmanship: fitness and appearance of the sales staff; knowledge about the stock and the use of notebooks – the example of CWS biscuits is detailed with scenes at the biscuit factory at Crumpsall; organising the stock and shelf allocation – the use of a plan and number references; methods for stock control; dealing with difficult customers; the use of advertising.

V George sums up the lessons of the film.

Remarks

Possibly the first training film of the Co-operative Movement. Plans for the preparation of a film on salesmanship were first discussed early in 1939, when it was noted that such films had been effectively used by the Swedish Movement and by competitors such as the Bacon Marketing Board. The proposed cost of £1000 seems to have put an end to that project. However, with the establishment of the CWS Film Unit in 1940, the prospect of a training film, this time for counter staff and branch managers, became more feasible. Although praised on its release in 1941, the film was apparently restricted in its screenings, no doubt due to the war, and was re-released successfully in 1946. Some of the Co-op store scenes were shot on the premises of the South Suburban Co-operative Society. The plot of the film is curiously altruistic, in that George, in helping his uncle, is aiding a competitor to become more efficient in the running of his store.

See also: xxxii, NCFC 110

NCFC 094
Manchester Took It, Too (1941)

b/w · 10m 42s · sound · 16mm · NFA, NFTVA, NWFA
pr CWS Film Unit

▪ A film record of the Manchester "Blitz", December 1940.

I Various shots of fire-fighters, burning buildings and smouldering rubble.

II The remains of Martins Bank and firemen wielding hoses on Corporation Street; the burning roof of the Co-operative Union building, Hanover Street; the CWS Furnishing Block, Balloon Street, ablaze; the CWS company of the Home Guard keep people away from the danger zone; CWS employees returning to work at the central premises, Corporation Street, with its windows shattered; the gutted Mitchell Memorial Hall, former meeting place of the CWS; the devastated roof of the CWS Furnishing Block; scars left by incendiary bombs which failed to burn through the roof of the CWS Bank building; Manchester's Piccadilly in ruins – also Miller Street, St Mary's Gate, the Victoria Arcade, the Oldham Road Goods Station, the Corn Exchange, the Market Place, the Free Trade Hall, the Royal Exchange and Manchester Cathedral.

III The salvage squads at work, demolishing buildings and making structures safe; work squads clear debris; troops taking a break at a mobile canteen; US presidential candidate Wendell Willkie tours the city; CWS firemen give a demonstration of their life-saving skills; CWS Home Guard ever on the alert; Manchester's men and women resume the task of work – it's business as usual.

Remarks

The film's title clearly derives from the celebrated Crown Film Unit documentary, *London Can Take It* (1940), and indicates the resentment felt at the time that the metropolis was receiving excessive attention. The CWS Film Unit had been established early in 1940, and thus was in a fortunate position to capture the Manchester "Blitz" of late-December 1940. Particularly heavily hit were the districts around the headquarters of the CWS and the Co-operative Union, and the Unit claimed advantageous positions on top of CWS buildings to get their powerful images. Visiting US politician, Wendell Willkie, had just been defeated in the November 1940 presidential election, which saw Franklin Roosevelt returned for an unprecedented third term of office.

NCFC 095
A Romance of Co-operation (1941)

b/w · 5m 30s · sound · 16mm · EAFA
pr WFA *d, comm* Joseph Reeves
cam Emmanuel Yospa

▪ A propaganda film for the Peterborough

Co-operative Society (PCS).

I   Views of Peterborough, including the cathedral.
II   A Co-op delivery boy arrives with a housewife's purchases; the society's new model bakery (exterior); bread is loaded onto a horse-drawn delivery van; milk is delivered to a doorstep by a milkwoman; scenes of the society's dairy herd, pigs and hens; the society's model dairy (interior) and milk floats; a fleet of vans and lorries leave the depot.
III   A PCS branch store (exterior); a housewife is greeted by the store assistant on the steps; Co-op chemists (exterior); the society's central premises (exterior); branch store (exterior); the members' magazine, the *Peterborough Co-operator*.
IV   Long-shot of Peterborough Cathedral. *(End missing)*

Remarks
In 1938, Joseph Reeves, Education Secretary of the RACS, had been instrumental in the establishment of the Workers' Film Association (WFA), of which he became Secretary-Organiser. With his aim of a film production body representative of the entire Labour Movement apparently realised, the Association was immediately restricted by the advent of war, and only a few commissions for films were forthcoming. The mainstay of demand came from Co-operative societies and this film commissioned by the Education Committee of the PCS, which has only recently come to light, is the only example so far located. It is of considerable historical interest, being both directed and narrated by Reeves, the only known instance from a man more renowned for his administrative, rather than technical, abilities. That was probably a necessity brought about by wartime staffing difficulties. In 1941, the PCS had 55 000 members and distributed over £100 000 in dividend annually. It is interesting to note the appearance of a Co-op milkwoman, once again a consequence of wartime employment circumstances. Surprisingly, the film does not include any store interiors, perhaps reflective of the Association's lack of lighting equipment in those difficult times. Manny (Emannuel) Yospa and Joe Reeves were two of the three full-time employees at the WFA. They were ably assisted by their secretary, Gladys, whom Joe later married. *A Romance of Co-operation* was Manny Yospa's first film assignment as cinematographer.

NCFC 096
Display By the National Fire Service (1942)

b/w · 8m 5s · silent · 16mm · NWFA
pr Bolton Co-operative Society *d* Alfred Booth

▪ Men and women of the National Fire Service, Bolton, demonstrate their skills.

I   Moss Bank Park: spectators line the display area; a brass band entertains; senior officers inspect the men and their fire-fighting equipment; arrival of dignitaries; a march past by men and women of the National Fire Service; parade ground drill.
II   The display: the construction of temporary water-tanks; the use of hand-drawn engines; the bicycle despatch riders and a mock communications exercise; display with a large motorised engine; a body-lift using the engine's giant ladders; fire-fighting from on top of a ladder; descent by wire from the tall ladders; historic horse-drawn engine enters the arena; a comic display with a theatrical horse; display with the large powerful hoses; "blow football" with the power hoses.

Remarks
The display took place at Bolton's Moss Bank Park, 1 July 1942, and was conducted by Fire Force Area 28, "A" Division. Although not a Co-operative subject, it was one of a series of local civic films produced by Alfred Booth, manager of the Pharmacy and Photographic Department of Bolton Co-operative Society's Market Street store. Numerous regional propaganda films were undertaken for the Movement by the Bolton Society, but only a small number survive. The National Fire Service had been created in May 1941, when, as a consequence of the Blitz in 1940, it was essential that a system of unified control be brought over the whole country. The NFS replaced the 1666 local fire brigades which operated before the war. As some material is repeated twice in this film, it is unlikely that it represents the release version enjoyed by audiences at the time.
See also: NCFC 082

NCFC 097
Eastern Rose (1942)

b/w · 5m 32s · sound · 16mm · IWM, SFA

- A promotional film for Co-op tea.

I   Tea plantations on the island of Ceylon: workers with baskets leave their village for the day's work; tea-picking on a plantation; children of the workers are taught in special schools; foremen examine the newly plucked leaves; baskets are weighed and transported to the nearby factory by an overhead cable mechanism.

II   The tea factory: the leaves are laid out to dry; the rolling machines; the rolling floor; the drying ovens; the tea is sifted and graded; packing in the tea chests.

III   Loading of the chests onto cargo ships; a wartime convoy.

IV   Testing and tea-tasting in the UK.

V   At home, a housewife makes a pot of tea and praises the virtues of Co-op tea.

VI   Graphic card: "Co-operative Tea. Available ONLY at CO-OPERATIVE STORES".

Remarks
As the surviving prints carry a British Board of Film Censors "U" certificate, the film was obviously screened in commercial cinemas, which was not particularly unusual. Of the seven CWS films produced in 1943, six were released theatrically into cinemas, and four screened non-theatrically by Ministry of Information roadshows. The film has similarities with the earlier *Rose of the Orient* (1935; NCFC 041), and indeed uses some of the same footage. This film brings the story up-to-date with its wartime convoy scenes, illustrating how the Co-op was ensuring the provision of the nation's favourite beverage.

NCFC 098
Golden Leaves (1942)

b/w · 5m 16s · sound · 16mm · NFTVA
pr CWS Film Unit

- An information film about cigarette-manufacture by the CWS, especially promoting the Raydex brand.

I   Brief scenes at a tobacco plantation in the United States; hogsheads of American tobacco are spilt open.

II   Scenes showing the testing of tobacco in a laboratory; tobacco leaves are weighed at the start of the blending process; leaves are softened in steamers and rotary moisteners;

female operatives remove the stalks; the leaves are shredded by mechanical cutters; the drying process; the tobacco is combed by large rollers; the tobacco is rolled into paper and cut into convenient lengths; the inspection process whereby faulty cigarettes are removed; making-up packets of twenty.

III   A packet of Raydex Navy Cut cigarettes.

IV   Graphic card: "Obtainable at Co-operative Stores Only".

Remarks
The CWS Manchester tobacco factory was purchased in March 1898. Initially, there was a powerful lobby within the Movement against the production of tobacco products, and the views of the Anti-Narcotic League were actively represented. One commentator realised the dilemma: "This progress is not comforting for a member of the Anti-Narcotic League, unless he should be a Co-operator, in which case there is a consolation in the conquest of the co-operative tobacco trade by the CWS" (quoted in Percy Redfern, *The Story of the CWS* [Manchester: CWS, 1913]). The CWS Film Unit, formed in 1940, busied itself in the early phases with films focusing on tobacco, with several titles on the subject released by 1942: *Tobacco*, *Golden Harvest* (both c.1942; NCFC 397 and NCFC 395), *Calling All Smokers* (1948; NCFC 117) and this film.

NCFC 099
The Machine is Mastered (1942)

b/w · 9m 17s · sound · 16mm · EAFA, IWM, NFTVA
pr Publicity Films *prod* Cecil Musk
d Terence Egan *cam* T R Thumwood
sd Charles Poulton *ed* C Beaumont
mus Leslie Bridgewater *ad* Harold Watson

- A film promoting the need for a planned and Co-operative approach to production.

I   A sequence of close-shots of machinery in operation.

II   Consequences of the machine: it has built cities – shots of London's buildings; improved communications – a train, aeroplane, road haulage; shaped thoughts – the printing press (producing *The Reynold's News*), a couple listen to the radio; produced modern architecture – including the De La Ware Pavilion, Bexhill;

increased leisure – shot of a busy beach.

III Failure in the machine age: idle men outside a Labour Exchange; unemployed miners scrambling on a slag heap; city slums.

IV The history of the machine: stone tools; an ancient potter; an Elizabethan tailor; specialisation and the division of labour; the threat of the machine to workers' skills – the Luddites smash machines; the unhealthy 19th century industrial landscape – factories and slums; the exploitation of the common people – scenes of toil and poverty; a gluttonous industrialist, his whims and the trade cycle.

V The Co-operative way: scenes of model industrial conditions.

VI Sir William Bradshaw, President of the CWS, speaks about the history and aims of the Co-operative Movement.

VII The planned system of Co-operative production: scenes of industrial manufacture within CWS factories; CWS leisure and welfare – sports, canteens, and so on; Co-operative store interior – a housewife purchases from a counter assistant; a sequence of close-shots of machinery in operation – The Machine is Mastered!

VIII Graphic card: "Towards the Co-operative Commonwealth".

Remarks
Following the worst of the Blitz in 1940/41, the progressive section within society was putting its mind to rebuilding the country in peacetime. Capitalism was felt to have failed the people during the Depression, and faith was being put in planning. Here is an early film contribution to the debate, whereby a planned system of Co-operative production was hailed as the future saviour of the workers, and capable of humanising the regime of the machine. This film and similar progressive documentaries were distributed widely by organisations such as the Ministry of Information and the Workers' Film Association, and, it has been argued, contributed to the Labour Party's stunning victory in the 1945 General Election. Some of the material reappears in the even more strident and impressive film, *Song of the People* (1945; NCFC 105). Sir William Bradshaw was elected Chairman of the CWS Board and President of the society in July 1936. His first post within the Movement was as a check boy with the Ripley Co-operative Society, Derbyshire. (A check boy was a menial junior post

involving the filing of members' purchasing details for dividend purposes.) Bradshaw was knighted as a Coronation honour in 1937. Edward Cecil Musk was a member of the Film Producers' Guild, and, as a producer-director, worked on numerous productions in the war years, including the celebrated documentary, *The Mosquito.*
See also: NCFC 105

NCFC 100
Out of the Box (1942)

b/w · 11m · sound · Scotland · 35mm: NFTVA / 16mm: SFA
pr Merton Park Studios Production *d* Terence Bishop *cam* Cyril Jenkins *sd* Charles Tasto *ed* C Beaumont *ad* Harold Watson *sc* H V Purcell *cast* Gordon McLeod, Hay Petrie

■ A dramatic account of the Fenwick Weavers, pioneer 18th century Co-operators in Scotland.

I James Hargreaves demonstrates his new revolutionary invention, the spinning jenny. A narrator explains the distress caused to weavers by the widespread introduction of the new process.

II The weavers of Fenwick, Ayrshire, meet to discuss their problems. They resolve to commission a strong-box and begin a mutual savings scheme. The box is ordered and collected from the local carpenter.

III A members' financial assistance scheme is commenced and payments are paid to members in need.

IV March 1769. Due to excessive demand, an emergency meeting is held. The idea of the society buying flour wholesale – with concomitant savings for individual members – is hit upon. The birth of the Scottish Co-operative Movement is declared.

V Brief montage of working-class strife in the early 19th century, including Luddites breaking machinery.

VI 1830. An address by Scottish pioneer Alexander Campbell advocating Co-operation as the means for the working classes to alleviate their distress, interspersed with the dates of establishment of Co-operative societies in Scotland.

VII 1867. Campbell argues for the establishment of a SCWS. In 1868, after an initial failure, a successful Wholesale society is launched.

VIII The growth and development of the SCWS until 1941, with a brief examination of the Shieldhall manufacturing complex, Glasgow.

IX The SCWS in the First and Second World Wars; shots of trench warfare and the "Blitz" of Glasgow (?).

Remarks
Out of the Box was the first major film commissioned by the SCWS. The film invites some intriguing speculation. Produced two years prior to the Rochdale centenary, cynics might argue that the Scottish Movement sought to pre-empt the celebrations planned by the English Movement; 1944 was not widely celebrated as the centenary of Co-operation in Scotland. A particularly striking feature of the film is the absence of reference to Rochdale in a sequence noting the establishment of Co-operative societies, although, in fairness, the film aims only to chart the emergence of Co-operation in Scotland. It was claimed that the film was shot in both Technicolor and black and white. Only the monochrome version is known to have survived. Filmmaker Terry Bishop was to serve in the Royal Naval Film Unit, and later worked as a director for Greenpark Productions.
See also: xxxi, NCFC 103, NCFC 116

NCFC 101
Progress (1942)

b/w · 42m 50s · sound · 16mm · EAFA
pr Pioneer Films

▪ A record of 60 years of Co-operative enterprise in Coalville and district, Leicestershire, 1882-1942.

I   A sketch artist draws the frontages of the Coalville Working Men's Co-operative Society's original branch stores. The actual contemporary stores are then viewed: branch no. 1, Ellistown (exterior); branch no. 2, Whitwick (exterior). The device of the sketch artist leading into actual shots of the stores is consistently used throughout the film.

II   The Whitwick branch store (interior): counter staff at work; a busy counter; preparing bacon and butter.

III The Swannington branch (exterior); the Ibstock branch (exterior and interior); the London Road branch (exterior); the Hugglescote branch (exterior); the Ashby Road branch (exterior); interior views show busy counter staff and the preparation of parcels for home delivery to customers; the Thringstone branch (exterior); the Bagworth branch (exterior); the Desford branch (exterior); the Central Allied Departmental Store (exterior); the Markfield branch (exterior) – interior scenes of the provisions and grocery department and the drapery department; the Emporium at Ashby de la Zouch (exterior) – internal scenes of the drapery, mantles, furnishing, grocery and provisions departments; the Donisthorpe branch (exterior) – interior scenes of the grocery and provisions department and women's clothing department; the Measham branch (exterior) – interior scenes of grocery and provisions department and women's clothing department; the Moira branch (exterior); the Barlestone branch (exterior); the Newbold branch (exterior); the Broomleas (?) branch (exterior); the Worthington branch (exterior) – interior scenes of the busy grocery and provisions department; the new branch store at Heanor (?) (exterior).

IV   Charts and tables illustrating the society's progress in membership, assets and sales, and so on, 1882-1942.

V   The central premises, Belvoir Road, Coalville: exterior views; interior scenes – millinery department; mantles department; drapery department; men's tailoring department (with shots of tailors and seamstresses at work); clothing accessories; footwear department (with shots of cobblers at work); hardware department; chemists department (exterior); fancy goods department (interior); furnishing department (interior); restaurant (interior); grocery and provisions department (interior); butchery department (exterior and interior).

VI   The society's abattoir, Ravenstone Road: exterior view; cattle are led into the premises; weighing of carcasses; cold storage of carcasses and poultry.

VII The society's bakery, Mantle Lane: exterior view; the granary storehouse; flour is fed into a hopper; the mixing of dough in huge drums; the fermentation process; the proving machine; a conveyor takes the cuts of dough to the ovens; loaves are taken

from the oven and racked for cooling; preparation of cakes and confectionery – various samples, straight from the oven, are viewed.
VIII The dairy fleet leaves the depot.
IX The society's garage. Mechanics at work.
X The society's distribution centre (exterior): various scenes of stored goods; goods are checked onto the vans.
XI The administration offices: the General Manager's Office; the Secretary's Office; the Finance Officer.
XII Payment of dividend: a queue of members forms outside the offices; inside, membership credentials are checked, and cash dividends are issued.
XIII The General Offices: clerks work at their ledgers; the work of the Check Office; the Mutuality Office; the Board of Directors in session – the members are introduced; the Education Committee in session – the members are introduced.
XIV A junior Co-op choir.
XV The Superannuation Joint Committee in session – the members are introduced.
XVI A brief montage of the varied activities of the society; the artist's sketchbook of society branch stores is rapidly gone through.
XVII End-card: "Each for All".

Remarks
An extraordinarily detailed film record of a local Co-operative society with its 25 branch stores. The Coalville Working Men's Co-operative Society was formed in 1882, and the film was made to commemorate the 60th Jubilee Year of the society – no doubt a difficult task in the austerity years of the Second World War. The film is particularly rich in dealing with the trading aspects of the society, whilst the educational and cultural activities are poorly served. The scenes dealing with dividend payout are the most detailed captured on film. The film was made by Pioneer Films, the film production unit of the London Co-operative Society, headed by noted Co-op film pioneer, Frank Cox. The unit was particularly active in the early war years, and *Progress* appears to be their only surviving film from that period. In 1942, Pioneer Films became the 16mm production outfit for the Workers' Film Association, and this film was probably a commission awarded by the WFA.
See also: xxvii

NCFC 102
"A Romance of the Century" (1942)

b/w · 4m 53s · sound · 16mm · EAFA
pr Pioneer Films *comm* Mrs C S Ganley JP

▪ A propaganda film for the London Co-operative Society.

I Medium-close-shot of Mrs Ganley, President of the London Co-operative Society, who begins her presentation.
II Facts and figures about the society – capital, membership, trade.
III Map of the trading area of the LCS, 70 miles wide from east to west.
IV Stills of society trading and productive premises – stores, bakery, garage, mobile delivery van, creamery, etc.
V A montage of Co-operative products and premises – biscuits, ceramics, shoes, shirts, boots, store interiors, farm, bread, transport, opticians, furnishings, laundery, real estate, pharmacy, the LCS Film Unit – Pioneer Films.
VI Ganley exhorts the audience to become active members – to join the Women's Co-operative Guild, the Co-operative Party, youth organisations, etc.

Remarks
A unique film record of Co-operator and Socialist, Caroline Ganley (1879-1966). A board member of the LCS between 1921 and 1946, she was the first woman President, elected in 1942. She had joined the Labour Party in 1918 and sat on the National Executive Council for many years, serving as its Vice-President (1921-23). She was the Co-operative and Labour Member of Parliament for Battersea South (1945-51). Her extensive social and political interests extended to the Women's Co-operative Guild and to civic matters.
    The film boasted an innovative construction with an obvious "bridge" between sections V and VI. That was to allow for the screening of other LCS films at that point, directly after the introduction to the LCS Film Unit (a unique glimpse). Available titles would have included *Towards Tomorrow: Pageant of Co-operation* (1938; NCFC 078), *Peace Parade* (1937; NCFC 061) and *The People Who Count* (1937; NCFC 062). Pioneer Films was particularly active during the war years, despite having its production facilities in Grays Inn Road destroyed by bombing. Unfortunately, only two of their films from that period have so far been located.

NCFC 103
Two Good Fairies (1943)

b/w · 14m 46s · sound · Scotland · 16mm ·
NFTVA
pr Norman's Film Production *d* Germain
Burger *sc* C E M Joad *ph* Harry Orchard
ed Eric Purcell *cast* Philip Friend, Drusila
Wills, Hay Petrie, Enid Lindsey, Ian Fleming,
Leslie Osmond, Neil S Beaton
comm Frederick Allen

■ A film commissioned by the SCWS and
promoting the aims of the Beveridge Report.

I   Frederick Allen, sitting in a armchair
        and reading from C E M Joad's *Two
        Good Fairies*, begins his narration.
II   John, a young soldier on leave, buys
        a copy of the Beveridge Report (1942),
        reads it and falls asleep.
III   Dream sequence: the war has ended
        and the young soldier seeks
        employment at the Labour Exchange.
        He accepts a position on a
        government training scheme; some
        time has passed and John is now
        married with a new home, furnished
        with a £10.00 marriage grant; financial
        worry is eased by the prospect of a
        maternity grant and allowance; John
        and his wife feel optimistic for the
        future of their newborn son, who can
        expect better opportunities and
        education than were available to his
        father; John's parents explain how
        their association with the SCWS has
        helped them through illness and
        prepared them for retirement, although
        admitting that the Beveridge Report
        was a good thing; John wakes from
        his dream – "Well, Sir William, You
        Seem To Have Thought of Everything".
IV   Neil Beaton, President of the SCWS,
        makes an address to camera,
        endorsing the Beveridge Plan and its
        aim to remove "Want". He outlines the
        aims and ideals of the Co-operative
        Movement, and its commitment to the
        comprehensive social insurance
        scheme.

Remarks
Published in the winter of 1942, the
Beveridge Report, with its proposals for a
comprehensive scheme of social insurance,
became an instant bestseller, with an
unprecedented total of 635 000 copies sold.
The Report was a key component of the
forces for social change that emerged in the
early war years: where official channels
remained lukewarm towards considerations

of peace aims, progressive groups worked
tirelessly to facilitate discussion of radical
issues. The Workers' Film Association
(founded 1938) provided numerous films
shows, screening Labour and MoI
documentary films in which the ideals of
health, employment and
planning were debated. The WFA was
instrumental in the production and
distribution of this film, which was possibly
the first to deal with the report. *Two Good
Fairies* – clearly represented in the film by
the Beveridge Plan and the Co-operative
Movement – was scripted by the noted
philosopher, C E M Joad, a popular
member of BBC Radio's "Brains Trust"
programme. Included in this film are some
sequences from the earlier film, *Out of the
Box* (1942; NCFC 100), about the 18th-
century Co-operators, the Fenwick Weavers.
Germain Burger was a senior figure in the
industry, having worked as a cameraman at
the Ideal Film Company between 1916 and
1934. He had also worked on projects at
UFA in Germany. During the war he directed
some minor features for the Butcher
company.
See also: NCFC 107

NCFC 104
Men of Rochdale (1944)

b/w · 38m 50s · sound · 16mm · EAFA,
NFTVA, NWFA, SFA
pr CWS Film Unit/Verity Films *d* Compton
Bennett *prod* George Wynn/Sydney Box
sc Reg Groves *cam* Reginald Wyer
sd Charles Tasto *mus* John Greenwood
conductor Muir Mathieson *cast* Brefni
O'Rourke, Julian Somers, Margaret Withers,
Cecil Brock, John Laurie, John Boxer,
Patrick Curwen *ad* James Carter *pm* William
McQuitty

■ A celebratory film marking the centenary
of the establishment of the Rochdale
Equitable Pioneers Society, and telling the
story of the opening of their first Co-op store
in 1844.

I   A narrator reads passages from G J
        Holyoake's *The History of Co-operation*
        over scenes of industrial Rochdale.
II   1843. A meeting of the working people
        of Rochdale, where they discuss their
        difficulties, the merits of Chartism and
        Owenism, and the possible responses
        to their bleak conditions. Small-scale
        activities in Co-operative buying have
        commenced, and plans are in motion
        to open a shop.

III   A young couple, Sam and Sally, discuss their future. Sam has faith in Co-operative endeavour, of benefit to all, whilst Sally insists on a more certain and secure future for themselves. Charles Howarth and Miles Ashworth puzzle over a form of organisation and constitution that would ensure success.

IV   In the middle of the night, Charles Howarth has a brainwave and rushes to tell his comrades. He has hit upon the idea of a dividend paid on purchases.

V   The Pioneers search for premises for their store and come up against hostility from the local traders. Eventually, they secure a suitable building on Toad Lane, leased by a local doctor.

VI   21 December 1844. Opening night for the new Co-op store. The local storekeepers gather to deride the venture and harass the customers, but it proves a modest success.

VII   The store is now seen as a success, with its range of articles for sale having greatly expanded, along with its trade and membership. Sam has been taken on as the full-time storekeeper.

VIII   The local traders, enemies of Co-operation, meet to conspire against the Pioneers. They start malicious rumours suggesting that the society is insolvent. The Pioneers must act to forestall a run on the society's funds.

IX   A dramatic scene in the store, as worried members and creditors demand the return of their investment. Cashier William Cooper remains calm, and his clever handling of the situation saves the day.

X   The 1860s – a new crisis threatens the society. The Civil War in America restricts the import of raw cotton, and economic distress comes to industrial Lancashire. The enemies of Co-operation are ebullient, believing that the industrial distress will weaken the Co-op. William Cooper, in a speech to the society, explains why Co-operators must remain firm in their ideals and continue to support anti-slave-owning Northern states, despite their blockade of the cotton-producing South.

XI   The continued development of the Rochdale Equitable Pioneers Society and the Co-operative Movement: a series of Co-op store fronts; aerial view of a CWS factory; exterior of a CWS factory; Co-operative milk production; a Co-operative ship; the CWS banking department; various industrial scenes and processes within Co-operatively-owned factories; a Co-operative farm; testing milk in a laboratory; and so on.

XII   Individual Pioneers, the Men of Rochdale, look down upon the state of society in 1944 and declare that much work still requires to be done to proceed to the glories of a "Co-operative Commonwealth": Miles Ashworth; James Standring; James Smithies; Charles Howarth; William Cooper.

Remarks
The most ambitious and lavish production in the collection. A major contribution to the Movement's centenary celebrations, this film was budgeted at £15 000. To help provide the necessary polish, and to handle the extensive dramatic sequences, independent producer Sydney Box was enlisted as co-producer, bringing with him his contract technicians, Compton Bennett as director, and Reg Wyer as cinematographer. That trio would work on the 1945 hit, *The Seventh Veil*, the success of which led Box to head of production at Gainsborough Studios. Box had previously been involved with Publicity Films as scenario manager, a role which would have brought him into contact with the CWS, who commissioned numerous films from the company in the 1930s. The impressive score to *Men of Rochdale* was provided by accomplished film composer, John Greenwood, who worked extensively at Ealing Studios. The music was played by the London Symphony Orchestra, which formed itself as a co-operative in the war years. The film was widely screened to national Co-operative Movements around the world, and, closely based on the history of the Rochdale Pioneers by G J Holyoake, stands as a consummate history lesson.
See also: xxxi, NCFC 105, NCFC 164, NCFC 165, NCFC 192

NCFC 105
Song of the People (1945)

b/w · 27m 22s · sound · 35mm: NFTVA / 16mm: IAC, NWFA
pr CWS Film Unit *d* Max Munden
prod George Wynn *sc* Reg Groves, Paul Potts *cam* Ray Elton *sd* Charles Tasto *mus* Mischa Spoliansky *cast* Bill Owen (listed under his original name, Bill Rowbotham), John Longden *additional*

production credits Billy Asher, Sydney Box, Alfred Burlinson, Geoffrey Busby, The Debonaires, Michael Golden, Tony Heller, Bob Hill, Philip Hill, Peter Hoyle, Edward Law, London Symphony Orchestra, Jim Mason, Muir Mathieson, Derek Morgan, Gerry O'Hara, Bob Pearce, Phil Cardew's Dance Band, Albert Rayner, Alec Snowden, Eddie Turner, Peter Ward, The Wardour Choir, Harold Watson. "And many more in the factories, fields and streets of Britain."

■ An innovative musical pageant charting the irresistible rise of the workers.

I A long tracking shot of a busy city street; a group of workers enters a factory; a long overhead tracking shot of workers inside a factory, accompanied by the music of Phil Cardew's Dance Band.
II A group of workers sings a song about British heroes in history. A foreman intervenes and tells them of the real heroes – the workers.
III A short scene at an English country church and graveyard, with young children playing. Buried there are England's "anonymous" heroes.
IV The 14th century – the struggles of working people led by Wat Tyler. Scenes at harvest time (played in modern dress).
V The English Republic – the struggles of the Diggers and the Levellers; the Diggers seize the common land for community use.
VI The Industrial Revolution – the oppression of the urban workers; scenes of modern working conditions and welfare facilities enjoyed by contemporary workers, gained through the toil and hardships of previous generations; Luddites raid a workshop and smash machines.
VII Rochdale 1844 – workmen combine in a mutual association, and the great Co-operative Movement commences. Brief scenes at the Toad Lane store.
VIII 1848, the People's Charter – presented with the images of contemporary newspapers, cartoons, literature, etc.
IX Recent labour struggles: the Dockers, 1910; the Co-op foodship sent to the strikers in Dublin, 1913; the railwaymen's strike, 1919; the General Strike, 1926.
X A busy urban shopping street. Ordinary people watch as a wealthy lady passes by, her bags and parcels carried by her chauffeur. The audience is asked where their sympathies lie –

with the many or the few?
XI International conflict: a montage of recent events – Manchuria, Stalingrad, Liberation by the Allies, Nazis marching, Guernica, Chamberlain.
XII The lessons for future unity and world Co-operation – be attentive to the world's oppressed and underprivileged: Britain's colonial peoples; Africans; American negroes; the Chinese; the Jews; the defeated enemies.
XIII Scenes at a funfair.
XIV Graphic card: "This film was made for the People, with the People by some of the People". "It was sponsored by the CWS in the year 1944 in the belief and faith that the people are The End and the Beginning".

Remarks
During the period 1938-45, the Movement produced several films offering a "workerist" slant on British history, including *The Voice of the People* (1939; NCFC 085), *The Machine Is Mastered* (1942; NCFC 099) and this film, the most ambitious and remarkable of the series. Some of the material in *The Machine Is Mastered* is again included here. An inspiring ensemble piece, with the contributors listed collectively rather than hierarchically, it combines the talents of noted artists and technicians from both the Labour Movement and the British cinema industry, reflecting the progressive wartime consensus which centred on hopes for a better postwar world – a New Jerusalem! Max Munden had been a busy director on wartime Mol films, and directed at least one further title for the CWS in the postwar years, *It's Magic* (1953; NCFC 150). It is worth noting that the scene detailing the Rochdale Pioneers utilises actors from *Men of Rochdale* (1944; NCFC 104), which was shooting at the time, but is a new sequence original to *Song of the People*. There is surprisingly little contemporary reference to this remarkable and outstanding film. In the late-1930s Maxwell Munden had been staff scenarist at Merton Park Studios. In 1941, he left to join his colleague, Sydney Box, at Verity Films. Both companies had worked on commissions for the CWS.
See also: xxviii, NCFC 099

NCFC 106
Brighton International Children's Camp (1946)

b/w · 5m 10s · silent · 16mm · EAFA

- A film apparently produced by the French contingent at the International Children's Camp.

I   A girl sits beneath the Rainbow Flag of Co-operation. The camera pans right, and a camp comes into view.
II   A slow panning shot of the camp.
III Youngsters check the camp information board.
IV A group giving a display of folk-dancing; closer portraits of some of the campers; a large group playing a circle game; mealtime; scenes around the camp-site; a group files past the camera behind the flag of the International Falcon Movement; a camp meeting, an adult leader makes an address; a group poses with flags and banners; games and dancing enjoyed by the camp; portraits of some of the young delegates; some performers; some camp activities; out on a ramble; farewell and departure on double-decker buses.

Remarks
The European Socialist youth Movements had been dealt a bitter blow by the events of the Second World War. The International Children's Camp at Brighton has been appreciated as "an important factor in the postwar rebirth of the International Falcon Movement" (Basil Rawson, "Brown Eagle", *The Woodcraft Way* [London: The Woodcraft Folk, 1962]). The camp was organised by the British Woodcraft Folk, and, according to John Attfield, was attended by 1000 of their members, plus 250 children from Dutch, French, Belgian, Swiss and Jewish youth organisations. The film also refers to representatives from Finland, Austria, Sweden and Czechoslovakia. It must have been an extremely difficult journey for all. Quite perversely, the WCF's association with the International Camp was a major reason for the ejection of the Folk from the official Co-operative Youth Movement, as being contrary to CYM policy. Several societies would have little to do with that judgment, and continued to recognise the Folk and provide facilities to the organisation. It is probable that a copy of the film was purchased by a supportive Co-operative society from the French youth organisation.

NCFC 107
They Found a Future (1946)

b/w · 24m 52s · sound · Scotland · 16mm · SFA

prod Edward Cook *cam* O Burn/S Clinton *mus* W L Trytel *cast* M Gordon, T Delaney, Leslie Osmond, Hay Petrie

- A young couple are assured of a bright future as part of the Scottish Co-operative Movement.

I   Two women await their men folk among the returning servicemen. George is sick and Mary helps tend him in hospital. Something seems to be worrying him.
II   George falls out with Mary's mother, who believes he has no prospects. At the outbreak of the war, he had sold the family retail business.
III A friend counsels the disheartened George, and suggests that he try for a job with the Co-operative Movement which had acquired his old family store.
IV The friend tells of a recent visit to the SCWS tobacco factory at Shieldhall, Glasgow, and the impressive industrial activities there: a detailed sequence of the production of cigarettes at the factory.
V   George rushes back to Mary and asks her to marry him: he has got his ambition back.
VI At a dinner party hosted by the local Co-operative society, George is welcomed as the new branch manager, responsible for his own former store. His mother-in-law is suitably impressed.

Remarks
Judging by the credits, this is an abridged version of the film, as certain specified characters do not make an appearance. With its extensive narrative sequences, this is an unusual example from the collection of surviving films from the SCWS. The film is an interesting historical document articulating the fears of returning servicemen about their prospects in the new postwar society. Three years earlier the SCWS had commissioned a film from the Workers' Film Association, *Two Good Fairies* (1943; NCFC 103), promoting the ideals of the Beveridge Report and outlining the Scottish Movement's responsibility in postwar reconstruction. Taken together, the two films indicate the Movement's concern to play its part in building the peace. Producer Edward Cook was a senior figure in the British documentary film industry, and had produced the first documentary sound film in Britain, *Liquid History*, for Shell-Mex Ltd.

NCFC 108
[Children's Sports Fete] (c.1946)

col · 5m 30s · silent · 16mm · ETV

■ A short film record of a junior sports meeting.

I   A large crowd enjoys boys' and girls' sprint races; boys' and girls' relay races; a race in fancy dress; boys' high-jump; a boy with an injured ankle; girls' high-jump.
II   Fancy dress carnival – many dressed as popular Co-op products.
III Fathers' race (?).
IV Massed dancing; massed singing; firework display.

Remarks
I have been unable to identify the specific place and occasion of this event, although it is probable that it was sponsored by the RACS as an annual sports meeting and gala for children of society members. It is possible that it is an International Co-operative Day celebration – sports, fancy dress, dancing and fireworks were traditional activities enjoyed on ICD – although the absence of a direct reference to that important calendar event is curious. Sporting and recreational get-togethers such as this one were staged by societies around the country and perceived as important communal expressions. They were a popular subject for filming, and numerous film records survive.

NCFC 109
Best Foot Forward (1947)

b/w · 16m 50s · sound · 35mm: NFTVA / 16mm: EAFA
pr CWS cam R O'Brien prod George Wynn sd S Rider ed Cath Miller

■ A general commentary on the manufacture of CWS footwear. A very detailed examination is provided, and the following are the basic sequences.

I   The various requirements of footwear: walking; marching; relaxing; playing.
II   The various processes of tanning the hides. A sequence shot at the CWS Grappenhall and Street tanneries.
III Exteriors of three CWS Wheatsheaf boot and shoe factories (unidentified). The various processes in male footwear manufacture: cutting; sewing; heel sections.

IV The manufacture of female footwear.
V   The manufacture of children's shoes.
VI Historical personages and their shoes: Henry VIII; Elizabeth I; Charles II.
VII Some of the contemporary Wheatsheaf styles.

Remarks
Co-operative boot and shoe production began at Leicester in 1872. By the eve of the Second World War, footwear had developed into one of the CWS's largest productive groups, employing 4199 in seven factories, and with a combined output of £1 987 732. The "Wheatsheaf" was a central Co-operative logo, and correspondingly a brand name, symbolising the binding together of the many into a mutually supportive whole. The film is more concerned with its "public information" role regarding footwear manufacture, than with an inherent Co-operative message. To that extent, it conformed to a growing postwar trend whereby Co-operative ideals and ideology were downplayed in favour of the central productive processes involved.

NCFC 110
Counter Courtesy (1947)

b/w · 18m 32s · sound · Scotland · 16mm · SFA
pr Orion Picture Corporation d Germain Burger prod Gordon O'Connell cam Ronnie Pilgrim cast Carl Pearson, Helen Christie, Beth Ross, Maurice Rhodes sc Barry Delmaine, James Eastwood ed Victor Gray

■ A training film for SCWS retail store counter staff.

I   The audience is introduced to the counter staff of a typical Co-op food store: Robert, a 16-year-old trainee; Jenny, a trainee saleswoman; Mary, a saleswoman; Mr Kearns, the manager.
II   A housewife makes a purchase of SCWS Unitas breakfast oats. Kearns explains the nature of employment in the retail trade: the importance of punctuality and cleanliness; the importance of personal appearance; dealing with customers – the customer who knows what she wants, the shy and nervous type, the vain and snobbish type.
III Tips for counter staff: know your stock and where to find it; keep notes on stock and its place of manufacture; always serve Co-op goods unless specifically asked otherwise; important

points in selling shoes; keep aisles clear; keep stock that is in regular demand close at hand; the correct use of the bacon machine; cutting and weighing butter and cheese; tidy-up service areas after each rush of customers; instruments of the trade – string, paper, scissors and carrier bags; avoid obstructions; give prompt service; utilise spare moments to study the stock; spare moments should be devoted to trainees to help bring them on; do not fob off battered goods onto customers; check stock for soiled and defaced goods; keep discussions with customers to the business at hand – do not gossip!; keep the storeroom tidy, as well as the front counter.

IV Kearns summarises the points necessary for a successful Co-op branch store.

Remarks

The SCWS commissioned three films in a "Training Film Series" from the Orion Picture Corporation in 1947, all of which survive; the other titles are *Know Your Business* (NCFC 111) and *Your Silent Salesman* (NCFC 114). The series was shot largely in a London studio, and an experienced retail manager, Mr J A Scott, was despatched from Scotland to ensure the accuracy of the store reconstructions and retail business. As in the case of the earlier English retail training film, *Behind the Counter* (1941; NCFC 093), the film contains excellent scenes of store interiors (albeit recreations) from the period before the wide-scale conversion to self-service outlets. Ronnie Pilgrim was an experienced lighting cameraman in the British documentary cinema. He eventually set up his own production company, Cine Industrial Productions. Scriptwriter Barry Delmaine was a member of the Film Producers' Guild, and wrote for radio, stage and screen.
See also: xxxii

NCFC 111
Know Your Business (1947)

b/w · 10m 39s · sound · Scotland · 16mm · SFA
pr Orion Picture Corporation *d* Germain Burger *prod* Gordon O'Connell *cam* R Pilgrim *ed* Victor Gray *cast* Harry Pringle, Campbell Singer, Helen Christie, Beth Ross, Maurice Rhodes *sc* B Delmaine, James Eastwood

■ A training film for SCWS retail branch managers.

I A Co-op store (interior). The camera tracks along the busy store counter.
II In his office, the branch manager discusses how to run an efficient store: the importance of punctuality; prompt opening; dealing with staff; cleanliness; checking stock and daily deliveries; how not to keep a stock room – a correct example; the use of advertising displays; stock records and control; interviewing new staff.
III Dealing with customers; make and keep friends for the society; discover if customers are dissatisfied; be cheerful.

Remarks

One of three surviving training films produced for the SCWS in 1947. This film, designed to aid branch managers in the efficient running of their store, contains excellent sequences of store interiors from the period immediately before the switch to self-service outlets. Like its counterparts, it is patronising in its approach, and some material is shared across films.
See also: xxxii, NCFC 110, NCFC 116

NCFC 112
Milk Salesmanship (1947)

b/w · 26m 14s · sound · 16mm · NFTVA
pr CWS Film Unit *d* George Wynn *sd* Syd Ryder *ed* C Beaumont *cam* Bert Hampson *sc* Selwyn Watson *comm* Geoffrey Sumner

■ A training film for Co-operative milkmen.

I A London Co-operative Society hand-drawn milk float; motorised milk floats of the Birmingham and the Bristol Co-operative Societies; a hand-drawn milk float in front of a Liverpool Co-operative Society store; motorised milk floats of the Manchester and Salford Co-operative Society and the Newcastle Co-operative Society.
II Two milk roundsmen are relaxing in a canteen. One has been receiving complaints about the other, who becomes disgruntled on hearing this.
III The dairy: empty bottles are cleaned and sterilised; the pasteurisation plant; the laboratory; the bottling department. No complaints here!
IV An unprofessional milk salesman: the roundsman clocks in late – a bad start. Time-wasting and unpunctuality

are two deadly sins of the milkman; noisiness can make him unpopular with customers; incivility loses customers – be obliging; further faults of a poor salesman are shown, and the audience is asked to spot them – leaving a delivery in the sun; not collecting empties; leaving a gate open, and so on; it is shown how customers are lost.

V   Graphic card: "We will now stop the film to allow us to discuss what we have seen so far".

VI   "Righting Wrongs": "Be friends with your job and your job will be a good friend to you". A good salesman at work – punctuality, getting on with the job, smartly dressed, obliging, refrains from smoking on the job. An extended sequence of him efficiently going about his work.

VII Graphic card: "Break for Discussion".

VIII "Know Your Product". An analyst at the dairy presents some facts about milk: nutritional value and health-giving properties – various scenes of children at play and adults enjoying recreation; the importance of pasteurisation – the elimination of various germs; how sterilised milk is produced.

IX   Graphic card: "Break for Discussion".

X   "Customers and Opportunities": various shots of people in busy streets; dealing with "Mrs Chatterbox"; dealing with the "business-like" type; the difficult customer; disputes over the bill; communicate with the manager; be punctual, polite, tidy and quiet for the successful selling of milk.

XI   Some tips on salesmanship: the three-point greeting – say it with a smile, say it politely, and call the customer by name; be instructive, diplomatic and tactful.

Remarks
A companion to the Movement's other "milk" film of 1947, *The Milk We Drink* (NCFC 113), which was targeted at general audiences. This film was felt to have considerable novelty value in its innovative use of discussion breaks. Pamphlets containing further consideration of the training points inherent to the film were also made available at screenings to help reinforce the learning situation. This approach was later adopted by a three-part 1952 film dealing with footwear (see NCFC 142-144). Apparently, the dairy industry had not previously employed training films, and the Movement thus opened up the field with *Milk Salesmanship*, the result of an original

suggestion by the Birmingham Co-operative Society's dairy department.
See also: xxi, xxxii, NCFC 113

NCFC 113
The Milk We Drink (1947)

b/w · 10m 46s · sound · 35mm · NFTVA
pr CWS *cam* Bert Hampson *prod* George Wynn

▪ A general commentary on the importance of pasteurisation in the production of milk.

I   The value of milk. Montage of scenes: dairy herd; children with their school milk; milking cows; processes in the creamery; farmyard scenes.

II   "What happens to the milk when it leaves the farm?": exterior shot, CWS creamery; the transportation of milk – lorries and tankers; laboratory testing of milk.

III The pasteurisation process: diagram explaining the elimination of germs; the heating process (two methods are detailed – the holding process [145°F] and the high-temperature, short-time process [162°F]); a diagrammatic representation of the pasteurisation process; the function of the flow-diversion valve; testing in the laboratory.

IV   The bottling plant.

V   Milk distribution: transportation from the creamery; a household delivery van.

VI   The importance of cleanliness: scrubbing the milk sheds; sterilisation of the milking apparatus and churns; the dairy plant; the responsibility of the consumer to ensure hygiene.

VII Summary – the benefits of a clean milk supply: farmyard scenes; healthy children.

Remarks
In 1947, the CWS Film Unit produced two films on the subject of milk. *Milk Salesmanship* (NCFC 112) was designed for training employees, whilst *The Milk We Drink* was intended for general audiences. This film is constructed as a public information film, and contrasts sharply with comparable Co-operative films of the interwar period in that emphasis is directed towards the specifics of milk production and preparation, whilst there is little exploration of Co-operative aspects of the business – the nature of ownership, the dominant position of the Co-op in the nation's milk supply, and

so on. Internal evidence indicates that the film was shot in the North-West; it is a Manchester and Salford Co-operative Society milk float that is evident in the short delivery sequence. It should be noted that during the immediate postwar period, a time when milk was being rationed, the Movement was having to confront proposed restrictions on their deliveries, designed to protect small independent distributors, being sponsored by the Council of Retail Distributors.
See also: xxi, NCFC 112

NCFC 114
Your Silent Salesman (1947)

b/w · 8m 55s · sound · 16mm · SFA
pr Orion Picture Corporation *d* Germain Burger *prod* Gordon O'Connell *cam* R Pilgrim *ed* Victor Gray *cast* John Maxwell, Campbell Singer, Miki Anderson, Charles Schofield, Patricia Downs *sc* B Delmaine, James Eastwood

▪ A training film about the value of promotional campaigns and display advertising for SCWS retail branch stores.

I An advertising manager lectures on the virtues of advertising. The sequence is illustrated with examples of press advertisements, posters, handbills and in-store display-cards. He stresses the background knowledge required of a successful advertising executive – knowledge of products, customers, and so on.
II Advertising workers – the copywriter, artists.
III A case-study in advertising: the Fraser family at breakfast; Mrs Fraser casually glances at an advert for SCWS Unitas oats in her newspaper. It has been a long time since she has found a retailer that stocks good porridge. Out shopping, she notices a poster on a hoarding advertising Unitas oats. She is prompted to enter a Co-op store, and is attracted by a display of Unitas oats – a product that has benefited from a coordinated advertising campaign. On the counter is a show-card for the product, and an aware counter assistant ensures a sale.
IV Window displays: example of a poorly laid-out window; well laid-out window displays.
V The advertising manager winds up with some final tips – the use of display cards and display materials.

VI The Fraser family at home enjoying breakfast – Unitas oats!

Remarks
One of three surviving training films produced by the Orion Picture Corporation for the SCWS in 1947. Improving the awareness of branch staff with regard to advertising was the aim of this film, and, with its mixture of documentary and narrative techniques, it conforms to the conventional pattern of the series. Another unifying feature of the films is their patronising approach! The important provision of advertising and publicity, although widely discussed within the Movement, were rarely broached on film. Co-operators were clearly uncomfortable with the notion of advertising, an activity which many on the Left felt was dishonest. Co-operation's maxim of "production for use and not for profit" evidently distanced the Movement from the capitalists, whom, it was thought, were exploiting consumers through extravagant promises and raising "false wants". Compromised by such a view of advertising, the Co-op's publicity endeavours were criticised as unimaginative.
See also: xxxii, NCFC 110

NCFC 115
26th Co-operative Day Celebration (1948)

b/w · 10m 32s · silent · 16mm · NWFA
pr AGCS Publicity Films

▪ A film record of a Co-op gala sponsored by the Guildford and District Co-operative Society.

I The Co-operative Queen, Miss Phyllis Francis, and her escort enter the field and take to the throne; the Queen is crowned by Mr Boxal, a member of the Management Committee, and she makes an address; the Queen and her maids of honour.
II Entrants in the fancy dress competition parade before the crowd; the prize-winners pose for the camera.
III The Queen leaves the field; busy crowds.
IV Sports and leisure activities: sprint race; side-shows, pony rides; miniature railway; brass band; Punch and Judy; milling crowds; queue for refreshments – inside the tea tent.
V "The Grand Entertainment" announced by the Co-operative Queen; bicycle display; dancing displays; acrobats;

wrestling; performing dogs; eurythmics; tent-pitching, fire-building, and a song by the Woodcraft Folk.

Remarks
This is the only film so far located of Co-operative activities at the Guildford and District Co-operative Society, although there is evidence that film work predated this film, when in 1935 the opening ceremony for a new federal dairy operated by the Aldershot, Guildford and Woking Societies was filmed. There was also a major production, commissioned in 1946 for £450, from the Workers' Film Association, recording a pageant, "This Precious Stone", staged by the Guildford Youth Council. This film record of the 26th International Co-operative Day celebrations on 3 July 1948, at Stoke Park, Guildford, presents a typical mix of cultural activities which would have been replicated in numerous towns around the country. The event was attended by 15 000 members, 3000 of them travelling in on special trains from outlying districts. In 1948, the Guildford Society claimed a membership of 28 865 and sales of slightly over £1 million.

NCFC 116
Achievement (1948)

b/w · 22m 56s · sound · Scotland · 16mm · SFA
pr Orion Picture Corporation *d* Germain Burger *prod* Gordon O'Connell *cam* Leslie Wheeler/A Burger *ed* Victor Gray *mus* De Wolfe *comm* Duncan McIntyre

■ A public relations film linking Co-operation to the great achievements of Scottish industry and enterprise.

I   Graphic card: "If we except the Athenians and the Jews – no people so few in number have scored so deep a mark in the world's history as the Scots have done" (J A Froude).
II Scenes of historic Scotland: Edinburgh Castle; Princes Street; historic Edinburgh; a Highland band; a loch; picturesque hills and glens; and so on.
III Scenes of Scotland's industrial heritage, including factories and pits.
IV The gas industry, founded on the genius of Scot, William Murdoch: his initial experiments into coal gas; his birthplace; a cave, the site of his early experimentation; modern industry and its debt to Murdoch; his work on steam engines.

V   The Jones Goods 046, the first railway engine with two pairs of coupled driving wheels, designed by a Scot: scenes of various shots of wheels; John Boyd Dunlop's pneumatic tyre; the Thornley Bank factory, Glasgow, manufacturer of tyres.
VI   Charles Macintosh's raincoat; Kirkpatrick MacMillan's bicycle – the original bike and modern counterparts out on the open road.
VII John Charmers of Dundee and the idea of the perforated gummed stamp.
VIII James Naismith's steam-hammer.
IX   The beautiful River Clyde; the river's mighty steamships and ship-building yard; the *Queen Elizabeth*, Clyde-built.
X   Future industries: the production of organic acids; the production of nitrocellulose.
XI   Native crafts – spinning thread.
XII Modern factories uphold the tradition of Scottish craftsmanship.
XIII Another Scottish innovation and gift to the world – Co-operation: the Fenwick Weavers; the steamship, *Scottish Co-operator*; the headquarters of the SCWS, Morrison Street, Glasgow; Glasgow Central Station, original site of the SCWS; factories, mills and warehouses of the SCWS; various interior scenes at SCWS factories and workshops; welfare provision for SCWS staff.
XIV The shoe factory at Shieldhall, Glasgow (exterior); a male operative at work; a senior cobbler talks about his work.
XV   The SCWS flour mill at Edinburgh (exterior); interior scenes; a senior miller talks about his work.
XVI The SCWS cabinet factory, Shieldhall, Glasgow (exterior); interior scene; a cabinet-maker speaks about his work.
XVII A sequence of lorries and trucks leaving SCWS works; SCWS Co-op store (exterior); SCWS products grouped on a counter; SCWS Luma lamp factory (exterior); Co-op store (interiors).
XVIII Graphic card: "Scotland's Strength Lies In Co-operation. Buy SCWS Products."

Remarks
One of a series of films produced by the Orion Picture Corporation for the SCWS in the postwar period. The film contains sequences from other productions, notably store interiors from *Know Your Business* (1947; NCFC 111), and even a few scenes from the earlier *Out of the Box* (1942; NCFC

100), the dramatisation of the Fenwick Weavers, pioneer Scottish Co-operators. The film would have been conceived as an informational subject within a programme of films screened to Co-operative and progressive groups. A similar approach, linking the Co-operative Movement to Scotland's social and industrial development, was adopted for a film in the following year: *Pride and Progress* (NCFC 124). In 1948, the SCWS conducted trade to the value of £55 million. Of particular interest in this film is a brief view of the SCWS motor vessel, *Scottish Co-operator*, launched in October 1938, with a dead weight of 650 tons. The ship initially plied trade between Leith and London, but was requisitioned by the Government in February 1940. Later that year, it was part of the heroic fleet which conducted the evacuation of Dunkirk.
See also: NCFC 085, NCFC 124

NCFC 117
Calling All Smokers (1948)

b/w · 4m 53s · sound · 16mm · NFTVA
comm Leslie Mitchell

▪ A publicity film for CWS pipe tobacco.

I   Crates of tobacco leaves arrive from all over the world – the United States, India, Nyasaland [now Malawi], Canada – and are unloaded.
II   Processing the tobacco: the dry leaves are steam-treated; the leaves are conveyed to a rotary moistener for washing; female operatives remove the stalks; the tobacco is weighed and put into a forming box, and compressed into a cake; stacks of tobacco cakes are further pressed and baked; the cakes are cut into bars, and the bars shredded into flakes; in the packing room, the flakes are weighed and packed by hand.
III   A young couple relaxing at home. The wife, who enjoys the smell of pipe tobacco, has no objections to her husband smoking at home.
IV   Close-up of a packet of Mahogany Flake tobacco.
V   Graphic card: "Obtainable at Co-operative Stores Only".

Remarks
Tobacco products were ranked first in volume of sales for the CWS by the eve of the Second World War. A CWS tobacco factory was established in Manchester in 1898, amidst some opposition from those who did not wish to encourage people "to poison themselves" (Percy Redfern, *The Story of the CWS* [Manchester: CWS, 1913]). The ratio of demand for cigarettes against tobacco gradually began to favour the former, and so this film is a rare discussion of a neglected product. Although an important item to the CWS, stiff competition was faced from private manufacturers, with their massive investment in advertising and consequently huge sales. The narration is provided by Leslie Mitchell, a popular commentator and broadcaster, and voice of British Movietone News from 1938. He can be glimpsed playing a radio interviewer, struggling with Will Hay as his subject, in the wartime comedy classic, *The Black Sheep of Whitehall* (1941).
See also: NCFC 098

NCFC 118
Co-operation (1948)

b/w · 7m 46s · sound · 16mm · NWFA
pr CWS *d* George Wynn *cam* Bert Hampson *sc* Reg Groves

▪ A propaganda film promoting the ideals of Co-operation to help build the postwar world.

I   A narration on the nature and extent of the Co-operative Movement. Various shots of Co-operative society central premises (Doncaster and Newcastle) and store interiors.
II   Co-operative society members' meeting. The principles and function of democratic participation are explained.
III   The "Co-operative Difference" is explained over images of Co-operative stores (Chingford), products (tea and margarine) and store interiors. Emphasis is given to the Co-operative dividend.
IV   The CWS headquarters, Manchester (exterior). Inside the boardroom.
V   Productive activities: baking; biscuits; shoe-making; flour; cloth-making; canning; carpentry; bed-making; cigarettes; farming; banking.
VI   75th Co-operative Union Congress, Brighton. Conference hall and delegates.
VII   Stress on the importance of International Co-operation. Shots of industrial activities; victory parade; Palace of Westminster.

Remarks
Produced to an impressive standard by the CWS Film Unit, the film represented a typical project for screening at members' meetings or additionally to progressive organisations, to educate audiences about "their business", and its functions and ideals. Importantly, its agenda embraced the circumstances of the postwar world, stressing the opportunities and responsibilities facing Co-operators. The film clearly conformed to the aims and aspirations of world peace and security offered by the United Nations.
See also: xxxvin73

NCFC 119
A Tale of Two Houses (1948)

b/w · 11m 20s · sound · 16mm · EAFA, NFTVA
pr CWS Film Unit *d* Max Munden *pr* George Wynn *cam* Bert Hampson *sd* Syd Ryder *ed* C Beaumont *cast* Jack MacGowran (?)

▪ A promotional film for CWS washing-powder, Solvo.

I	The office of Professor Snodgrass DRIP, a hapless domestic economist. He introduces the audience to two of his case histories: Mrs Brown and Mrs Smith. It is Monday, washday.
II	The Brown household: the browbeating and mean Mr Brown worries about the household budget.
III	The Smith household: the browbeating and extravagant Mrs Smith argues for a labour-saving washing-machine.
IV	Mrs Brown finishes her washday early with the aid of a washing-machine. Mrs Smith is on top of things despite her lack of modern conveniences.
V	Eventually, the husbands return from work. Mr Brown is impressed by his wife's labours; Mr Smith is upset that, despite his wife's extravagance, her results are less impressive – he points out that "the essence of the washing is the soap!".
VI	Back at the Professor's laboratory, he and his assistants explain what Mrs Brown and Mr Smith knew all along – that CWS Solvo washing powder ensures a first-rate wash.
VII	Graphic card: "Sooner or later it <u>had</u> to come! SOLVO. A superlative soap powder from Co-operative Stores everywhere."

Remarks
A rather strained comic narrative is enlisted in an attempt to promote the well-known CWS washing powder, Solvo. The film is unusual in being a single-product publicity film that dispenses with the documentary sequences of Co-operative manufacturing, an integral part of the Movement's approach to pre-war promotional films. A CWS research department was established in Manchester in 1917, which went some way to centralise activities which had previously been conducted on site, notably at the CWS soap works. By the time of this film's production, the Co-operative Movement was the country's third largest manufacturer of soap. Although the film lacks credits, it is possible that Professor Snodgrass is played by well-known Irish actor, Jack MacGowran.

NCFC 120
Their Great Adventure (1948)

b/w · 31m 19s · sound · 16mm · NFTVA
pr CWS Film Unit *d* John Curthoys
prod George Wynn *cam* Bert Hampson
sd Gerry Turner *ed* C Beaumont
mus Edward Williams *cast* Cecil Trouncer, Henry Longhurst, Eve Gray, Jan Pilbeam, Frank Webster, Blanche Fothergill, Tom Webster *sc* Stephen Black/Vincent Brome *ad* George Haslam

▪ A narrative film promoting the achievements and ideals of the Labour Government elected in 1945.

I	We are introduced to the well-to-do Copeland family – father Henry, mother, and daughter Peg; and the working-class Jackson family – father Tom, mother, and son Dick.
II	Dick and Peg meet and fall in love. About to get married at the Registry Office, they are interrupted by an irate Mr Copeland who brings the proceedings to a halt. Acting on the Registrar's advice, Dick applies to a magistrate's court for their consent to marriage. It transpires that Mr Jackson is also against the marriage.
III	In court: Dick puts his case for the marriage; Mr Jackson puts his case against – he thinks his son is marrying above himself; Dick defends himself; Peg makes her views known; Mr Copeland makes his objections – he believes Dick would be unable to provide for his daughter. A Conservative businessman, he considers that the Labour Government

has put the country in a mess. In reply, Mr Jackson blames his sort for the poverty of the 1930s.

IV The final witness, Stephen Vincent, the local Labour MP, arrives in court. He puts the case for Dick and Peg's future, safe in the hands of a Labour Government – cut with scenes of modern industrial activity, modern hospitals, house-building and modern estates, developing educational provision, and so on.

V The verdict is left in the balance – what would be the audience's decision?

Remarks

In 1946, the Co-operative Movement, Labour Party and Trades Union Congress joined in the National Film Association, a body responsible for the film and audiovisual work of the entire Labour Movement. Film production was undertaken by the Film Unit of the CWS. *Their Great Adventure* was the largest project undertaken by the National Film Association, and was a direct commission from the Labour Party. The script was vetted by Cabinet Minister, Herbert Morrison, who was also a visitor to the set. The film, like the National Film Association, can now be judged a disappointment. The preliminaries concerning young love are stodgily constructed and reflective of the worst of a stagy, hidebound, British filmmaking tradition. Only in the last sequence dealing with Vincent's speech does the film come to life, and the whole purpose of the project become apparent at all.

Popular character actor Cecil Trouncer's professionalism is telling here, and one can only wish that audiences were still awake at that point to benefit from a passionate espousal of Labour's "New Jerusalem". Relatively few reports of screenings for the film are apparent in the contemporary press, and one presumes that the film was quietly forgotten. However, the film remains of some historical significance as the Labour Party's first film commission. *See also:* xxvi

---

NCFC 121
A Change For the Better (1949)

col · 2m 16s · sound · 16mm · NFTVA
pr Signal Films *comm* Stanley Holloway

▪ A model-animation featuring a monologue narration by Stanley Holloway – the story of P C Ramsbottom.

I P C Henry Ramsbottom is directing traffic (c.1900). He is an old-fashioned soul and is still at his post half a century later.

II But Henry has worries that he cannot balance the household budget; his dinner table is very bare.

III He calls in at the house of the doctor to meet his friend the cook, who provides a nice spread. "How does the Doctor manage so well?", inquires Henry, and she explains the benefits of shopping at the Co-op.

IV Henry has risen in the world. He is now a sergeant, and he shows everyone how the "divi" brings living costs down.

Remarks

Apparently the third contribution to a CWS film by celebrated musical comedian, Stanley Holloway – see also *Co-operette* (1938; NCFC 071) and *Sam Goes Shopping* (1939; NCFC 084). It is also noteworthy that this 3-D animation (incorrectly described at the time as a puppet film) was shot in Technicolor, making it the only surviving Co-op film produced in that lavish colour process. In fact, it is the only narrative animated film produced for the Movement so far located beyond brief television/ cinema advertisements. A small number of cartoons were made before the war, but have not been traced. The film received a theatrical release, appearing on the Odeon and Gaumont circuits. It exhibits some skilful model animation with excellent use of lighting and colour photography.
See also: NCFC 071

NCFC 122
Co-operator's Day Colchester 1949 (1949)

b/w · 3m 40s · silent · 16mm · EAFA
pr A C Butcher

▪ A film record of a Co-op gala.

I Procession passing the town hall led by a pipe band. Vehicles are dressed as Co-operative tableaux.

II A crowd of 7000 meet at the recreation ground.

III The Co-operative Queen arrives escorted by pipers and her maids of honour. The Queen is crowned by Captain C Smith MP, and makes her address.

IV Snap shots of Co-operative officials.

Remarks

The first in a series of films recording International Co-operative Day celebrations sponsored by the Colchester and East Essex Co-operative and Industrial Society. A competent amateur production by A C Butcher – no doubt a local ciné enthusiast and possibly a society member. Recording Co-operative Day at Colchester became an annual event, and film records survive marking the celebration during the early 1950s. It is possible that film from other years will resurface in time.

film project would have been his responsibility. The Co-operative Movement has traditionally supported various youth groups and activities. Such groups were the responsibility of the local society's Education Committee. Younger children were organised into Playway groups (7-10 years), and older children were organised into Pathfinder groups (11-14 years). The Woodcraft Folk was an autonomous democratic young people's organisation which found support from many Co-operative societies.

NCFC 123
Junior Sports Day (1949)

col · 8m 58s · silent · 16mm · ETV
pr RACS Film Unit *cam* George Durham

■ A sports meeting of the Pathfinders, Playways and Woodcraft Folk, groups of the RACS, Charlton Park, 12 June 1949.

I   Unloading the RACS Education Department's "Sport's Day Box"; placing signs; arranging tables and the sports field; the CWS mobile film unit; setting up the public address system; officials lay out the medals and badges; erecting the refreshment tent, expertly supervised by the Woodcraft Folk; catering arrangements.
II   Spectators and participants gather; children amuse themselves.
III The starter pistol is made ready.
IV   A sequence comprising of girls', boys' and adult races; the work of the officials, and so on.
V   Field events: long-jump pit; high-jump; obstacle race.
VI   Track events: races; sack races; egg and spoon races.
VII Mrs E Todd, Chairman of the Education Committee, presents the Shield to the Captain of the Foresters Pioneer Woodcraft Folk.
VIII The RACS's sport's box is repacked.

Remarks

George Durham, previously of the LCS, replaced Anthony Bingham as Education Secretary at the RACS in 1947. He brought a new impetus to the society's film work, having developed some experience in 16mm film production for the Woodcraft Folk and the LCS. He remained the RACS Education Secretary until 1958. Although the credits only list George Durham's contribution as cinematographer, the entire

NCFC 124
Pride and Progress (1949)

b/w · 28m 19s · sound · Scotland · 16mm · SFA
pr Orion Picture Corporation *d* Germain Burger *prod* Gordon O'Connell *cam* R Pilgrim/A Burger *cast* Frank Phillips, Patrick Macnee, Thea Wells, Betty Taylor *sc* James Eastwood

■ A public relations film for the Co-operative Movement in Scotland.

I   A young Scot returns by air from the Dominions to his native land. His colleague, piloting the plane, explains some of the landmarks and heritage of Scotland as they fly over: Berwick-upon-Tweed; Melrose Abbey; the mountainous Law at North Berwick; the Firth of Forth; Edinburgh.
II   Scotland's recent achievements are detailed: Comrie Pit; the new industrial estates of Dundee and its modern shopping centre; new initiatives in forestry in the Highlands; Loch Sloy hydroelectric power station; small Highland airport; Renfrew Airport; busy Clydeside; Prestwick Airport.
III The land of Robert Burns: Burns' House: the Tam O'Shanter Inn; Burns monument and statue; rural Ayrshire.
IV   Fenwick, Ayrshire, home to the pioneers of Scottish Co-operation, the Fenwick Weavers.
V   Back on land, the wife of the pilot explains the benefits of Co-operation, an example of Scottish progress: the production processes of SCWS Shieldhall coffee essence; the production of SCWS Snowdrop salt; the production of SCWS jelly.

Remarks

The film assumes the air of a travelogue, commenting on Scottish achievements past

and present, and is clearly a companion piece to *Achievement* (1948; NCFC 116), produced in the previous year. In both films, the Co-op is situated as continuing a long tradition of Scottish invention and innovation. Those attentive to the actual geography of Scotland will be highly amused by the patently "improbable" nature of the air journey.
See also: xxxii, NCFC 116

NCFC 125
Co-operative Day Colchester, July 1950 (1950)

b/w · 9m 8s · silent · 16mm · EAFA
pr A C Butcher and L H Sparks

▪ A film record of a Co-op gala.

I The President of Colchester and East Essex Co-operative and Industrial Society, Mr B Pye, opens the celebrations with an address to the gathered crowd.
II Sports: children's races; shots of the spectators.
III Display by the pipe band.
IV Display of Highland dancing.
V Shots of the milling crowds.
VI The arrival of the Co-operative Queen, flanked by pipers and maidens of honour.
VII Mrs John Strachey crowning the Queen and Princess.
VIII An unidentified gentleman addresses the crowd. Further shots of the platform guests, Co-op Queen and her entourage.
IX The Queen makes her exit, followed by the dignitaries.
X Sideshow attractions. Councillor Morris tries his strength! He is watched by society officials.
XI A brass band entertains.
XII Secretary of State for War, John Strachey, addresses the crowd of 15 000.

Remarks
A much more complete and extensive record of Colchester's Co-op Day festivities than the effort of 1949. Considerable attention is paid to individuals who are presumably society officials, managers and local dignitaries. The film was made during the final period of the postwar majority Labour Government, and senior Cabinet Member John Strachey MP is evident as guest of honour. The film finishes abruptly on his speech and it is possible that the end

sequence is lost. The Colchester and East Essex Co-operative and Industrial Society had a membership of 40 000 by the middle of the century, and operated 25 branch stores.

NCFC 126
Get It At the Co-op (1950)

b/w · 24m 43s · sound · Scotland · 16mm · SFA
pr Gate Film Productions *d* Gordon O'Connell *cam* P Barralett *ed* I Milligan *cast* James Urquhart, Howard Douglas, Jock McKay, Olga Dick, Patricia Mason, Josephine Cromp *sc* James Eastwood

▪ An informational film outlining the nature and extent of the SCWS.

I A "Propaganda Meeting" of a local Co-op society. The Chairman welcomes to the platform Mr R A Andrews of the SCWS. He delivers an address on the Scottish Co-operative Movement.
II Aberdeen: the Movement's stake in the traditional herring industry – the SCWS fish-curing factory. The factory also deals with poultry.
III A male audience-member enquires about the new SCWS jute mill at Dundee. He is informed by a fellow audience-member who had recently visited the mill: various scenes at the SCWS jute mill and the production of jute thread and fabric.
IV A spinster asks about the dividend and whether it is safe to leave her investment to accumulate. She is reassured.
V The SCWS hosiery factory at Shieldhall. Some production processes are examined, together with the varied fabrics produced.
VI A question about SCWS furniture is offered. Details of the Movement's cabinet works are explained with particular reference to the SCWS furnishing warehouses, where buyers inspect the products.
VII SCWS blanket-making: various processes at the factory at Galston, Ayrshire, are examined.
VIII The production of Co-op milk: Monkton Hill model farm; the milking of the dairy herd; processing the milk at a SCWS creamery; the bottling process; testing in the milk laboratory; a doorstep delivery.
IX Graphic card: "Get it at the Co-op –

SCWS goods of course! Dividend on all purchases."

Remarks
The film provides a valuable examination of certain trades that do not appear to have been detailed in the numerous other industrial films of the SCWS – fish-curing, jute-milling, blanket-making, etc. The SCWS first acquired a jute mill at Dundee in 1917, an important centre of the jute industry. The Ayrshire blanket mill, overlooking the Burnawn at Galston, was acquired in 1913, supplementing the Ettrick tweed mill, at Selkirk, acquired in 1896. The SCWS took its place on the Aberdeen Fish Market in 1899, business expansion being such that three premises were quickly acquired. A hosiery factory at Glasgow was one of the original productive works of the SCWS, begun in 1886. It eventually found larger premises on the Shieldhall site. A further factory was acquired at Leith in 1912. The first SCWS furniture warehouse was opened in Glasgow in 1897, and one soon followed in Edinburgh. The annual trade of the SCWS in 1950 was in excess of £68 million.

All characters in the film are played by actors. This appears to be the first film commissioned by the SCWS from Gate Film Productions, a company which would continue to be the main producers for the society throughout the 1950s. The company apparently emerged from a split in the Orion Picture Corporation, previous producers for the SCWS, with technicians Gordon O'Connell and James Eastwood moving into the new firm.

NCFC 127
International Meeting of the Red Falcons (1950)

b/w · 6m 20s · silent · Austria · 16mm · EAFA

■ An international meeting of the Socialist youth organisation, the Red Falcons, at Klagenfurt, Austria, 1950.

I   Graphic card: "25 years of the Red Falcons. 6000 Red Falcons from all over Europe meet in Klagenfurt."
II   A train pulls into a station and many Red Falcons disembark, making new friends and meeting old acquaintances; a long file of Falcons marches away; the marchers with banners are photographed from a moving train; the Red Falcons march down crowd-lined streets and into the main square.
III   Members, delegates and friends congregate in the square for a main ceremony; the English contingent of Woodcraft Folk (WCF) are evident with their banner.
IV   Overhead shots of the massed Falcons in the square; civic dignitaries welcome the Falcons – General Mandl, General Wedering; the founder of the Red Falcons, Anton Tesarek, makes a presentation.
V   A demonstration of folk-dancing; flags are paraded onto the platform; General Mistelberger, of the Federation of Falcons, hands over souvenirs to representatives of the participating organisations; a close-shot of two hands clasped in friendship.

Remarks
The film was acquired, probably as a presentation, by the British WCF, who are clearly present in the parade within the film. A number of films of international congregations and camps were collected by the Folk, and represent an important record of the European Socialist youth Movement.

NCFC 128
Pathfinders In Camp (1950)

col · 15m · silent · 16mm · ETV
pr George Durham

■ A record of a camp organised by the Education Departments of Gillingham, Gravesend, Grays and Royal Arsenal Co-operative Societies at Westbourne, Hampshire, July 1950.

I   The camp, a disused Ministry of Defence site: settling-in in the dormitories – a girl attempts making a bed; the girls' dormitory; boys in the shower; cleaning and drying clothes; writing postcards home; the camp secretary and fellow organisers; morning assembly; a Co-op delivery van arrives with supplies; food preparation; scrubbing tables; mealtime; early morning exercises on the parade ground; on a ramble with "Uncle George"; the busy tuck shop; the recreation room – table-tennis, darts, dominoes, draughts.
II   Visitors from the Royal Arsenal and Grays Co-operative Societies.
III   The sports field: fun on a tractor; football; cricket; wheelbarrow races;

egg and spoon race; obstacle races; fun and games; the injury room; on the beach at Prinsted.

IV   Assembled campers wave goodbye to the camera.

Remarks
Filmmaker George Durham had begun his film work with recordings of Woodcraft Folk camps in the immediate pre-war period. After the war, he was appointed to the post of Education Secretary of the RACS, and continued the progressive film policy established by Joseph Reeves in the interwar years. Once again, Durham's eye for composition and excellent control of the colour photography are both evident. Pathfinder groups were part of the Co-operative Youth Movement, and catered for 11-14 year olds. The annual camp, involving four local Co-operative societies, was an interesting example of regional collaboration to make the best use of available resources. 200 children were in attendance at this particular camp. The film of the following year's annual camp also survives.

NCFC 129
Brighton Follies (c.1950)

b/w and col · 10m 38s · silent · 16mm · EAFA
pr Departmental Managers' Association, Barnsley British Co-operative Society

▪ A jokey record of the trip to Brighton enjoyed by the Departmental Managers' Association of the Barnsley British Co-operative Society (BBCS).

I   Two of the trippers are collected by a chauffeur-driven car.

II   Out on the road with the coaches; the passengers enjoy a convivial drink; a break at the White Post Inn, Nottinghamshire; some fun and games in the coach; sightseeing in an unidentified town; further scenes on the coach.

III   At Brighton: scenes of the sea front and promenade; the hotel (exterior).

IV   Strolling down the promenade; on the pier; at sea on a pleasure steamer; scenes of the sea front and beach; it is the birthday of one of the wives, and she opens her present – a doll; in the pleasure gardens; a coach trip along the coast – scenes on top of a cliff; at a stately home, enjoying the floral displays and grounds *(colour)*.

Remarks
One of two surviving films recording the annual outing of the Departmental Manager's Association of the BBCS. One of their members was responsible for the film work and obviously had some competence and a sense of humour. It is probable that two other films of the BBCS – *Sports Day at Oakwell* (1951; NCFC 138) and *Then and Now, 1862-1952* (1952; NCFC 145) – were made by this filmmaker. It is interesting to note that the coaches belonged to the BBCS. Many retail societies ran profitable tour operator's businesses. BBCS was a major regional Co-operative society, which by the mid-century claimed over 110 000 members, served by nearly 100 branch stores. The society had been formed in 1862.

NCFC 130
Did You Know? Number 1 (Preserves) (c.1950)

b/w · 3m 51s · sound · 16mm · NFTVA
pr CWS Film Unit

▪ The processes that go into the production of CWS jam.

I   A fully-laden tea-table, but what is missing? Jam. No tea-table is complete without it!

II   The jam-making process: fresh fruit is boiled in steam-heated pans; the hot liquid is poured into cooling trays; jars are filled with the rich preserve; lids are placed on the jars which are then thoroughly sterilised; labels are stuck to the jars.

III   Close-ups of CWS raspberry jam, apricot jam, damson jam, strawberry jam, blackcurrant jam, marmalade.

IV   Graphic card: "These brands are obtainable at your Local Co-operative Stores".

Remarks
The first in a series of instructional films providing details of the production of well-known CWS products. There were apparently seven or eight films under the generic title of *Did You Know?*, of which five have been located. The series would have been suited to the recently inaugurated CWS mobile film service, whereby free cinema shows were made available to Co-operative society members, and to whom knowledge of Co-operative production, as well as products, would have been deemed desirable. The CWS operated

four preserve works – at Middleton, Reading, Acton and Stockton – and postwar difficulties were experienced in sustaining demand. As the CWS Board reported in 1954, "there was a most disquieting tendency to decline CWS productions in favour of those of competitors!" (Sir William Richardson, *The CWS in War and Peace 1938-1976* [Manchester: Co-operative Wholesale Society, 1977]). That situation might explain the subject of this film – preserves – which required a boost in sales.

NCFC 131
[Gravesend Co-op Opera] (c.1950)

b/w · 10m · silent · 16mm · ETV

▪ A film record of a dramatic performance of Gilbert and Sullivan's *Pirates of Penzance*, mounted by the Gravesend Co-operative Society.

Remarks
A rather static recording of four brief scenes from the production. The camera assumes only two positions to capture the action: for most of the film it is at the front of the circle, but closer shots are briefly achieved. The production appears competently staged; however, without sound-recording, it is impossible to make an assessment of the talent. One of the most widely supported cultural activities across the Movement was drama, and numerous groups and societies trod the boards in Co-op halls. The ending of the film is missing. The Gravesend Co-op had been founded in 1884, and by the middle of the 19th century was claiming nearly 20 000 members, and operated sixteen branch stores, a bakery, dairy, specialist pharmacy, drapery, butchery and confectionery stores, amongst other businesses.

NCFC 132
Pattern of Light (c.1950)

b/w · 22m 45s · sound · Sweden/Scotland · 16mm · EAFA, NFTVA
pr Kino Centralen *d* Gösta Werner *cam* Sten Dahlgren *mus* Gunnar Sonstevold *comm* James Harker *poems* Emily Dickinson

▪ An information film about the Co-operatively-owned Luma lamp factory in Sweden.

I   Images of light and darkness – a candle, the sun, dawn and dusk; flowers and people putting their faces to the sun; the galaxy; the electric light bulb – man masters light.

II   The Luma lamp factory, Sweden (exterior): making filaments from tungsten bars; the automatic blowing of small glass bulbs; the assembling of the electric light bulbs; the making of special lamp bulbs by hand.

III   The specially designed lighting equipment on the panel of a modern aircraft; Sweden's smallest-produced light bulb and largest-produced light bulb.

IV   The burning bulbs of the lamp-testing room. A variety of bulbs are examined in close-up; scenes in the laboratory where research and development work is carried on; the work's machine shop; staff dining-rooms and welfare facilities; the trophy cabinet of the factory sports club; educational classes for employees; the meeting of the photography club; the periodical room and library; general scenes around the factory; children at play in the factory grounds (crèche?); 5.00 pm and the workers leave the factory; a meeting of the works' committee.

V   Graphic card: "And over in Scotland is the British Luma factory where UC Lamps are Made. Next time you need lamps ask for UC obtainable only from Co-op Societies".

Remarks
Various films of Co-operative projects around the world were acquired by Co-operative organisations in the UK for educational screenings to their members. Generally, I have omitted such titles so far located, except where they contain material directly relating to the activities of the British Movement. This is a case in point. The film deals with the successful Co-operative lamp manufacturer, Kooperativa Förbundet (KF), Sweden, operated by the Swedish Co-operative Union, a federal body. The final section of the film, added for the benefit of British Co-operators, provides basic information on the British Luma Co-operative Electric Lamp Society. This was established in 1936, and represented the first international Co-operative production unit, a joint venture between KF and the SCWS (in 1948, the English CWS took up a one-third shareholding in the business). The British Luma factory, of which a still is featured in the film, was completed in 1939, designed by architects of KF and built by the building department

of the SCWS. With its glass conning tower, it was an impressive and important modernist building of the interwar period.

NCFC 133
Bits O' Sticks (1951)

col · 23m 32s · sound · Scotland · 16mm · SFA
pr Gate Film Productions *d* Gordon O'Connell *sc* James Eastwood *cam* P Barralett *ed* I Mulligan *mus* John Reynders *cast* Joanna Scott, James Liggat *anim* S Harvey, P Griffin, E Smith-Morris

▪ An information film about SCWS furniture-making.

	Animated sequence (4m 54s)
I	Various comic episodes involving the lumber business and furniture-making. The hapless carpenters, Chip and Dale, visit a SCWS cabinet factory, "The Home of Good Furniture".
	Live-action sequence (18m 38s)
II	A craftsman polishes a finished wardrobe; a display of other completed items.
III	Designers at work in the drawing office; draughtsmen working on blueprints.
IV	At the factory: timber is delivered and cut; the veneer is prepared and applied; furniture fittings are cut and trimmed; craftsmen work on chair legs; various operations are carried out by machines; the finished parts are stored.
V	Assembly: tallboy drawers; fixing drawer-bearers; inspection procedures; staining, spraying and polishing; upholstery; loading a delivery van.
VI	A young couple plan to furnish their new home. Bare rooms are transformed by the addition of SCWS furniture.

Remarks
SCWS furniture production was carried out at two centres, at Shieldhall and Beith. One of the busiest periods of production was during the Second World War when wartime contracts were completed for Anderson shelters, ambulance stretchers, bomb cases and repairs to the Navy Army and Air Force Institute (NAAFI) chairs. The construction of wartime utility furniture was another important task: sideboards (4911); tables (6036); chairs (38 684); and beds (19 785). Furniture manufacture was not a success for

the postwar SCWS, and constant annual deficits had to be met; total aggregate losses for the period reached £217 278. The trend to hire purchase, allied with the acceptance of furniture as an expendable fashion item, proved problematic to the Co-operative cabinet-makers whose products were traditionally expensive quality items. Two factories, at Janefield, Beith, and at Shieldhall, Glasgow, were forced to close before the centenary of the SCWS in 1969. The film exhibits an unusual construction, combining animation, documentary and live-action dramatic sequences.

NCFC 134
The CWS (Manchester) Band (1951)

b/w · 11m 55s · sound · 16mm · NFTVA
pr CWS Film Unit *prod* George Wynn *conductor* Eric Ball

▪ A performance in the studio by the CWS (Manchester) Band.

I	"County Pallatyne", the signature tune of the CWS Band.
II	An Australian march by Wilbur Sampson, "High Command".
III	The Gay Bolero (?).
IV	A special arrangement of "When Day Is Done" by Robert Katscher.

Remarks
An earlier film from 1935, now thought lost, recorded the performance of the original CWS Tobacco Factory Prize Band, which had been formed in 1907. This film of the renamed CWS (Manchester) Band was designed as a replacement. The band broadcast regularly on BBC Radio and achieved considerable success in brass band competitions, winning, among other events, the Belle Vue Open Championship of Great Britain in 1947, and the City of Edinburgh Pre-Festival Trophy in 1949 and 1950. The film was made at the Manchester studios of John E Blakeley, where the popular northern comedies of Frank Randle and others where produced. The CWS (Manchester) Band also gave a performance in the later *Symbol of Success* (1963; NCFC 259).

NCFC 135
Did You Know? Number 2 (Peas) (1951)

b/w and col · 5m 45s · sound · 16mm · EAFA, NFTVA
pr CWS Film Unit

■ An informational film about the canning of CWS peas.

I   Peas are cut on a Suffolk farm for canning at the CWS canning factory at Lowestoft; the cut vines are collected by a special loader. Two and a half hours from field to can is the boast of the CWS at Lowestoft.
II The peas arrive by lorry at the CWS factory: the load is passed into the viner, a pea-shelling machine; peas are removed from the pod by beaters; the peas pass onto a conveyor for weighing and cleaning in a rotary high-pressure shower; peas are stored in large holding tanks; preliminary cooking in a blanching machine; passing on an inspection belt, the peas are scrutinised by female operatives; the peas are canned; the filled cans roll down to the sterilising machine; the quality-control laboratory; the cans are labelled and packed into cartons.
III A close-up of a can of CWS garden peas *(colour)*.

Remarks
A series of short films detailing CWS productions was commenced around 1950, under the generic title of *Did You Know?* The Lowestoft canning factory was one of the biggest concerns of the CWS, and one of the factory's prime products was canned peas. As an official historian of the CWS wrote: "The British have a great appetite for canned peas, and at Lowestoft, adjacent to where the best peas grow, a big CWS factory worked night and day during the canning season on processing and canning peas and on many other canned products in the rest of the year" (Sir William Richardson, *The CWS in War and Peace 1938-1976* [Manchester: Co-operative Wholesale Society, 1977]). By the 1950s, colour photography was becoming cheaper and easier, and this film innovatively utilises the process for the final shot. Later in the series, at least one title, *Did You Know? Number 5 (Sweets)* (c.1952; NCFC 148), was shot on colour stock. By the mid-1950s, all CWS films, apart from television advertisements, were produced in colour.
See also: NCFC 191

NCFC 136
Festivity (1951)

b/w · 9m 33s · silent · 16mm · EAFA
pr Departmental Managers' Association,

Barnsley British Co-op Society

■ A jokey record of the trip to the Festival of Britain organised by the Departmental Managers' Association of the Barnsley British Co-operative Society.

I   The journey: it rains at Barnsley, Bawtry, Leicester and Banbury; Curly and Dinkie keep up everyone's spirits.
II In London: leaving the Ambassadors Hotel; catching a London red bus; approaching the South Bank site; entry through the turnstiles; general views of the site, including a shot of the Dome of Discovery, a centrepiece of the exhibition (exterior); among the exhibits (in the Lion and Unicorn building?); further scenes around the site; a funeral manager forgets where he is and measures a statue for burial; break for a cup of tea and a bit of a nap; the Skylon; the site lit-up at night, viewed from across the river; Big Ben; fountains.
III At the coast: the White Cliffs of Dover (?); on the cliffs, looking down on a lighthouse; the group of wives pose for a photograph; making friends with a horse.
IV Leaving the hotel and loading the luggage into the coach, which belongs to the Barnsley British Co-operative Society; the coach sets off and the passengers enjoy a sing-song and some comic turns; a break of journey at the George Hotel – a female passenger requires some assistance to get back on board the coach, which eventually pulls away.

Remarks
An interesting amateur film record of the 27-acre South Bank site, centre-piece to the huge national cultural event that was the Festival of Britain which ran throughout the summer of 1951. Nearly 8.5 million visitors were attracted to the South Bank, which, together with the Festival Pleasure Gardens at Battersea, were rare bright moments for the fun-starved populace in drab, austere postwar Britain. The Exhibition consisted of a number of pavilions, such as the Dome of Discovery, which presented British achievement in exploration and discovery, and the Lion and Unicorn building, which celebrated British character and tradition. The Skylon, designed by Powell and Moya, was an architectural centre-piece to the Festival, and was described as "a Vertical Feature in steel and aluminium" (*The South Bank Exhibition: A Guide* [1951]). The CWS

was refused permission to exhibit alongside other British manufacturers, and an alternative Co-operative festival was staged in Birmingham over two weeks in May.

This humorous "people's" record of the event is in welcome contrast to the rather respectful "official" documentary films which were produced. Being good Co-operators, the Departmental Managers' Association stayed at the Ambassadors Hotel, North London, owned and managed by the London Co-operative Society.

NCFC 137
Pathfinders Camp (1951)

col · 14m · silent · 16mm · ETV
pr George Durham

▪ A film record of the Kessingland Youth Camp, August 1951, organised by the Gravesend, Gillingham, Royal Arsenal and Grays Co-operative Societies.

I   Various scenes at camp: tuck shop; group-shot of the organisers; groups out on a walk.
II   Morning assembly; drawing funds at the camp "bank"; money is exchanged for goods at the "canteen".
III Sports: rounders; cricket; fun on the playground.
IV   A ramble to the "wreck", an old beached ship.
V   Visitors from Grays and Royal Arsenal Society's Education Committee.
VI   Scenes at mealtime.
VII Sports day: sprint races; sack race; relay races; three-legged races; obstacle race; pleasure boats.
VIII A visit to the CWS canning factory at Lowestoft.
IX   On the seashore: playing ball on the beach; climbing rocks; fun in the water.
X   The coaches leave for home.

Remarks
The second annual Pathfinder camp to be filmed by the talented George Durham, this time on the Suffolk coast at a camp operated by the Holiday Fellowship. The Co-operative Youth Movement (CYM) was a national youth scheme initiated by the Co-operative Union in 1944; it sponsored two groups, the Rainbow Playways (7-11 years) and the Pathfinders (11-14 years). Attempts to incorporate the autonomous children's organisation, the Woodcraft Folk, were never entirely satisfactory and the two organisations split in 1946. As the 1950s

progressed, the CYM went into decline as Co-operative societies cut back on resources, and the organisation's lack of democratic structure came in for criticism.

NCFC 138
Sports Day at Oakwell (1951)

b/w · 2m 10s · silent · 16mm · EAFA
pr Barnsley British Co-op Society

▪ A film recording a Co-op sports gala sponsored by the Barnsley British Co-operative Society.

I   Panoramic shot of the sports field.
II   The day's sporting events: women's egg and spoon race; happy spectators; boys' sprint race; the officials at the finishing-line; girls' sprint race; boys' sack race – includes a "dramatic" slow-motion sequence; an injured competitor receives first aid from the St John's Ambulance crew; the large crowds in the grandstand.

Remarks
One of four surviving films from the Barnsley British Co-operative Society. The sports day would have been an annual event timed to coincide with the International Co-operative Day celebrations. In 1951 it was held on 7 July. Numerous films have survived of similar activities from societies around the country, this example being rather brief. ICD celebrations usually included fancy dress parades, entertainers, displays, singing, dancing, and so on. It is not possible to ascertain if such activities were absent from the event or merely "missed" by the filmmaker.
See also: NCFC 129

NCFC 139
[Colchester Co-op Society International Co-op Day] (c.1951)

b/w · 12m 30s · silent · 16mm · EAFA

▪ A film record of a Co-op gala.

I   The gathered spectators watch children's racing.
II   Fancy dress parade.
III Children's pony rides.
IV   Fancy dress parade.
V   The Co-operative Queen and pipers arrive and take up their positions on the platform.
VI   The crowning of the Queen and

VII A display of Highland dancing; young ballerinas; folk-dancing.
VIII The Co-operative Queen makes her address.
IX A ballet display and folk-dancing are watched by the large crowd.
X Preparing the "Grand Balloon Race".
XI Pipers and Queen make their exit. The pipers provide a marching display.
XII Little Bo Peep, plus sheep!
XIII An acrobatic dancer is enjoyed by the crowd; judging the fancy dress parade; a choir entertains.
XIV Viscount Alexander addresses the crowd of 18 000.
XV The Co-operative Queen makes the prize draw for a television set.

Remarks
One of a series of surviving films (1949-54) recording International Co-operative Day celebrations at Colchester and East Essex Co-operative and Industrial Society. Of particular note is the guest of honour, Co-op and Labour luminary, A V Alexander (1885-1965). In 1922, he had entered Parliament as a pioneer, Co-op-sponsored candidate for Hillsborough, Sheffield. He rose to become the Movement's pre-eminent parliamentarian: twice First Lord of the Admiralty; the first-ever Minister of Defence; Minster without Portfolio. He was created a Viscount in 1950, becoming leader of the Labour Peers in 1955, and created an Earl shortly before he died. By 1951, the Colchester and East Essex Co-operative and Industrial Society had a membership of 40 000, and operated 25 branch stores in the district. The television set raffled as a prize is a Defiant model, manufactured by the CWS.

NCFC 140
Co-operative Day Celebrations (1952)

b/w · 15m 2s · silent · 16mm · EAFA
pr CWS Film Unit

■ A film record of a Co-op gala sponsored by the Colchester and East Essex Co-operative and Industrial Society.

I Scenes of Colchester, old and new: the High Street; the castle; the War Memorial; the Old Siege House; St Botolph's Priory.
II Some of the premises of the Co-operative society: central premises; Brooklands Co-operative Education and Youth Centre.

III A banner welcoming the Co-operative Day Fete and Demonstration. Programmes are distributed.
IV Children's sports: girls' sprint races; boys' sprint races.
V The Co-operative Queen and Princess enter the arena piped in by the Stewart and Lloyds Pipe Band.
VI Opening address by Mr H H Fisher JP, President of the society.
VII Crowning ceremony by Lady Hartley Shawcross. The Co-op Queen addresses the crowd.
VIII Dancing display by the Kelvedons; female gymnast; children's folk-dance troupe; marching and Highland dancing display; funfair and side-shows; Sir Hartley and Lady Shawcross try their luck at prize fishing with magnets; children's pony rides; fancy dress parade; the toddler's race; a portrait shot of the Co-operative Pathfinders concert party; Punch and Judy is enjoyed by the large crowd; tug-of-war – winners are the funeral department; the Brooklands Co-operative Youth Choir.
IX Speech by Sir Hartley Shawcross.
X Film shows are projected in a tent.
XI The Co-operative Queen makes the prize draw – first prize is a Co-op Defiant television.
XII Old-time and Highland dancing.

Remarks
One of a series of films (1949-54) recording International Co-operative Day celebrations by the Colchester and East Essex Co-operative and Industrial Society. 1952 was the first occasion the film record was produced by the CWS Film Unit, and, correspondingly, it is a more complete and professional production, as is evident in the first sequence of historic Colchester, which extends the project beyond a simple film record of the day's events. The guest of honour was Labour luminary, Sir Hartley Shawcross, the Attorney General (1945-51), and briefly in 1951 President of the Board of Trade, before Labour lost power. The trade name, Defiant, was adopted in 1934 when the CWS entered into the manufacture of radio sets as a result of a trade boycott introduced by the Radio Manufacturers' Association.

NCFC 141
Did You Know? Number 7 (Soap) (1952)

b/w · 3m 31s · sound · 16mm · EAFA, NFTVA

pr CWS Film Unit

- The manufacturing processes behind CWS soaps.

I   Exterior of CWS Irlam soap works, Manchester; the large pans of the boiling-room; the chief boiler tests the mixer with his trowel; storage for cooling; cutting of the slabs into bars; the bars are stacked for drying; cutting the bars into tablets; the stamping of the tablets of soap; packing the soaps into cartons.

II   Boxes of soap pass on a conveyor: CWS White Windsor soap; CWS Congress soap; CWS Newsheaf soap; CWS Microl soap.

III   Graphic card: "These Brands are obtainable at your LOCAL CO-OPERATIVE STORES!".

Remarks
The last surviving example from the series, dealing yet again with soap manufacture, one of the products most examined by the Movement's films. One reason for the relatively high attention might be that, in the postwar years, the productive works shared the downward trend with retail performance and efficiency (although the situation really began to worsen after 1953), and the soap works in particular were losing ground. A particular concentration on the manufacture of soap in its film work could have been an attempt to boost demand.

NCFC 142
Shoe Salesman Part 1: "Your Product, Your Shop, and You" (1952)

b/w · 13m 21s · sound · 16mm · EAFA
pr CWS Film Unit *prod* George Wynn
d, sc Max Munden *cam* Bert Hampson *ed* C Beaumont *sd* Pip Pearson

- The first instalment of a three-part training film for Co-op shoe sales staff.

I   A busy shoe department.

II   An experienced manager of a shoe department in a film studio. He "conjures up" a shoe department, and introduces us to his sales assistants. He dismisses the slovenly "don't-care Charlie", and "sloppy Sally", preferring the smart and attentive "courteous Charlie" and "service Sally".

III   Know your stock: get to know what is in the window; check up on stock in spare moments – aids in stock control;

double-check the placement of your stock for efficiency – "a place for everything and everything in its place"; keep the particulars of all surgical, and made-to-measure customers, on file.

IV   Be attentive to your customers and their requirements. Do not lose customers.

V   The wrong and right ways of handling and presenting merchandise. Treat customers and their feet with respect.

VI   The senior salesman invites the audience to discuss the learning points raised by the film.

Remarks
See entry for *Shoe Salesman Part 3: "Your Customers"* (1952).

NCFC 143
Shoe Salesman Part 2: "Feet and How to Fit Them" (1952)

b/w · 12m 53s · sound · 16mm · EAFA, NFTVA
pr CWS Film Unit *prod* George Wynn
d, sc Max Munden *cam* Bert Hampson *ed* C Beaumont *sd* Pip Pearson

- The second instalment of a three-part training film for Co-op shoe sales staff.

I   Various shots of people's feet, resting and walking; a model's bare feet are analysed at rest and in motion.

II   The skeletal construction of a human foot and the functions of particular bones, muscles and ligaments are explained.

III   The essentials of fitting shoes: fitting for size; fitting for shape; dealing with abnormal feet; fitting children's shoes – the use of the "pedicator", a specially designed CWS measuring device.

IV   A display of CWS Wheatsheaf Nature-Fit shoes for boys and girls.

V   What parents should be told about their children's shoes – size, fit and shape – to ensure the healthy development of a child's feet; a display of children's shoes.

VI   CWS Wheatsheaf shoes ideal for adults and their occupations: farmers' boots; nurse's shoes; the ballroom dancer; the docker; the policeman; the hiker; manual worker; the family is catered for with a range of Wheatsheaf footwear.

VII   Trainees are asked to discuss the learning points arising from the film.

Remarks
See entry for *Shoe Salesman Part 3: "Your
Customers"* (1952).

NCFC 144
Shoe Salesman Part 3: "Your Customers"
(1952)

b/w · 11m · sound · 16mm · EAFA, NFTVA
pr CWS Film Unit *prod* George Wynn
d, sc Max Munden *cam* Bert Hampson *ed* C
Beaumont *sd* Pip Pearson

▪ The third instalment of a three-part training
film for Co-op shoe sales staff.

I   A senior salesman in a Co-op shoe
     department introduces his assistants,
     Sally and Charlie. We are going to
     witness some typical customers and
     sales situations.
II   Situations which customers do not
     like: lack of tact, rather than politeness
     – do not embarrass customers;
     inadequate attentiveness – do not
     make customers feel unimportant.
III   Different types of customers and how
     to deal with them: "the can't make up
     her mind type"; "the superior type";
     "the bad-tempered type"; "the chatter-
     box".
IV   The senior salesman brings the
     training session to an end and asks
     the audience to discuss the sales
     situations and techniques examined in
     the film.

Remarks
This three-part film produced by the CWS
Film Unit was considered a "brilliant training
film" by the Co-operative trade journal, *The
Producer*. The film was broken into three
parts to allow for discussion. To assist in
that aim, "Discussion Notes" accompanied
the film's screening, together with a leaflet
containing the "Shoe Selling Alphabet",
designed to assist the society's footwear
manager in leading a discussion. Special
screenings of the film to footwear staff were
provided by the CWS mobile film units when
they were visiting a trading area to present
a conventional film programme. It appears
that the complete training film was not
necessarily played as a single programme,
since separate prints of parts 2 and 3 have
been located, and were suitable for
screening in isolation. The Movement first
set up a committee to report on the efficacy
of training films in 1939, but ultimately little
was invested in this vocational aid.
See also: NCFC 142, NCFC 143

NCFC 145
Then and Now, 1862-1952 (1952)

col · 11m 58s · silent · 16mm · EAFA
pr Barnsley British Co-op Society

▪ "Being A Record of 90 Years Service And
Enterprise" of the Barnsley British
Co-operative Society (BBCS).

I   Dressing the society's transport fleet
     for the 90th anniversary parade.
     Various products and trades are
     represented: Co-op tea, the Education
     Committee, Co-op flour, Co-op milk,
     and so on. Participants get into their
     historical costumes; the procession
     takes to the road; a Highland pipe
     band leads the parade through the
     city streets, and is cheered on by
     spectators; busy scenes in the main
     retailing district.
II   The crowds follow the parade to the
     Oakwell playing-fields; the crowd is
     addressed by the society President
     (?); two clowns entertain; two acrobats
     perform on top of a high structure; a
     display of tricks by an Alsatian dog; a
     demonstration cricket match between
     the "Pioneers" and current members; a
     fireworks display.

Remarks
An impressive record of the Jubilee
celebrations held by the society in 1952,
particularly noteworthy for the excellent
quality of the colour photography. The
detailed preparations for the parade are
captured by the film, and the numerous
dressed vehicles are quite astounding in
their ingenuity and execution. A strong local
Co-operative society such as BBCS held an
important place in the fabric of a
community, which is clear from this film in
the resources lavished on the procession,
the celebrations and obvious wide-scale
community interest. Several films detailing
Co-operative activity in Barnsley have
survived from the period. From the scant
evidence, it appears that one of the
society's departmental managers was a
talented amateur ciné enthusiast and
responsible for the charming productions. In
its Jubilee year of 1952, the society claimed
a membership of 119 000.
See also: NCFC 129

NCFC 146
[Co-op 3-D Film] (c.1952)

col · 29m 36s · silent · 16mm · NFTVA

- A compilation stereoscopic film.

I Scenes around Doncaster – including a drive past by a Doncaster Co-operative Society (DCS) delivery van; a doorstep delivery by a DCS bread van and roundsman; a DCS milk roundsman by his float; a wooden DCS prefabricated store (exterior); a DCS supermarket (exterior); the central premises of the DCS (exterior).
II A short sequence promoting the CWS detergent, Spel: a display of packets of Spel; a housewife cleans a work surface and window with Spel.
III "Meet Me At The Zoo" – scenes at a zoo.
IV "Cowboys and Indians" – children play a game of cowboys and Indians.
V A man throws biscuits, from a carton marked "CWS", towards the camera – to gain the maximum 3-D effect!; a display of CWS packed biscuits.
VI "North Wales in Springtime" – various scenes of picturesque North Wales.
VII "Smooth as Velvet" – a woman smokes a cigarette and blows the smoke towards the camera; scenes of cigarette manufacture; cartons of CWS Navy Cut cigarettes; a man throws packets of cigarettes towards the camera; a display of CWS Navy Cut cigarettes.

Remarks
This 3-D stereoscopic film – a rarity in the collection – clearly exploits the new process which, for a brief period in 1952-53, was widely popular with cinema audiences. This reel is made up of several distinct sequences, with sections I, II, V and VII containing Co-operative material. The first sequence is particularly noteworthy, providing a unique record of Co-operation in Doncaster. It is also interesting to note the crude attempts to exploit the visual qualities of 3-D by throwing objects at the camera.

NCFC 147
Did You Know? Number 4 (Tobacco)
(c.1952)

b/w · 3m 29s · sound · 16mm · NFTVA
pr CWS Film Unit

- Promotional film for CWS cigarettes.

I A hopper machine processes raw tobacco; cigarettes roll forward on a conveyor.
II Hogsheads of tobacco, marked from Virginia and Rhodesia; a workman breaks open a hogshead to reveal the raw tobacco leaves; the leaves are fed into rotary moisteners and passed through to the cutting machines; the shredded tobacco is "combed out" to ensure even cigarettes; paper is stamped with the brand, and the cigarette rolled, sealed and cut; the action of the rotary knife is presented in slow-motion; automatic testing for quality-control to ensure correct size and weight; female operatives further examine the cigarettes for quality; the cigarettes are fed into the packing machines and boxed into tens and twenties.
III CWS brand cigarettes: Jaycee, Navy Cut, Raydex.
IV Graphic card: "These brands are obtainable at your LOCAL CO-OPERATIVE STORES".

Remarks
Throughout the wartime period, Co-op tobacco sales and production had remained buoyant, substantially aided by War Office contracts for cigarettes. The CWS tobacco factory also supplied, on behalf of retail societies, thousands of parcels of duty-free cigarettes and tobacco to Co-operative employers in the forces. In the postwar period of relative decline, the Manchester Tobacco Factory was one of several famous CWS factories to experience heavy falls in value and volume of sales. The film was an effort to help build demand within the Movement for Co-op brand cigarettes. By the early 1970s, the position was such that the tobacco factory became a joint enterprise with a Canadian firm, part of a general tendency at rationalisation within the Movement.

NCFC 148
Did You Know? Number 5 (Sweets)
(c.1952)

col · 3m 12s · sound · 16mm · EAFA, NFTVA
pr CWS Film Unit

- The processes that go into the production of CWS sweets and confectionery.

I The manufacture of CWS Assorted Fruits: after the boiling process, the toffee confection is laid out to cool; the pliable toffee is shaped and moulded into a long string; individual Assorted Fruits are stamped out at the rate of 2400 per minute; the sweets are transferred to packing-machines; the sweets are packed into hygienic wrappers.

II   A selection of CWS sweets in attractive display boxes: Eclairs; Liquorice Allsorts; Family Assortment; London Mixture; Congress Caramels; Assorted Fruit Whirls; Brazil Nut Caramels; Peter Pan Mixture.

III   Graphic card: "As Good As They Look. CWS Sweets."

Remarks

Apparently the only example in the series made in colour, and used to great advantage in the choice of product – Assorted Fruits sweets. The production sequences were filmed at the CWS sugar confectionery works at Reddish, Stockport, a site acquired in 1937 for development purposes. Confectionery/sweets was one of the first manufacturing trades entered into by the CWS, and commenced at the Crumpsall (Manchester) works purchased in 1873. After the Second World War the manufacture of sweets largely centred on the Reddish plant.

See also: NCFC 135

NCFC 149
Co-operative Day Celebrations (1953)

col · 13m 43s · silent · 16mm · EAFA, NFTVA
pr CWS Film Unit

▪ A film record of a Co-op gala sponsored by the Colchester and East Essex Co-operative and Industrial Society.

I   Shot of the "Co-operative Day Fete and Demonstration" welcoming banner.

II   Children's sports: girls' sack race; boys' sack race; girls' three-legged race; girls vs. boys relay race; mixed toddlers' race.

III   The procession of the Co-operative Queen enters the arena: the marching band; the "Queen" and her maids of honour; the crown borne upon a cushion; the "royal party" on the platform; official opening by Mr H H Fisher JP; the crowning of the "Queen" and "Princess".

IV   Marching by the band of the 1st Battalion, Northamptonshire Regiment.

V   The "Queen" addresses the gathering.

VI   More selections from the band (seated).

VII   "Impromptu entertainment". A young child at play.

VIII Fancy dress parade and judging.

IX   The side shows: darts; balloon games; puppet show.

X   Display of international dances by the Brooks School of Dancing.

XI   Display of physical training by the Co-operative youth clubs.

XII   Display of self-defence.

XIII The guest of honour, Herbert Morrison MP, makes a speech, followed by Roy Thomas.

XIV   Prize draws.

XV   "Old Tyme Dancing" as dusk falls.

Remarks

One of a series of such films (1949-54), this film record conforms to the established pattern. This was the second of the films produced by the CWS for the Colchester and East Essex Co-operative and Industrial Society. As was the convention, a well-known Labour politician was invited as guest of honour. Of all such guests recorded by the film series, Morrison was the most senior, having been Home Secretary during the war, and Lord President and Foreign Secretary for the previous Labour administration. The obvious readiness of leading Labour politicians to attend Co-operative celebrations testifies to the important and influential place of the Co-op within the Labour Movement.

NCFC 150
It's Magic (1953)

b/w · 11m 30s · sound · 16mm · EAFA, NFTVA
pr CWS Film Unit *d* Max Munden *prod* George Wynn *cam* Bert Hampson *ed* Steve Cox *mus* Francis Chagrin

▪ A promotional film for the CWS detergent, Spel.

I   Various cleaning jobs around the house – washing dishes, scrubbing floors, washing clothes, and so on.

II   A housewife is sceptical about the merits of a "new" washing powder, and demands action rather than words: a young housewife uses Spel to wash her delicate fabrics – with excellent results; another housewife uses Spel to wash the dishes – no scum!; dirty marks are removed from the paintwork using Spel; a man cleans his car using Spel; stains are cleaned from a carpet using Spel; Spel is used for a general clothes' wash – with excellent results.

III Graphic card: "Spel does it all because Spel makes the water do the work!".

IV Various scenes of manufacture at the CWS soap works, including the laboratory, and animated diagrams which attempt to explain the benefits of Spel.

V The sceptical housewife is convinced, and deems to buy Spel at her local Co-operative store.

VI Graphic card: "SPEL Contains Laurex That Looks After Your Hands. SPEL Tomorrow's Miracle Today. Exclusive To Co-operative Societies".

Remarks

Despite difficulties posed by restrictions on labour and materials in austere postwar Britain, the CWS did manage remarkable expansions and new developments in the period. The business in soft drinks grew; new fertilisers were added to the existing range; and the CWS Defiant television set was launched with the assistance of the Plessey company. In August 1952, after exhaustive research and market-testing, Spel, the Co-operative synthetic detergent, reached Co-operative store counters. The historian of the CWS in the postwar period has commented on the launch: "In a savagely competitive market 'Spel' was a Co-operative success story" (Sir William Richardson, *The CWS in War and Peace 1938-1976* [Manchester: Co-operative Wholesale Society, 1977]). The new cleaning product was marketed aggressively with a competition for sales staff to place in order of value as sales aids. An example of the Spel promotional campaign – for which 14 000 entries were received – was an ambitious local scheme involving the Wellingborough Co-operative Society in a tie-in with the local Lyric Cinema, with free cinema tickets on offer to children who collected sufficient packet tops. A shorter colour film with the same title was also released at this time.
See also: NCFC 105

NCFC 151
Magic Feet (1953)

b/w · 8m 44s · sound · 16mm · NWFA
pr Anglo-Scottish Pictures *cast* Stanley Matthews

▪ A promotional film for CWS "Stanley Matthews" football boots.

I A crowded football ground. Various shots of football legend, Stanley Matthews, conjuring his "magic" on the right wing.

II Slow-motion sequence of Matthews's footwork.

III Matthews in action against Scotland; the 1953 "Coronation" FA Cup Final, Matthews in action for Blackpool against Bolton; Matthews receiving his cup winners' medal.

IV The Stanley Matthews football boot, made exclusively by the CWS; Stanley demonstrates the numerous virtues of the boots; a young boy trying out his new pair of Stanley Matthews football boots.

V Graphic card: "The CWS Stanley Matthews football boots are sold through Co-operative Societies everywhere".

Remarks

One of the most successful CWS celebrity product endorsements was the CWS Stanley Matthews football boot. Football legend Matthews helped to design the boots which were manufactured at the CWS Heckmondwike boot and shoe factory beginning in 1949. Special promotional displays were mounted in stores at which *Magic Feet* and a complementary film, *Play with the Best* (1950s; NCFC 412), were screened. "The Wizard", Matthews, was sometimes in attendance to help with sales. A number of testimonials were forthcoming for the quality of the CWS football boots: several players in Scotland's international squad ordered pairs, including winger Willy Waddell, and captain, George Young; Bob Jackson, manager of Portsmouth Town kitted out his whole team in them!
See also: NCFC 177

NCFC 152
A Tribute To Beauty (1953)

col · 6m 28s · sound · 16mm · NWFA
pr CWS Film Unit

▪ A promotional film for CWS toilet soaps.

I A woman arranges a colourful display of flowers – nature's beauty of colour and perfume.

II The making of fine CWS toilet soaps: a vat of soap chips, to which is added a beaker of colouring and perfume; the mixing of CWS Green Olive soap; the milling process; the cutting of tablets; shaping and embossing; the wrapping process; packing into cartons for despatch.

III The various fragrances of the popular CWS Galatea brand -- lavender, rose, floral bouquet and eau-de-Cologne.

IV Hand-finishing of toilet soaps: hand-stamping of CWS Cream of Lavender toilet soap; trimming and polishing; boxing of Cream of Lavender soap; displays of Cream of Lavender, Green Olive, Toilet Carbolic, White Olive, Bath Tablets, and Coronation boxed set.

V The flower arranger compares the fragrance of CWS toilet soap with that of her floral display.

Remarks
Soap-making was a regular topic of Co-operative promotional films, this example concentrating more on the luxury end of the market. By 1953, the CWS was Britain's third largest manufacturer of soap, with its large factory situated at Irlam, Manchester. Of particular interest is the souvenir boxed set of Coronation soap, just one of a range of CWS products to commemorate the event, which also included crested teapots, biscuit tins, a 9" Coronation plate, tea-caddy and embossed silver-plated teaspoons. Here is a clear example where the Co-operative Movement was integrated into the official culture, boldly getting into line behind the royalists.

NCFC 153
It's Magic! (c.1953)

col · 1m 44s · sound · 16mm · NFTVA

■ A short promotional film for the new CWS detergent, Spel.

I People are talking about a new product -- shot of busy street and Co-op self-service store front.

II A packet of CWS Spel.

III A dirty rag is immersed in a jar of hot water and Spel -- it floats the dirt away! Spel makes the water do the work!

IV Two packets of Spel: handy size, 1/-, and economy size 1/11.

V Graphic card: "SPEL is a CWS Product".

VI Shop window of a Co-op self-service store with a display of Spel.

VII A packet of CWS Spel.

Remarks
One of two surviving films from the period

promoting the CWS's successful new synthetic detergent, Spel. This example is particularly interesting for its inclusion of early colour footage of the new self-service Co-op stores, a distinct postwar development. It is surprising that there appears to have been no film produced by the Movement on the phenomenon of the self-service store, in the innovation and development of which the Co-op played a decisive role.

NCFC 154
Summer Fete (c.1953)

col · 7m 32s · silent · 16mm · EAFA

■ A film record of a Co-op gala sponsored by the Ipswich Industrial Co-operative Society.

I A dog show. Alsatians, followed by Labradors, are paraded around the showground.

II A marching band entertains.

III Funfair and sideshow attractions.

IV Athletics: ladies' sprint; male competitors warming-up; men's sprints; men's long-distance races; more men's sprinting.

V Motor cycle stunt displays: dragging men on boards; weaving between obstacles; seven men on a bike; riding a bike backwards; driver and passenger switching places; trick balance displays; leaping over human bodies.

VI Acrobats performing atop a high structure.

Remarks
It is probable that the eponymous summer fête was International Co-operative Day, 1953. It is notable how, in this last addition to the cycle of such films commemorating the celebrations sponsored by Ipswich Industrial Co-operative Society, all evidence of Co-operative and Labour activism has gone. Sports, recreation and entertainment are now completely foregrounded, and the historic/symbolic significance of Co-operative Day has vanished. For instance, no promotional material or displays are evident for either the local society or the CWS, always features of the earlier occasions/films.

NCFC 155
Celebration Dinner and Dance (1954)

b/w and col · 11m 41s · part-sound · 16mm · EAFA
pr Birmingham Co-operative Society

■ An "amateur" film record of a celebration dinner and dance, which was sponsored by the dairy of the Birmingham Co-operative Society.

I	Close-shot of programme and menu.
II	Guests are greeted by senior managers and board members.
III	The assembled guests are served dinner in the ballroom; speeches are made from the top table.
IV	The orchestra on the stage; dancing on the ballroom floor; prize-giving.
V	Guests are greeted *(colour)*.
VI	Speeches from the top table.
VII	The assembled guests join in a toast; further speeches; the tables are cleared away from the ballroom floor.
VIII	Civic dignitaries are welcomed and greeted *(colour)*.
IX	The mayor's speech; prize-giving ceremony.
X	Performance by a troupe of dancing girls; trick-cycling; juggler; acrobat; French cancan.
XI	Guests enjoy ballroom dancing, cut with shots of the orchestra; the singing of "Auld Lang Syne"; the guests disperse to go home.

Remarks
The event was held at the Tower Ballroom, Edgbaston, in commemoration of attaining weekly sales of 350 000 gallons of milk. Some of the sections are clearly out of sequence, and the voice-over merely provides an explanatory introduction. The Birmingham Co-operative Society was formed in 1881, and quickly grew into one of the largest regional societies. By the middle of the 1950s, it had a membership of 300 000, and owned nearly 200 branch stores.

NCFC 156
Co-operative Day Celebrations, 1954 (1954)

col · 7m 38s · silent · 16mm · EAFA
pr DATA Films

■ A film record of a Co-op gala sponsored by the Colchester and East Essex Co-operative and Industrial Society.

I	Poster – International Co-operative Day celebrations, 3 July 1954.
II	A large crowd awaits the day's events.
III	A series of children's races, interspersed with shots of the crowd.
IV	A succession of athletics events: boys' sack race; young ladies' sprint; girls' three-legged race; mixed relay race.
V	A marching band (Newark Imperial Carnival Band) and arrival of the Co-operative Queen.
VI	The Co-operative Queen is crowned by the Mayoress, Mrs E Morris, and makes her address. Return of the marching band.
VII	A fancy dress contest. A portrait shot of the winners.
VIII	A children's Punch and Judy show. Several close-ups of youngsters enjoying the entertainment.
IX	A classical dancing display by young girls.
X	An address by Mr W T William MP.
XI	Various sideshow attractions.
XII	The title poster flutters away in the wind.

Remarks
One of a series of surviving films of that period depicting International Co-operative Day celebrated by the Colchester and East Essex Co-operative and Industrial Society. A mix of sporting and musical events, speeches and funfair entertainment, made for a typical itinerary that would have been replicated around the country. This example is distinct for not involving a senior Labour parliamentarian.

NCFC 157
CWS Shop Window (1954)

col · 5m · silent · 16mm · NFTVA

■ A compendium of animated advertisements for CWS brand products.

I	A night-time scene: a divan set materialises from the heavens and disappears into a nearby house; "Slumber...in sweet luxury. Society sheets and pillowcases."
II	A young penguin is distressed in the rain. Adult penguins shield him with umbrellas: "You'll Be Smart And Gay On The Wettest Day. CWS Penguin umbrellas, from as little as 16/9 in several colours. Born in Manchester, raised Everywhere."
III	A magical fairy, balancing on top of a large ball, waves her wand to produce CWS polishes – CWS floor polish, tile polish, Viola wax, Pelaw polish:

"PELAW Polishes. The Wax in Pelaw REALLY Polishes. PELAW Polishes for a Brilliant Performance. CWS."

IV   Two bottles of CWS cleaning products declare their worth – "We do all the cleaning jobs around the house": Laundene – 101 uses around the home, 1/9; Laundazone – cleans and disinfects, 1/-; Laundene handy-size joins them, 1/-; "We're Pelaw products for easier cleaning. At your Co-operative Society Now. CWS."

V   A young woman on the telephone – "I've got the number I want" – Number One Navy Cut: "A Brand New. A Grand New, Cigarette. A New Larger Cigarette Made From Skillfully Blended Fine Quality Tobaccos. The Largest Size Quality Cigarette. 1/9 for 10. For 20, 3/7."

VI   A radio mast beaming out signals – "Tune In To Radio Luxembourg 208m. Silver Seal Margarine, Shilling a Second Programme. Britain's Most Hectic And Hilarious Quiz! A Brand New Idea In Entertainment. Tune in 8-8.30 pm To Radio Luxembourg 208m, Every Friday."

VII   An attractive plate of "CWS Biscuits" – cream crackers, Ginger Nuts, Digestive Sweetmeal, Aladdin, Chocolate Marshmallows, Marie, Shortcake, Chocolate Raglan, Fig Bar. "Go Down Well With Everyone".

VIII Graphic card: "These CWS Goods Are Obtainable From All Co-operative Societies. You'll Save When You Say "CWS Symbol of Sound Value".

Remarks
A collection of seven advertisements for use in cinemas. An excellent example of the plethora of brand names utilised by the Movement which critics considered were confusing to the general public. It was assuming much that audiences were aware that the CWS was the brand manufacturer of Co-op products, even more that they could decode the historical and geographical significance of brand names such as Pelaw. Advocates of a simpler, unified approach won the day in 1967, with the adoption of the now-familiar Co-op logo for all brand products. The Co-op-sponsored radio show, "Shilling a Second", commenced broadcasting in October 1954, and was compèred by Paul Carpenter. The show specifically promoted CWS Silver Seal margarine.

NCFC 158
It's Up to You! (1954)

b/w · 9m · sound · 16mm · EAFA
pr DATA Films *d* R Pickering *cam* Wolfgang Suschitzky/Ken Reeves *comm* John Slater

▪ A propaganda film for the London Co-operative Society.

I   A dairy of the LCS. A milk transporter, freshly loaded, sets off on its journey; a coal horse is led out to its cart; a bakery roundsman on his deliveries; the coal cart leaves the depot; vans and lorries leave the garage; a store prepares for opening – the first customer walks in – the owner of the shop has arrived.

II   A garage of the LCS (exterior); a funeral car draws away; tailoring, household goods and electrical departments of a Co-op departmental store; a modern self-service store (interior); Harlow branch store (exterior and interior); a prefabricated store (exterior and interior); various store exteriors and crowds of shoppers on busy streets.

III   Board meeting of the London Co-operative Society – the commentary discusses the key principles of the Movement.

IV   Co-operative Education: scenes at a Co-op youth camp; the Co-operative College, Stanford Hall; a meeting of the WCG; Guild women canvassing on the street; a discussion group of the National Co-operative Men's Guild; a Co-op drama group in rehearsal.

V   The importance of democratic participation: a quarterly general meeting with full attendance; a quarterly meeting with sparse attendance and apathetic members.

VI   A housewife, with full basket, leaves a Co-op store.

Remarks
DATA Films (Documentary Technicians' Alliance) had been formed in 1944 by a group of documentary technicians, notably director Donald Alexander and cinematographer Wolfgang Suschitzky, as a Co-operative production unit. Most had previously worked with celebrated filmmaker, Paul Rotha. Several commissions were gained from the Co-operative Movement, and this one, probably unique, attempted to instruct the membership in the necessity for participation in a democratic organisation. Increased member apathy was

felt to be a mounting problem in the 1950s, a time when member loyalty and Co-operative ideals were being lost to the attractions of the "affluent society". Although Suschitzky's credit appears collectively on the film, he does not recall any actual participation. It is possible that some of the scenes were his work. He would later work widely in the feature film industry, shooting such celebrated films as *Ulysses* (1967), *Get Carter* (1971), and *Theatre of Blood* (1973). The film is imaginatively constructed, proving the general skill and competence of DATA as a production outfit.

NCFC 159
Seal of Success (1954)

col · 20m 32s · sound · 16mm · NFTVA
pr Anglo-Scottish Pictures *d* John Spencer *cast* Jacqueline Rose, Hilda Fennimore, Gordon Bell, Bridget Stenner.

■ A promotional film for CWS baking ingredients, including Silver Seal margarine.

I   Mrs Drake and her daughter are shopping at the Co-op for items for the young girl's birthday party.
II   "Aunty" Jacqueline Rose, the famous television cook, arrives to help prepare the birthday feast; Mrs Drake demonstrates how to bake an ideal birthday cake; making a plain cake; Jacqueline Rose demonstrates how to make a "mushroom cake" – named after its appearance rather than after its ingredients; the daughter and her friend are surprised at how nice the butter icing is, being made with CWS Silver Seal margarine.
III Scenes at the CWS margarine factory showing how Silver Seal margarine is made, wrapped, tested and despatched.
IV Other uses for CWS Silver Seal margarine: improves white sauce; served on baked stuffed cod and vegetables; parsley sauce; with scrambled eggs; for sauté potatoes.
V   Mr Drake arrives and, tempted by the feast, begins tucking in prematurely.
VI The party is a great success, with the children greatly enjoying all the goodies made with Silver Seal margarine. Resting with the other adults whilst the children play in the garden, Mrs Drake declares that she has found the answer to better cooking – CWS Silver Seal margarine.
VII Graphic card: "CWS Silver Seal

Margarine. That's the Stuff to Spread, 10½d per lb."
VIII Graphic card: "Gold Seal. The luxury spread contains 10% butter, 1/- per lb."
IX Graphic card: "CWS Gold Seal and Silver Seal Margarines. From Co-operative Societies Everywhere."

Remarks
CWS cooking fats and baking products were heavily promoted through films and screened by the CWS Publicity Film Service. The service was available free of charge to societies, with the CWS providing the following: specially designed posters advertising the show; a monthly £50 prize competition; window bills; invitation cards and recipe booklets for distribution; materials for local press advertising announcing the show, and promoting the featured products. A new "Woman's Hour" show was inaugurated in 1954, and *Seal of Success* was the special interest film produced to launch it. Future cookery demonstration films, ideal for the programme "to arrest and hold feminine interest" (*The Producer* August 1954), included *The Right Mixture* (c.1955; NCFC 183), *Father Takes the Cake* (1957; NCFC 200) and *Choice of Quality* (1958; NCFC 207). 1954 saw some urgency in the production of margarine, since on 8 May the product was derationed, and open competition in its supply began once again. This film thus represents the Movement's opening gambit in the "battle of the brands", over a product whose consumption had doubled since before the war. Jacqueline Rose was a well-known celebrity television cook and described as television's "youngest chef". Her expertise was further drawn upon in the later film, *Father Holds the Fort* (1955; NCFC 163). This print suffers from some colour-fading.
See also: xxii, xxxiii

NCFC 160
[CWS Meat Plant] (c.1954)

b/w · 8m 27s · silent · 16mm · NFTVA

■ Various scenes of empty premises apparently acquired by the CWS for use as a meat-processing plant.

Exterior shots of the buildings and grounds are combined with interior views, the material apparently edited "in-camera". A small group of men inspects the site; later, they are grouped around a scale model of the area.

Remarks
The film was probably an aid to assist the architects in their plans for redeveloping the site. There is no evidence from which to deduce the actual whereabouts of the location or much about the intentions of the CWS for establishing productive activities there. In the 1950s, the meat trade was a significant business for the CWS. Principal supplies were obtained from New Zealand, and considerable investment was made in plant, especially in the area of pre-packaging. For 1955, the Movement's trade in meat was approximately £70 million, representing 10-11% of the total. The value of meat sales for the CWS in that year was £18.5 million.

NCFC 161
[Co-operative Fashion Show] (1955)

b/w and col · 3m 34s · silent · 16mm · NFA
pr Turners (Photography)

▪ A Co-operative fashion show in Newcastle.

I　Female models parade a selection of summer dresses on a catwalk.
II　Mature models parade evening wear with fur stole.
III　The latest in bridalwear and bridesmaid wear.
IV　The fashion models pose in front of the main hoarding of the CWS Family Fare Exhibition *(colour)*.

Remarks
The fashion show was almost certainly a feature of the CWS Family Fare Exhibition that had visited Newcastle in August 1955. It is probable that this fashion show sequence had "detached" itself from the film record of the exhibition made for the Newcastle Co-operative Society. A surviving film of the 1960 CWS Family Fare Exhibition includes footage of the fashion show, a regular feature of such trade exhibitions. For this film, it is interesting to note that the models parade solely for the camera, the event being staged without an audience! A further sequence (2m 22s, b/w) of what appear to be out-takes from the fashion show is also preserved at the Northern Film and Television Archive.

NCFC 162
CWS Family Fare Exhibition (1955)

b/w and col · 8m 18s · silent · 16mm · NFA
pr Turners (Photography)

▪ A record of the CWS Family Fare Exhibition, Newcastle, 1955.

I　Exterior of the CWS Family Fare Exhibition marquee; visitors arrive through the main entrance; long-shot of the exhibition site – several large marquees; arrival of the civic dignitaries and representatives of the Board of Management who enter the main marquee *(colour)*.
II　Interior of the main exhibition marquee. Visitors take their seats; the civic dignitaries and representatives of the Board of Management are led onto the platform; an opening address by Councillor Mrs D A Starkey; an address by Mr J M Sanderson of the Board; a musical interlude by the CWS (Manchester) Brass Band; an address by Mr W H Patterson (General Manager); bouquets of flowers are presented to the female guests on the platform.
III　Scenes around the exhibition: recruitment at the "membership booth"; busy crowds milling around the stalls; busy trade at a mock self-service store.
IV　A performance by the CWS (Manchester) Brass Band.
V　Further scenes among the exhibits; refreshment at the café; the CWS Aerated Waters Stand *(b/w)*.

Remarks
The first of two films recording the CWS Family Fare Exhibition at Newcastle. The touring Family Fare show was considered excellent propaganda for trade by the CWS, "a shot-in-the-arm for Co-operative business and prestige. Non-Co-operative families flock to its doors to see, probably for the first time, the visible evidence of the Movement's claim to the title of universal provider" (*The Producer* January 1960). The Family Fare was a "flexible" show able to adapt to large hall or small, or, as seen here, to the tented field. A typical exhibition boasted 45 stands, a furnished bungalow, furniture-testing, cookery demonstrations, fashion parades and film shows, with the CWS (Manchester) Band as a special "top-liner" – some of those exhibits being evident in this record of the Newcastle show. The site for the Newcastle show was the Town Moor, between Newcastle and Gosforth, and the exhibition ran for two weeks in August, attracting over 250 000 visitors. The

film footage taken of the exhibition was intended for incorporation into a general film dealing with the many ramifications of the Newcastle Co-operative Society. I have found no evidence that such a project ever came to fruition.

NCFC 163
Father Holds the Fort (1955)

col · 15m 17s · sound · 16mm · IAC, NFTVA
pr Anglo-Scottish Pictures *d* John Spencer
prod Bert Hampson *cam* Bernard Davies
cast Jacqueline Rose, Roy Godfrey, Maureen Davies, Edwin Ellis, Tim Turner, Derek Prentise *sc* Tom Twigge *ad* Don Russell

■ A comic narrative film promoting CWS Shortex cooking fat.

I   On the train to work on Monday morning, George recounts to colleagues his cooking adventures over the weekend.
II   It is Saturday afternoon, and George pops into the local Co-op store expecting to find his wife. The counter assistant explains she has not been in, but his daughter, Mary, had forgotten the CWS Shortex cooking fat.
III   Upon returning home, he finds his wife is ill and his daughter is out house-hunting. He is asked to "hold the fort", as Mary's friend Jackie is expected for supper. George rolls up his sleeves and prepares a steak and kidney pie – he is not a natural chef. After putting it in the oven, he retires to the garden for a nap.
IV   Mary returns home with her friend Jackie Rose, the famous television cook. They decide to make a real steak and kidney pie – but not to tell George. Jackie Rose demonstrates how to bake a perfect steak and kidney pie with flaky pastry, using CWS baking ingredients: how to make short-crust pastry; using Shortex in cake-making; using Shortex as a hot cooking fat – sandwich dreams, French toast, curry, frying, etc.
V   A dream sequence where Mary imagines herself the cook of mouth-watering delicacies made with Shortex, and her perfect man is there to enjoy them.
VI   George returns to the kitchen and is proud of "his" steak and kidney pie. The two women do not shatter his illusions.

VII   Graphic card: "Jacqueline Rose says:- 'Be Sure of Success with Shortex'. From Co-operative Societies Everywhere."

Remarks
One of a series of humorous story films promoting CWS baking ingredients and commissioned from Anglo-Scottish Pictures in that period. Such films were integral to the CWS Publicity Film Service "Woman's Hour" shows which began in 1954. The c.1963 *CWS Film Catalogue* described the film as a "domestic comedy film for women". This particular film concentrates mainly on Shortex, described within the film as the "good cook's dream". Rose makes her second appearance in a CWS film production, being well-known at the time as a popular television cookery expert. Like many television announcers and celebrities of the 1950s, her Roedean accent betrays her class origins as being somewhat more comfortable than those of her audience. This print suffers from some colour-fading.
See also: NCFC 159, NCFC 207

NCFC 164
Getting Together: A Story of Co-operation (1955)

b/w · 28m 37s · sound · 16mm: EAFA / 35mm: NFTVA
pr Anvil Films for COI

■ An information film about the course for overseas students at the UK Co-operative College.

I   Exterior shots of the Co-operative College. A voice-over gives details about the courses and international students.
II   Sporting facilities: putting; swimming in the lido; tennis; cricket.
III   Two new students arrive at the college and settle in. Students from around the world congregate and introduce themselves to each other in the common-room: Sudan, Iceland, Denmark, Germany, Finland, Vietnam.
IV   A student is interviewed by the College Principal, R L Marshall, and by College staff.
V   The College library; the student's common-room; squash courts; snooker; dining-hall; an address by the College Principal; classroom work.
VI   Staff tutor Arnold Bonner screens a film of the Rochdale Pioneers, and narrates the history.

VII   A brief montage of tutorials, lectures
       and discussions.
VIII   Student visits: an agricultural
       Co-operative; the Kettering Clothing
       Manufacturing Co-operative Society.
IX   Students talk of Co-operation (with
       accompanying shots) in their own
       countries: Gold Coast; Cyprus;
       Trinidad and Tobago; Uganda;
       Malaysia.
X   Term ends. Students return home to
       put into practice the lessons they have
       learned about Co-operation.

Remarks
A film sponsored by the Central Office of
Information to spread information regarding
the Co-operative Movement. It provides a
detailed view of the Co-operative College,
Stanford Hall in Leicestershire, established
in 1945 as a centenary memorial to the
Rochdale Pioneers, the founders of the
modern Movement. The film concentrates
on the work of the International
Co-operative Studies Department, and was
presumably aimed at overseas audiences.
Staff tutor Arnold Bonner, who in 1961
would publish a seminal study entitled
Co-operation, features prominently. The film
which he screens to give the Rochdale story
is the Movement's centenary film, *Men of
Rochdale* (1944; NCFC 104), presented
here in an abbreviated form without its
soundtrack, but with a voice-over from
Bonner.
See also: NCFC 226

NCFC 165
It's All Yours! (1955)

b/w · 11m · sound · 16mm · EAFA
pr DATA Films *comm* John Slater

▪ An information film about the extensive
business of the CWS.

I   Montage of productive processes:
       manufacturing; agricultural; and
       distribution. The narration emphasises
       that such activities are conducted on
       behalf of the members/audience: "It's
       All Yours!".
II   Presentation at a society members'
       meeting, explaining the role of
       Co-operative democracy and the
       contribution of the local society to the
       wider Movement of over eleven million
       members.
III   Exposition on the birth of the modern
       Co-operative Movement in 1844
       replayed over scenes from the 1944

CWS film, *Men of Rochdale*.
IV   Contemporary store exterior, LCS, and
       interiors of departmental store and
       self-service grocery.
V   The nature of Co-operative
       democracy, with voting at members'
       meetings, and a board meeting.
VI   The worldwide success of the
       Co-operative ideal. The loading and
       unloading of trade goods at the docks.
VII   The CWS, Manchester, "Britain's
       Biggest Business": HQ Manchester;
       banking; boardroom; agriculture;
       manufacturing; food-processing;
       laboratory research; packaging;
       market research; distribution; store
       interiors.

Remarks
One of several films made for the
Co-operative Movement by DATA Films.
However, Wolfgang Suschitzky, cameraman
and founding member, has expressed
disappointment that, since DATA was a
Co-operative Co-Partnership, more film
commissions had not been forthcoming
from the Movement. The film "illustrate[s]
some of the extensive ramifications of the
CWS and show[s] that these could not exist
without the support of individual
co-operators" (*The Co-operative News* 30
July 1955).

NCFC 166
The Man From Ballymena (1955)

col · 26m 44s · sound · Australia · 16mm ·
NFTVA
pr Letona *prod* Peter Whitchurch *sc* Ken
Saunders *cam* Dennis Hill *sd* Rob Kellett
ed Jack Gardiner

▪ An information film about the Leeton
Co-operative Cannery, New South Wales,
Australia.

I   Views of the arid Australian outback;
       the Leeton district, marginal land
       subject to periodic draught; busy main
       street, Leeton; aerial view of Leeton;
       daily scenes around Leeton – children
       in a playground; the arable lands
       around Leeton.
II   The original sheep station of Samuel
       McCaughey, the "Sheep King" of the
       world; how he irrigated the arid land
       using a local river; the ruins of his old
       workings; the modern dam which
       controls the local water supply
       through a system of canals; fields of
       peas in the irrigated plains.

III   A field officer from the Leeton Co-operative Cannery and a local farmer examine the pea harvest; the peas are harvested by Co-operatively-owned machinery.

IV   The Leeton Co-operative Cannery: the vines are led into the factory; the peas are washed, graded, checked, canned and cooked; the cans are stacked in a giant storeroom.

V   A display of Leeton canned products; canned goods are packed into cartons; exteriors of the Leeton Co-operative Cannery.

VI   Exterior of Samuel McCaughey's house and estate; the coat of arms and portrait of Sir Samuel McCaughey; interiors of the house – a stained glass window; young boys run down the staircase – the house is now an agricultural high school; boys at their farming duties around the estate; technical training classes.

Remarks
New South Wales was a distinct centre of Co-operative endeavour in Australia. The Leeton district saw the establishment of several important producer Co-operatives, Leeton and District Poultry Farmers Co-operative Society (1943), Leeton Fruitgrowers Co-operative Society (1932) and the Leeton Co-operative Cannery (1935). By the early 1950s, the cannery was employing 1300 workers. Sir Samuel McCaughey's house became an agricultural school in 1927. The Rochdale strand of consumer Co-operation was also successfully supplanted in the NSW territory.

NCFC 167
Spot the Likeness [Baking Products]
(1955)

b/w · 1m 10s · sound · 35mm: SFA / 16mm: NFTVA
comm Patrick Allan

▪ A television advertisement promoting CWS baking ingredients.

I   Three women are individually presented in cameo mid-shots. Viewers are asked to "Spot the Likeness".

II   Mrs Jones, pianist, uses CWS Federation plain flour.

III   Mrs Brown, lift attendant, uses CWS Federation self-raising flour.

IV   Mrs Smith, fruit-seller, uses CWS mixed dried fruit.

V   "Can You Spot the Likeness?" – the three women are again individually presented in medium close-shot clearly demonstrating their associated product.

VI   In a three-shot, it is revealed that they are all left-handed!: "Of course they all buy CWS flour and fruit at their Co-op as well!".

VII   Graphic card: "Everyone who wants the best insists upon CWS".

Remarks
The CWS was amongst the first businesses to advertise on the Independent Television Network (ITN) when it began broadcasting in the London region in September 1955. "Spot the Likeness" was the Co-op's first campaign and was thought to "have all the attractions of a panel game" ("C.W.S. and Commercial TV", *The Co-operative News* 17 September 1955). The cost of £1000 per minute for commercial advertising was thought high, yet the value of the new service was conceded and advertising spots were booked as far into the future as possible. Special window and counter displays were made available to societies to tie in with the promotions. Various CWS brand products were promoted utilising the "Spot the Likeness" gimmick – Gold, Silver and Red Seal margarine, White Olive soap, Spel washing powder, Pulvo pan-cleaner, Newsheaf soap, Paddy washing powder, and so on.

NCFC 168
Spot the Likeness [Cleaning Appliances]
(1955)

b/w · 1m 15s · sound · 16mm · NFTVA
comm Patrick Allan

▪ A brief television advertisement for CWS cleaning appliances.

I   Three women are introduced to the audience, who are asked to decide why they are all alike – Spot the Likeness!

II   Joan gets excellent results with her CWS Invincible upright vacuum cleaner – her dog is a little wary; Jane can remain houseproud with her CWS Society sweeper, it certainly intrigues her kitten; newly-married Jill gets straight down to her task with a CWS Invincible cylinder vacuum cleaner, she can spend more time with her pet parrot.

III "Well, did you Spot the Likeness?". They were all alike because they had pets! Of course they all buy their cleaning appliances at the Co-op – but that's too easy!
IV A display of CWS vacuum cleaners and sweepers.
V Graphic card: "Everyone who wants the best insists upon CWS. The mark of a thousand good things."

Remarks
One of the Co-op's first television advertisements, part of the innovative "Spot the Likeness" series. The commentary was provided by popular radio personality, Patrick Allan, star of Radio Luxembourg's "Shilling a Second", a show sponsored by the CWS.

NCFC 169
Spot the Likeness [Confectionery] (1955)

b/w · 1m 50s · sound · 16mm · NFTVA
comm Patrick Allan

■ A brief television advertisement for CWS confectionery.

I Three young people are introduced to the audience, who are asked to decide why they are all alike – Spot the Likeness!
II Interior of a sweet shop: Susan knows that CWS sweets are best, where pocket money buys you more; Jim is there to buy sweets for his party, CWS sweets last you longer and cost less; Marie is after variety, for CWS has 90 different kinds of sweets.
III "Well, did you Spot the Likeness?". They were alike because they all had shopping bags! Of course they all buy their sweets at the Co-op – but that's too easy!
IV A display of CWS confectionery.
V Graphic card: "Everyone who wants the best insists upon CWS. The mark of a thousand good things."

Remarks
Another in the innovative series of television advertisements that helped launch the Independent Television Network (ITN) in 1955. The "Spot the Likeness" approach drew on the vastly popular quiz show format heavily utilised by commercial radio and television.

NCFC 170
Spot the Likeness [Lingerie] (1955)

b/w · 1m 14s · sound · 16mm · NFTVA

■ A brief television advertisement for CWS Belmont lingerie.

I Three young women are introduced to the audience, who are asked to decide why they are all alike – Spot the Likeness!
II Bride-to-be Betty buys a new CWS nightie for her bottom drawer.
III Belinda is out to buy a CWS petticoat and knicker set.
IV Bright girl Betty dotes on a lace-trimmed petticoat, Belmont brand.
V "Well, did you Spot the Likeness?" They were all alike because they had the same hairstyles! Of course they all ask for Belmont lingerie at the Co-op too – but that's too easy!
VI A display of CWS Belmont lingerie.
VII Graphic card: "Everyone who wants the best insists upon CWS. The mark of a thousand good things."

Remarks
One in a series of television advertisements using the "Spot the Likeness" game show theme. This example was the only commercial not to utilise the voice-over of popular radio personality, Patrick Allan. The unidentified female narrator was presumably considered more suitable for the delicate product line under discussion. "Belmont" was the name of the CWS garment factory at Birmingham (before 1932 known as the Underclothing Factory), and provided the brand name.

NCFC 171
Spot the Likeness [Paint] (1955)

b/w · 1m 14s · sound · 16mm · NFTVA
comm Patrick Allan

■ A brief television advertisement for CWS home decoration products.

I Three husbands are introduced to the audience, who are asked to decide why they are all alike – Spot the Likeness!
II Mr A selects CWS water paint – there are twenty washable shades to choose. Mr B selects CWS oil paint – there's no mess. Mr C selects CWS white ceiling paste – quick to mix and no waste.

III "Well, did you Spot the Likeness?"
They were all alike because they wore
glasses! Of course they all buy CWS
paints from the Co-op, but that's too
easy!
IV Display of CWS paints.
V Graphic card: "Everyone who wants
the best insists upon CWS. The mark
of a thousand good things."

Remarks
The Co-op's first television advertising
campaign, "Spot the Likeness" was used to
promote various CWS products. Special
window-stickers for display by stores were
designed to link in with the television spots:
"CWS products. *See* Them on Television.
Buy Them Here!."

NCFC 172
Spot the Likeness [Raincoats] (1955)

b/w · 1m 15s · sound · 16mm · NFTVA
comm Patrick Allan

■ A brief television advertisement for CWS
raincoats.

I Three male characters are introduced
to the audience, who are asked to
decide why they are all alike – Spot
the Likeness!
II A young boy puts on his sturdy CWS
Strolite trenchcoat, under his mother's
watchful eye.
III A young salesman out and about in
his smart CWS double-breasted York
raincoat.
IV A middle-aged man is helped into his
CWS gaberdine raincoat by an
attendant.
V "Well, did you Spot the Likeness?".
They were all alike because they had
worn the same school colours! Of
course their raincoats all came from
the Co-op as well – but that's too
easy!
VI A display of CWS Strolite and York
raincoats.
VII Graphic card: "Everyone who wants
the best insists upon CWS. The mark
of a thousand good things."

Remarks
A further addition to the familiar series of
television advertisements sponsored by the
CWS. The CWS costume and raincoat
factory – or, as it was designated in the
trade, "Mantle Factory" – was situated in
Manchester, the general manufacturing
centre for the industry. To meet demand,

another site – on Commercial Road, East
London – had been acquired in 1933.

NCFC 173
Women's Co-operative Guild Congress
(1955)

b/w · 4m 11s · silent · 16mm · NFA
pr Turners (Photography)

■ A film record of the 1955 Women's
Co-operative Guild Congress, Newcastle.

I The banner for the Women's
Co-operative Guild Congress hanging
above the entrance of the City Hall,
Newcastle.
II Delegates entering the City Hall; the
busy foyer.
III Interior of the congress hall: overhead
views of the congress platform and the
delegates; banners of the Guild
branches hanging from the balcony;
the arrival of the Executive onto the
platform; the singing of "These Things
Shall Be"; the welcoming speech by
the Lord Mayor; fraternal greetings by
members of the Consumer
Co-operative Movement; the passing
over of the Presidential mantle; a floral
bouquet is presented to the Lady
Mayoress; the President begins her
opening address.

Remarks
One of two surviving films of a WCG
Congress following the earlier film record of
the 1939 Congress at Hull. This project
appears to have been prepared at the
instigation of the hosting Newcastle
Co-operative Society, which had engaged in
several film productions in 1955 using the
local photography firm of Turners. The new
President who is shown being welcomed
into her role was Mabel Ewan. The position
was held for one year by each incumbent.
See also: NCFC 261

NCFC 174
Your Sunday Newspaper (1955)

b/w · 37m 23s · sound · 16mm · ETV,
NFTVA
cam Layland-Ross/Norman Williams
sc Hubert Popplewell *comm* Franklin
Engelmann *sp* Nottingham Co-operative
Society

■ An information film about the Movement's
Sunday newspaper, *The Reynold's News*.

I   A Nottingham Co-operative Society dairyman delivers milk early on a Sunday morning.

II   Even London is quiet at that time: shot of a deserted Trafalgar Square. Shot of a deserted Old Market Square, Nottingham – apart from the news vendors who are doing a brisk trade with *The Reynold's News*.

III   A copy of *The Reynold's News* is delivered through a letter-box; Dad enjoys the sports pages in his armchair; mother is attentive to the women's page.

IV   Shots of busy London streets and landmarks – places where news is made.

V   Fashion designer Matli at work in his West End salon, a weekly contributor to the women's page; seamstresses at work; fashions being modelled.

VI   The Humphrey Lyttleton Jazz Band. The bandleader is a weekly columnist in the paper.

VII   Woodrow Wyatt, foreign affairs commentator and star of the television programme *Panorama*, at work in his office.

VIII   Columnist Tom Driberg hard at work.

IX   *The Reynold's News* library, information centre of the paper, completes a request from Tom Driberg.

X   Winifred Munday, Women's Page columnist, at her typewriter.

XI   The Photographic Laboratory.

XII   The Art Editor selects the pictures for the forthcoming edition.

XIII   Pioneer House, the home of *The Reynold's News* (exterior): the switchboard operators; the busy teleprinters supplying the world's news 24 hours a day; a reporter phones in a story to a journalist; an office of busy sub-editors turn the raw copy into news items with headlines; the sports reporters hard at work on Saturday afternoon, polishing their stories – the football results are marked up on a large board; the sports editor selects the photographs to illustrate the sports pages.

XIV   The printing process: compositors operating linotype machines; handprinting for proofing; pictures are processed onto metal plates suitable for printing; fine detail is achieved by hand; setting the page layout; an impression of the page is made on a "matrix"; in the foundry, metal casts are made from the "matrix" – the casts are shaped as a half-cylinder; the casts are cut, trimmed and washed; casts are fitted to one of the eighteen great printing presses at Pioneer House; the presses turn and printing commences; the completed newspapers come off the presses; the giant reels of newsprint, each weighing three quarters of a ton and sufficient for 10 000 copies of *The Reynold's News*; various shots of the printing process around the plant; up the mechanical conveyor the newspapers pour into the despatch room where they are made ready in bundles for the main inter-city expresses; the senior management team in consultation; the bundles are labelled for their destinations – Plymouth, Belfast, Liverpool, Glasgow, Birmingham, Edinburgh and Nottingham; a *Reynold's* delivery van unloads at Euston Station, the stacks of newspapers are conveyed to the trains which set off.

XV   An address by Cyril Hammlett, Chairman of *The Reynold's News*.

XVI   A newsagent's shop (exterior); a newspaper boy on his round.

Remarks

An extremely detailed examination of the Movement's Sunday newspaper, *The Reynold's News*. The paper had been acquired in 1929 by the National Co-operative Publishing Society, when it had fallen on hard times. A well-known Sunday journal, it had been started by the Chartist, G W M Reynolds, in the mid-19th century, and had quickly become an influential radical publication. *The Reynold's News* was never able to build a sufficient circulation to rival the leading Sunday papers; however, it did capture a respectable proportion of the nation's progressive readership. Eventually, the paper went the way of all centre-left newspapers – including *The Daily Herald* and *News Chronicle* – and folded in 1967. The change of name to *Sunday Citizen* had been unable to halt the decline.

A director and former President of Nottingham Co-operative Society, Alderman Walter Halls JP, sat on the Board of the Co-operative Press Ltd, and played a leading part in the acquisition of *The Reynold's News*. This probably explains the involvement of the society in the project. Throughout the 1950s, the NCS organised campaigns to increase the paper's circulation; in 1956, it lobbied to improve its contents.

See also: NCFC 246

NCFC 175
[Co-op Advertisement] (c.1955)

b/w · 41s · sound · Scotland · 16mm · SFA

▪ A television advertisement for the Co-op in Scotland.

I   A group of people converge, arriving on various types of transportation: horseback, motor cycle, car, penny farthing, helicopter.
II   Customers are welcomed into a Co-op store and are served at the busy counter.
III   End-card: "Remember the Dividend".

Remarks
It is difficult to determine if this film was commissioned by the CWS or by the SCWS. The advert, featuring a suitably banal jingle, attempts to entice people to "Shop at the Co-op", rather than promote a specific product. Surprisingly, the film features a traditional service store, which was already becoming dated by that time. If, in fact, the advert was produced and screened in 1955, it would have been amongst the Co-op's first television adverts. The Independent Television Network (ITN) began broadcasting in September of that year.

NCFC 176
[CWS Baked Beans Advertisement] (c.1955)

col · 36s · silent · 16mm · NFTVA

▪ A simple animated advertisement for CWS Waveney baked beans.

I   A housewife returns home from a shopping trip: "NOW – A treat to take home".
II   Graphic card: "On your way out get your free sample tin of Waveney Beans".
III   Graphic card: "In rich tomato sauce, after enjoying this delicious treat you'll be bound to want more. Your Co-operative Society will be glad to serve you. Ask for them by name. Waveney Beans."

Remarks
A rare surviving example of a special tie-in promotional film for use in local cinemas. It is probable that the Publicity Department of the CWS took responsibility for the logistics of the scheme, providing each participating

cinema with a quantity of tinned Waveney beans for handing on to audience-members. Some sort of foyer display for CWS tinned foods was also likely.

NCFC 177
[CWS Football Boot Advertisement] (c.1955)

b/w · 33s · sound · 16mm · NFTVA

▪ A brief advertisement for CWS Stanley Matthews football boots.

I   Crowded football terraces are mesmerised by the ball skills of the "Wizard", Stanley Matthews; Matthews in the dressing-room lacing up his boots; Matthews demonstrating the flexibility of the boot he helped to design; various styles are displayed.
II   Graphic card: "Stanley Matthews Football Boots. From Co-operative Stores Everywhere."

Remarks
The legendary footballer's boots were the Movement's highest profile celebrity endorsement. Two longer films, for use in in-store demonstrations and at members' film shows, were also produced in this period: *Magic Feet* (1953; NCFC 151) and *Play with the Best* (1950s; NCFC 412). Surprisingly, the film is narrated by a North American.

NCFC 178
[CWS Polish Advertisement] (c.1955)

b/w · 19s · sound · 16mm · NFTVA

▪ A brief television advertisement for CWS Pelaw wax polish.

I   A young housewife achieves a mirror finish on her table, using CWS Pelaw polish: "It cleans as it polishes. And what's more it lasts for weeks at a time."
II   Graphic card: "CWS PELAW Silicone Wax. From Your Co-op Store."

Remarks
A typical early television commercial. Traditionally, the CWS had used a variety of brand names, such as Pelaw, Wheatsheaf and Defiant, which were endowed with historic or geographical significance. Pelaw, for instance, was the district on Tyneside where the CWS's famous polish factory was

situated. Only a decade after the introduction of television advertising, the Movement felt compelled to establish a unified national brand identity – a response to the strengthened market position of nationally established competitors such as Sainsbury's and Tesco.

NCFC 179
[CWS Pudding Advertisement] (c.1955)

b/w · 10s · sound · 16mm · NFTVA

■ A brief advertisement for CWS tinned rice pudding.

I   A simple image of a tin of CWS rice pudding is presented.
    Commentary: "They all say YES to CWS Rice Pudding./From all Co-operative Stores."

Remarks
An advertisement probably intended for television use, since it was produced in black and white; cinema advertisements were invariably produced in colour to achieve maximum impact. This film is a good example of the extent to which television advertising could be unsophisticated in the pioneer days, when sponsors were unconvinced of the new medium and shy of the high costs involved.

NCFC 180
[CWS Shoe Advertisement 1] (c.1955)

b/w · 34s · sound · 16mm · NFTVA

■ A brief advertisement for CWS Ardington shoes.

I   A shoe salesman demonstrates three styles of CWS Ardington men's shoes: the famous Ardington 8150 in prime calf; a free and easy casual; and a smart "mud-guard" design.
II Graphic card: "Ardington Shoes. 65/11. From Your Co-op Stores."

Remarks
Made in black and white, the film would probably have been an early CWS television commercial. Television advertising was a considerable organisational problem for the CWS, which had to liaise with regional independent television companies and numerous local retail societies to maintain a consistent profile for a campaign. In a region where an advertisement was

screened, the CWS would have to ensure that societies stocked the specific item(s) at the prices stated.

NCFC 181
International Co-operative Day Grand Pageant (c.1955)

col · 10m 20s · silent · 16mm · BRO
pr F G Warne Ltd

■ A record of the mid-1950s International Co-operative Day (ICD) celebrations staged by the Bristol Co-operative Society.

I   The public are admitted at the entrance to the ICD event.
II   The arrival of the society parade: troupes of women members in highly coloured costumes carrying placards and banners; members and international guests wearing rainbow sashes; a contingent of the Women's Co-operative Guild holds up placards – "Co-operative Democracy in Action"; a contingent of international Co-operators from the Netherlands.
III "Prologue by the Herald – Christopher Hallett" – an address from the platform to the gathered crowd; a performance by the Co-operative Ladies Choir; scenes amongst the spectators; a performance by The Co-operative Rainbow Players – "Pretty Polly Perkins of Paddington Green"; The Kingswood Evangel Band; a sketch by the Co-operative Rainbow Players – "Co-operative Democracy".
IV   "Parade of Trading Departments and Social, Cultural and Political Groups" – grocery, laundry, greengrocery, milk, hotel, Women's Co-operative Guild, Holland visitors, drama group, adult and junior choirs, folk-dancing, verse-speaking groups, Playways and Pathfinder groups, Woodcraft Folk, coal.
V   Dancing display by the Woodcraft Folk; scenes around the park.
VI   Performance by the Co-operative Junior Choirs; an address by the Chairman, Mrs L M Lidington; guest speaker, Mr J M Peddie of the CWS; the Rainbow Flag of Co-operation.
VII Graphic card: "Co-operative Democracy in Action".

Remarks
The only film record so far located detailing the Bristol Co-operative Society. The society had been founded in 1905, and by the mid-

1950s served over 115 000 members. This extended record of ICD celebrations is superbly shot in colour, and illustrates how the event was an excellent local propaganda opportunity whereby a society could boast of its impressive trading and cultural achievements to the town and region. The guest speaker, J M Peddie, was a senior board member of the CWS and had been a former Chairman of the National Film Association, the film body established by the Labour Movement in 1946, but wound up in 1953.

NCFC 182
A Piece of Cake (c.1955)

col · 30m 16s · sound · Scotland · 16mm · SFA
d E Morris prod B Webb cam Gordon Dines

■ A promotional film for SCWS Lofty Peak flour.

I   A housewife in her kitchen is busily engaged in cake-making. She uses SCWS Lofty Peak flour.
II   The arrival of grain at the Meadowside granary, Glasgow.
III   Grain is delivered to a SCWS flour mill: screening the grain; blending the grain; washing and conditioning the grain; the disc separator; polishing the grain; the milling process produces semolina and coarse bran; the sifting process; the grinding of semolina into flour.
IV   In the laboratory: experiments in the blending of wheat; tests of the protein value and gluten quality of the flour; testing the purity of samples; tests on self-raising flour.
V   Test-baking in the mill: doughnuts; bread; common baking errors are outlined.
VI   Practical hints on successful cake-making; the Florence cake; the Swiss roll.
VII The packaging of Lofty Peak flour.
VIII A display of SCWS Lofty Peak prepared cake mixes.
IX   The production of prepared cake mixes.
X   The despatch of cartons to Co-op stores; Lofty Peak products on display in a Co-op self-service store.

Remarks
The initial title and some of the credits are missing. The flour mill featured is possibly the SCWS establishment at Leith, known as

Junction Mill, and acquired in 1897. Initially, it concentrated on the milling of oatmeal "in order to cope with the national demand for the food which builds up Scottish brawn and muscle" (J A Flanagan, Wholesale Co-operation in Scotland [Glasgow: SCWS, 1920]). Flour milling had made a substantial contribution to the trading account of the SCWS, to such an extent that the historians of the SCWS declared that the process "seemed to have an almost invincible place in the SCWS scheme of production" (James Kinloch and John Butt, History of the Scottish Co-operative Wholesale Society [Manchester: CWS, 1981]). Yet, even this commanding business activity suffered in the postwar period, and eventually the Scottish Movement's several mills were rationalised into a single new site at Leith in the mid-1960s. Considerable disillusionment was caused when 51% of that business passed to private enterprise in 1968.

This film would have been aimed at a housewife audience, for which special programmes were compiled and special shows arranged by the SCWS mobile film units. Information is provided regarding "free home-baking demonstrations", no doubt eagerly booked for Women's Guild meetings, where the promotion of the CWS's popular Lofty Peak flour and prepared cake mixes would have been the aim. The film's most striking credit is that of Gordon Dines. As the film – unusually and prestigiously – lists him as "director of photography", it is possible that it is the same Gordon Dines who worked as a contract technician at Ealing Studios, shooting such films as The Blue Lamp (1949).

NCFC 183
The Right Mixture (c.1955)

col · 15m · sound · 16mm · EAFA, NFTVA, NWFA
pr CWS Film Unit

■ A cookery demonstration film shot at the research laboratories of the CWS.

I   A selection of perfectly baked cakes.
II   Poor-quality cakes achieved through incorrect technique, the result of not paying attention to the recipe.
III   How to make a sponge sandwich. A demonstration of the importance of the correct technique; the poor results achieved by using too much baking powder.
IV   A diagnosis of a "collapsed" cherry

cake; a perfect example of a cherry cake.

V   How to make a cherry cake and achieve perfect results; the poor results obtained by using too much baking-powder and sugar.
VI   A summary of correct techniques: measuring accurately; mixing and preparing thoroughly; choosing the correct oven temperature; correct handling and cooling procedures.
VII A selection of perfectly baked cakes.

Remarks
A profoundly sexist film, particularly evident in the comments of the male narrator who sees baking as a wifely duty. Several cookery demonstration films of one type or another were produced in the 1950s for inclusion in the "Woman's Hour" programme offered by the CWS mobile publicity film shows. This example is by far the most simple and straightforward – little more than a cookery demonstration, in fact – whereas other titles absorb the cookery elements within some comic narrative business. Surprisingly little attempt is made to promote CWS baking products – another feature of its counterparts – although CWS Federation flour is clearly evident as a staple ingredient.
See also: NCFC 159

NCFC 184
[Woodcraft Folk Continental Trip] (c.1955)

b/w · 11m 50s · silent · 16mm · PC

▪ An "amateur" film of Woodcraft Folk activities.

I   Young adults of the WCF struggle along a rope bridge.
II   General scene at a camp.
III A WCF troupe poses for a photograph.
IV   Scenes onboard a train; boarding the ferry for France; scenes on board ship.
V   Travelling through mountainous scenery on board train.
VI   Arrival at destination – a German or Austrian lakeside town (?).
VII Bathing in the lake.
VIII A local parade through the town by the International Falcon Movement – marching with flags, members in local costume, a folk music troupe, the WCF march by with banner; a huge gathering in the town square; folk-dancing and singing by the WCF.
IX   General scenes at camp – a choir

entertains, folk-dancing, daily chores, writing home, mealtime.
X   A coach journey sightseeing into the Alps.
     (End missing)

Remarks
See entry for NCFC 185.

NCFC 185
[Woodcraft Folk Scenes] (c.1955)

b/w and col · 7m 43s · silent · 16mm · PC

▪ An "amateur" film of Woodcraft Folk activities.

I   Brief scenes at a branch meeting.
II   General scenes out in the country – hiking, beauty spots, a game of cricket.
III Mealtime at camp; the camp itinerary and duty rota; two boys preparing to sleep in their tent.
IV   Fun and games in a field; scenes of recreation and relaxation around the camp-site; the camp fire is lit; a display of dancing; breaking camp *(colour)*.
V   Further activities at a camp – morning exercises, games and sports, mealtime, first aid, the camp notice-board.

Remarks
Two films of WCF activities and camps in the mid-1950s, photographed by the same source. The first reel contains a miscellany of items but substantially comprises scenes from an international youth camp held in the UK. The second, more structured, film, follows a WCF group on a visit to an international camp in Europe. Both films suffer from some poor photography, but the scene of the march of the International Falcon Movement, attended by a WCF contingent, is well executed and offers a rare glimpse of the Folk participating in a political parade abroad.

NCFC 186
Come Clean (1956)

col · 9m 57s · sound · 16mm · EAFA, NFTVA
pr Anglo-Scottish Pictures

▪ An informational film promoting CWS cleaning products.

I   Packets of CWS cleaning products are animated into movement – Pulvo, Solvo, Spel, Crysella soap flakes, Floral soap flakes, Olive toilet soaps. "They're Magic!".

II The production of CWS soaps: the blending of selected oils and fats; drying into "soap chips"; adding of fragrant perfumes and blending; the milling process; shaping the soap into a long continuous bar; cutting into tablets; testing the soap bars; the stamping machine – "Wheatsheaf", the symbol of fine quality; the wrapping machine; packing for despatch – White Olive, Green Olive, Toilet Carbolic.

III Laboratory testing and inspection; research and development.

IV Luxury brands are stamped by hand; hand-trimming; hand-packing – Cream of Lavender.

V   A young woman in her bathroom with CWS Green Olive soap.

VI Other CWS cleaning products are quickly detailed – Pulvo pan-cleaner, Solvo washing powder, Floral flakes for delicate fabrics, Spel washing powder for whites.

VII Display of CWS cleaning products – "From Co-operative Stores Everywhere".

Remarks
The film was unusual for the time in having a commentary provided by a woman. Perhaps that was indicative of a new awareness on behalf of the marketing staff, who sought to construct a more direct address to housewives and the female consumer in general. Certainly, the entry for the film in the c.1963 *CWS Film Catalogue* was the most lyrical: "In each of us there is a love of beauty which responds to the glowing vividness and intriguing perfumes of flowers. Perfumes in this case refer to the making of fine toilet soaps." This print suffers from some colour-fading.

NCFC 187
[Co-op Dividends] (1956)

b/w · 40s · sound · Scotland · 35mm · SFA

▪ A television advertisement promoting the ideal of the Co-operative dividend.

I   A husband and wife are relaxing at home. The wife has been wisely spending her housekeeping money at the Co-op, and, with the money she

has saved, she intends to buy her husband a new suit for his birthday – to his obvious joy. By purchasing the suit at the Co-op, she can put the dividend towards a new coat for herself.

II In medium close-shot and direct to camera, the couple declares: "Yes, it pays to shop at the Co-op".

Remarks
A short advertising film probably intended for use in cinemas. Interestingly, the film does not promote a specific product, but rather the value to families of generally shopping at the Co-op, where aggregated purchases lead to a receipt of monies in the form of a cash dividend. Many working families had traditionally organised their shopping in that way, in order to facilitate the purchase of more expensive items such as shoes, clothes and furniture.

NCFC 188
Cuckoo In the Kitchen (1956)

col · 27m · sound · 16mm · NFTVA
pr Anglo-Scottish Pictures *cast* Kenneth Connor, Barbara Hicks, Roy Godfrey, Maureen Davis, Michael Segal

▪ A comic narrative film promoting CWS bakery products.

I   A mother and daughter have let the spare room to a lodger, a Frenchman, Monsieur DuBonne. They are worried about breaking the news to father.

II Mother visits the local Co-op store. She arouses the counter assistant's suspicions when she orders French mustard and snails.

III M. DuBonne is satisfied with the accommodation. He will cook for himself.

IV Father arrives home. Mother and daughter have put on a spread to cheer him up before breaking the news of the lodger.

V   After an ill-tempered early morning incident, Father demands that M. DuBonne must go. In the fracas, M. DuBonne's coat and the daughter's 21st birthday cake get ruined. Father storms out, refusing to attend the same party as the Frenchman.

VI To remedy the situation, M. DuBonne ushers the weeping women out of the kitchen and sets to work himself. Father returns and the two men are reconciled. M. DuBonne reveals

himself as a chef.
VII   M. DuBonne puts the family to work
and conjures up a spread for the
imminent party. CWS products such
as Gold and Silver Seal margarines
and Shortex are featured throughout.
The sequence is organised as a
cookery demonstration – fancy
sandwiches, canapés, savouries, etc.
VIII The party is a huge success, M.
DuBonne has saved the day. As the
guests tuck into the food, the praises
of Shortex and Gold and Silver Seal
margarines are sung on the
soundtrack.

Remarks
One of several films from the period
commissioned by the CWS from Anglo-
Scottish Pictures, this time promoting
bakery ingredients such as CWS Shortex,
and Gold and Silver Seal margarines. These
expensively produced "domestic comedy
films for women" were suited to the CWS
Publicity Department's film road-shows,
whereby samples of the featured products
were handed out after the screenings. The
c.1963 *CWS Film Catalogue* continued with
the following comment on the film: "The
entertainment nature of this film is equal to
the best of its type. Cookery
demonstrations, featuring C.W.S. Margarine,
are of a very high standard." Popular comic
actor Kenneth Connor appears as a Co-op
counter assistant, although his role is less
prominent than in the later *Father Takes the
Cake* (1957; NCFC 200). This print suffers
from some colour-fading.

NCFC 189
[CWS Margarine Advertisement 1] (1956)

b/w · 44s · sound · 16mm · NFTVA

▪ A brief animated advertisement for CWS
Gold and Silver Seal margarines.

I   Mrs Grey prepares her husband's
sandwiches, but she fears they are dry
and drab. A little bird whispers in her
ear that CWS Gold Seal margarine
would improve matters.
II   A steady stream of housewives files
into a Co-op store advertising Gold
Seal.
III   Graphic card: "Gold Seal Margarine
Contains 10% Dairy Butter".
IV   Graphic card: "Gold Seal Margarine/
Silver Seal Margarine – Sold Only At
Your Co-op".
Jingle: "Only your Co-op sells Gold

Seal Margarine,/With dairy butter 10%
it's full of honest nourishment./Every
appetite is content with Gold Seal
Margarine".

Remarks
CWS margarine was the first product
advertised by the Movement on broadcast
media, beginning in 1939. A considerable
amount of promotional resources went on
CWS brand margarines, and they were
heavily publicised on commercial television,
which commenced in autumn 1955. The
Co-op's leading brands were Gold and
Silver Seal margarines, both receiving a
similar animated film in this campaign, and
made in monochrome, since that was the
only broadcast standard at the time.

NCFC 190
[CWS Margarine Advertisement 2] (1956)

b/w · 43s · sound · 16mm · NFTVA

▪ A brief animated advertisement for CWS
Silver and Gold Seal margarines.

I   Mrs Jones is worried about the impact
of rising prices on the household
budget, until a little bird whispers into
her ear that value and quality are to be
had from CWS Silver Seal margarine.
II   A steady stream of housewives files
into a Co-op store advertising Silver
Seal.
III   Graphic card: "Silver Seal Margarine
With Added Sunshine Vitamins A and
D".
IV   Graphic card: "Silver Seal Margarine.
In Keep Fresh Silver Foil".
V   Graphic card: "Silver Seal Margarine/
Gold Seal Margarine. Sold Only At
Your Co-op".
Jingle: "Only your Co-op Sells Silver
Seal Margarine,/With Sunshine
Vitamins A and D for Health and
Strength and Energy,/And it saves you
£.s.d., Silver Seal Margarine".

Remarks
A simple monochrome promotional film for
CWS Silver Seal margarine, and a
companion to a similar cartoon publicising
CWS Gold Seal margarine. The Co-op was
an early and significant user of television
advertising. An article published in 1959
shows a clear faith in the potential of the
new medium: "When TV really produces
sales results it produces them fast –
jamming the wires if you proffer a phone
number, emptying the shops the following

morning if you have a new product with an appealing story" (*The Producer* April 1959).

NCFC 191
Inside Story (1956)

col · 12m · sound · 16mm · IAC, NFTVA
pr Anglo-Scottish Pictures

■ An information film about CWS Waveney processed products – the story of the "inside" of the can/packet.

I   A housewife fills her basket from the shelves of a Co-op self-service store and reaches the checkout. She has brought a can of Co-op peas.
II   Peas are harvested on CWS farms in East Anglia; the vines are fed into the factory, and the peas are separated from the pods and washed.
III The CWS cannery at Lowestoft: the peas are canned and fed into the giant cooker.
IV An animated diagram explains the process.
V   A technician checks the controls; grading and washing dried peas; empty cans are rapidly conveyed around the factory by chute; quality-control checks.
VI Various products are prepared at the cannery: baked beans in tomato sauce, Waveney processed peas, CWS garden peas.
VII The work of the laboratory – the tenderometer tests the quality of the peas.
VIII The processing of Waveney cheese spread: the giant cheddar cheeses are cut; the shredding machine; the milling process; the cooking process; quality-control; the packing process; cartons are packed for despatch.
IX A housewife stocks her larder with CWS Waveney products.
X   A display of CWS Waveney products.
XI Graphic card: "From Co-operative Societies Everywhere".

Remarks
One of several films on the CWS canning factory at Lowestoft. Others include *Kitchen Capers* (1937; NCFC 058), *Did You Know? Number 2 (Peas)* (1951; NCFC 135), *It's In the Can* (1963; NCFC 257), and so on. This example is unspectacular and merely efficient, and undoubtedly would have been part of a wider promotional campaign for CWS Waveney products. Samples of Waveney goods would have been distributed to audiences at the CWS film shows when this film was exhibited. With the decline of the fishing industry in the area, production was redirected to food-processing, with particular attention to cheese products. Food-processing remained one of the CWS's most profitable activities, and the Lowestoft operations had doubled its turnover in the period between 1950 and 1955.

NCFC 192
Punched Cards Pay Dividends (1956)

b/w · 20m 26s · sound · 16mm · EAFA, NFTVA
pr Kinocrat *d* Gerald Cookson *sc* L Winter *cam* Hubert Davy *ed* Brian Gibson *comm* Lionel Marson

■ A promotional film for the Powers-Samas punched cards machine, and featuring the Dartford Industrial Co-operative Society (DICS).

I   Extracts from the CWS film, *Men of Rochdale* (1944; NCFC 104).
II   A brief montage sequence detailing the extent of the British consumer Co-operative Movement: street scene; selection of CWS publicity posters.
III A profile of DICS: exterior of the society's three-storey emporium; graphs giving details of turnover and membership; window and showcase displays; interiors of grocery, pharmacy, toy, furnishing and electrical departments; the accounting department.
IV A brief acted sequence wherein a member makes her purchase in the millinery department, and the details are recorded for dividend purposes.
V   The Climax Check System, an administrative procedure for recording purchases for purposes of calculating dividend, is detailed: the cash office, the check office – generating punched cards which carry details of members' purchases; the tabulator machine calculates sales totals; members' punched cards are filed; analysis cards are punched, allowing for strategic planning; tabulation of members' punched cards for four-weekly accumulative totals; verification of punched card data; final analysis of members' purchases for the half-year; calculation of members' individual dividend and share interest.
VI The various analytical possibilities of

the data made possible by the mechanical handling and storage of the purchase information.

VII   Mr A E Johnson, Chief Executive of DICS, endorses the Powers-Samas punch card apparatus.

Remarks
The film was sponsored by the Powers-Samas company in order to promote its mechanical apparatus for handling dividend data, and would presumably have been widely screened amongst officials of Co-operative societies. It is most interesting for the insight it gives into a medium-sized regional society; there seems to be no other film material on DICS. At the time, the society had a membership of c.23 000 from a local population of c.38 000, and operated 23 branch stores. The society had been founded in 1888. The film provides an extremely detailed examination of the mechanised process of producing records, and of calculating dividend and share accounts. Although investment in the equipment would have been substantial, the labour costs involved in the traditional method of calculating members' dividends were an increasing concern for societies, making many receptive to the prospects of mechanisation.

NCFC 193
Your Business (1956)

b/w · 10m · sound · 16mm · EAFA
pr DATA Films

▪ A propaganda film about the importance of members' buying Co-op brand products.

I   Interior of a Co-operative service store. A housewife, Mrs Smith, purchases a range of articles produced by private businesses. The importance of Co-op brand loyalty is explained.
II   The range of CWS products: a young girl tries on a CWS summer dress; a young girl tests a CWS bicycle; a family examines CWS household furniture.
III   Mrs Smith takes a tour of CWS factories: a CWS furniture factory; the CWS corset factory, Desborough; the manufacture of glass bottles – a range of CWS bottled products; a CWS research laboratory; a combine harvester at work on a CWS farm, the huge tomato sheds; scenes at a CWS dairy; egg-packing.
IV   Back at the Co-operative service store,

Mrs Smith is purchasing only CWS brand products.

Remarks
One of several films from the mid-1950s period made for the CWS by the filmmakers' co-operative, DATA Films. This film addresses the Co-op's typical customer, the housewife, and, to aid in that task, untypically uses a female voice-over. During section III, the distinct ownership structure and benefits of Co-operative membership are explained in detail over the scenes of Co-operation production. It is interesting to note that a counter service store is selected for the film, missing the opportunity to present the Co-op's pioneering development of self-service stores in the previous ten-year period. It is worth noting the final statement of the film: the Co-operative Movement is the "largest single material possession ever to come into the hands of ordinary people".

NCFC 194
[Birmingham Co-op Carnival] (c.1956)

col · 1m 20s · silent · 16mm · EAFA

▪ A Birmingham Co-operative Society (BCS) carnival.

I   Street procession: junior military band and parade; various dressed vehicles promoting society trading departments and cultural groups; the parade passes along busy, crowd-lined streets; the local Co-operative Queen and her maids of honour on top of a horse-drawn wagon.

Remarks
A short film record of an impressive propaganda event. Probably made at the request of the dairy department, for which a number of films exist, and correspondingly good shots of the department's dressed milk float are presented. The BCS had been founded in 1881, and by the mid-1950s claimed a membership of 33 000.

NCFC 195
Educational Pleasures (c.1956)

b/w · 15m 34s · silent · 16mm · ETV
pr Woolwich and Plumstead Institute

▪ A film made by students sponsored by the RACS, which details the various cultural activities supported by the society.

I   Students prepare captions for a rostrum camera: ROYAL ARSENAL CO-OPERATIVE SOCIETY EDUCATION DEPARTMENT LEISURE TIME GROUPS. MADE BY THE FILM MAKING CLASS WAVERLEY SCHOOL.
II Music class. An orchestra rehearses at the Woolwich and Plumstead Institute.
III A drama group rehearses.
IV Youth activities: girls dance; boys play table-tennis, snooker and darts; girls listen to a presentation.
V   Adult activities: adult choir; adult language class – Russian.
VI A young audience listens to a debate.
VII Leisure time for the youth members: drinks; food; socialising; sport; music and dance.
VIII The Borough Hall (exterior).
IX A musical performance inside the hall.
X   Making a film: arranging a light; splicing film; story-boarding; setting lights; preparing captions – THE END.

Remarks
This amateur film, made by students supported by the RACS, provides a useful comparison with those films produced in the 1930s which examine the work of the society's Education Department. At times, the film betrays its production origins, and several scenes are inadequately lit. Another interesting comparison would be with Karel Reisz's well-known Free Cinema documentary, We Are the Lambeth Boys (1959), which examines the leisure time and lifestyles of South London's youth further up the river. It is worth noting the inclusion of the Russian-language class: the RACS, prompted by Joseph Reeves, their Education Secretary between 1918 and 1938, had been an early supporter of the Soviet Union, and pioneering tours to Soviet Russia were sponsored between 1929 and 1939.
See also: NCFC 262

NCFC 196
Pots of Gold (c.1956)

col · 10m 22s · sound · 16mm · EAFA, NFTVA
pr Anglo-Scottish Pictures

■ An information film about CWS preserves.

I   An English orchard in springtime; orange-picking in the groves of Sevilla, Spain.
II Oranges are unloaded at a CWS preserve factory; the eyes of the oranges are removed; machines remove the peel, which is shredded; the orange flesh is boiled; the sugar store – a sack of sugar is emptied into a chute; the making of the sugar syrup; the shredded orange peel is added to the syrup and the mixture boiled; the large boiling pans where the various jams are made; jars are filled with hot orange marmalade and then capped; samples are tested at the quality-control desk; further tests are conducted at the CWS laboratory; jars of marmalade and jam are stacked to cool; labels are applied to the jars; the packing department makes up cartons for despatch.
III A display of CWS marmalade and jams; a jar of CWS William of Orange marmalade.
IV Graphic card: "William of Orange Marmalade From Co-op Shops".

Remarks
At the time of making this film, the CWS operated five preserves works – at Middleton, Reading, Acton, Stockton and Reddish (Stockport). The productive scenes for this film appear to have been taken at Reading. However, the postwar trend for the business was downwards, as it was for soap and tobacco. The general rationalisations undertaken by the Movement in the late-1960s led to the concentration of preserve-making at Reddish, the most modern works where land was also available for development. The CWS first opened a depot in Spain in 1896, at the old fruit port of Denia on the Mediterranean coast, and much fruit passed through there destined for CWS preserves. The trade was dealt a serious blow by the outbreak of civil war in 1936.

NCFC 197
[Unitas Oats] (c.1956)

b/w · 39s · sound · Scotland · 35mm · SFA

■ A brief television advertisement promoting SCWS Unitas oats.

I   A saucepan of SCWS Unitas oats simmers on a cooker.
II A family of four dances a jig to the breakfast table. They tuck with relish into their meal of Unitas breakfast oats.
III Graphic card: "In 1lb and 2lb Packets at your Co-op. FULL DIVIDEND". Jingle: "When you go for your

breakfast be sure you always take,/A good plate of Unitas Breakfast Oats./ The value of them lies in, the fact they're appetising,/And eating them good health in you promotes./When once you taste their flavour, forever more you'll favour./Unitas, Unitas Breakfast Oats."

Remarks

With the exuberant family dance to breakfast and their expectant joy as they launch into the meal, this film represents the quaintest of the surviving SCWS television commercials. Oatmeal-milling was an important traditional business of the SCWS, and mills were established at Junction Mill, Leith (1897), Crichie Meal Mill, Aberdeenshire (1915) and Girtrig Mill, Ayrshire (1918).

NCFC 198
Working Together (c.1956)

col · 14m 48s · sound · 16mm · EAFA, IAC, NFTVA, WFSA
pr DATA Films d Peter Pickering cam Ken Reeves ed Eric Pask

▪ A general information film about the Co-operative Movement and the manufacturing activities of the CWS.

I   A simple animated sequence explaining the ownership and membership structure of a Co-operative society and the federal nature of the Movement.
II A craftsman at work at a CWS pottery; modern machine methods of production of ceramics; ceramic painters at work; a display of CWS china and earthenware; a foreman and manager discuss the latest designs.
III Cigarette production at the CWS tobacco factory – CWS Navy Cut and Jaycee cigarettes.
IV Gathering fruit at the CWS apple orchards, Cockayne Hatley, Bedfordshire; harvest thanksgiving in the local church; fruit-packing at the nearby CWS pre-packaging plant.
V   Bicycle- and pram-making at the CWS Tyseley cycle factory, Birmingham.
VI CWS Josie shoes are modelled for a group of buyers.
VII Cloth-making at a CWS mill; CWS fashion designer, Matli, at work; cutters and seamstresses work on the designs; fittings of the new designs; the clothes are modelled in a salon –

Lanfield clothes.
VIII Interiors of Co-op stores: jewelry; children's clothes; furniture – CWS Universe range; tailoring; shoes; grocery – self-service store.
IX A simple animated sequence explains the nature of the Co-op dividend and the importance of buying CWS brand goods.

Remarks

The film production unit, Documentary Technicians' Alliance (DATA), was a co-operative of film technicians formed in 1944. Several films were produced by DATA Films for the Movement in the 1950s, all distinguished by their imaginative construction and professionalism. The chief interest of this film is its attention to CWS productive activities not featured previously on film: for instance, the 1600-acre estate operated by the CWS at Cockayne Hatley, Bedfordshire, and the Tyseley cycle factory, Birmingham. The manufacture of cycles was yet another occasion when the Movement undertook the manufacture of an item in response to a trade boycott imposed by private interests. The factory was established in 1920 and, due to the seasonal nature of demand for its products, it soon began production of perambulators and, subsequently, toys and tubular furniture. At the time of the making of this film, the Movement operated 26 000 shops, and claimed around 12% of the nation's retail trade – the Movement's high point.

NCFC 199
Cogent Cigarettes (1957)

b/w · 1m 13s · sound · Scotland · 35mm · SFA

▪ A brief promotional film for SCWS Cogent cigarettes.

I   Graphic card: "Introducing Tremendous Value – Cogent Cigarettes".
II Factory production: leaf-softening process; high-speed cutters; cigarette assembly; cartoning of cigarettes; wrapping and sealing.
III A man relaxing in his armchair with a Cogent cigarette.
IV Graphic card: "Relax with Cogent Cigarettes. Sold at your Co-op."

Remarks

A fairly detailed cinema advertisement which finds time in its tight schedule to outline the

basics of the production process of SCWS cigarette-manufacture, as well as to promote the popular Cogent brand. The relaxed smoker appears to have been an associated image with the brand: see *Relax with a Cogent* (c.1957; NCFC 205).
See also: NCFC 205

NCFC 200
Father Takes the Cake (1957)

col · 25m 30s · sound · 16mm · NFTVA
pr Anglo-Scottish Pictures *d* L Reeve
cast Kenneth Connor, Toke Townley, Deidre Sheriff, Barbara Ashcroft.

■ A comic narrative promoting CWS baking products.

I   Father is disturbed when he hears that Mother is expected home in only four hours, after a stay with a friend. The house is in a mess and he must put it right.

II   The women decide to surprise Father and bake him a cake. The Co-op delivery man times his visit just right and leaves the required CWS baking products – including CWS Gold and Silver Seal margarines.

III   Father hits upon his own surprise – a cherry cake for when Mother returns. With his cupboard bare, he heads off to the Co-op store.

IV   In their kitchen, the women demonstrate how to make a perfect Victoria Sandwich cake using CWS baking ingredients.

V   At the Co-op store, Father buys his baking ingredients. Luckily for him, there is an in-store cookery demonstration, and his idea of a cherry cake is selected for demonstration.

VI   The women demonstrate various icing techniques.

VII   Father is in his kitchen proceeding with his cherry cake. He remembers his lesson from earlier in the day.

VIII   The women demonstrate how to bake the perfect chocolate cake, sponge boats, butterfly buns, Madeleines, the Puffin Billy cake – a train-shaped cake for children's parties, coffee and walnut cake, and pineapple cake.

IX   The Co-op counter assistant calls on Father to return his cigarettes, left at the store. They virtually polish off the cherry cake, and the incredulous assistant, disbelieving of Father's baking skills, is led to the kitchen for a demonstration. At that point, Mother returns laden with her own cakes.

X   A montage sequence of various home-made cakes baked with CWS ingredients.

Remarks
Although promoting CWS baking products generally, the film concentrates on Gold and Silver Seal margarines and Shortex cooking fat. The film was shot at Shepperton Studios, part of a series of brand product films undertaken for the CWS by Anglo-Scottish Pictures. These films were integral to the popular "Woman's Hour" programme offered by the CWS Publicity Film Section, which began in the early 1950s. Between October 1956 and March 1957, CWS mobile film units presented 2339 consumer shows to an aggregate audience in excess of 261 000. Representatives of the CWS Technical Research Department were on the film set to supervise baking demonstrations. A CWS trade journal at the time commented on the film: "In essence, it is a cookery demonstration in full colour, leavened with domestic fun, but all the time concentrating on its primary subject: to demonstrate how first-class cakes for tea-table and party can be made with CWS margarine, cooking fats, and other products of our own factories" (*The Producer* June 1957). Popular comic actor, Kenneth Connor, then best known for his participation in television's *The Goon Show*, puts in a predictable comic performance on the eve of his extensive *Carry on* career. The first *Carry on* comedy, *Carry on Sergeant*, was released in the following year, 1958. Leonard Reeve(s) had a long association with Anglo-Scottish Pictures where he directed numerous films going back to the war years.
See also: xxii, xxxiii, NCFC 159, NCFC 188, NCFC 207

NCFC 201
A Souvenir of Littlehampton (1957)

col · 9m 7s · sound · 16mm · ETV
pr RACS Film Unit *cam* George Durham

■ A film record of a day's outing for children, sponsored by the RACS.

I   A RACS coach arrives to collect a party of Playway and Pathfinder groups for an annual summer outing to Littlehampton, West Sussex. Soon it is out on the open road.

II   With Rainbow Flags flying, the children head for the beach.

III   Scenes on the beach: at the water's edge; on the promenade.
IV   The Punch and Judy show.
V   Young boy at the St John's Ambulance station.
VI   At the funfair: Big Dipper; toddlers' cars; big wheel; roundabout.
VII   Marching behind their banners, the children head for the green.
VIII   Folk-dancing inside a ring of Rainbow Flags. The congregation sings "Jerusalem".
IX   Procession of the children.
X   Waiting for the coaches.

Remarks
A record of the Co-operative Day outing for youngsters to the seaside resort of Littlehampton. The film is provided with a voice-over narration which, in one or two places, is damaged and inaudible. The film is particularly interesting for the excellent collection of banners and flags paraded by the children, and representing the various chapters of the Playway, Pathfinder and Woodcraft Folk groups. A silent version of the film also survives at the ETV archive.

NCFC 202
[CWS Margarine Advertisement 3]
(c.1957)

b/w · 34s · sound · 16mm · NFTVA
cast Desmond Walter Ellis (?)

■ A brief advertisement for CWS Gold Seal margarine.

I   A hapless young man attempts to praise the virtues of the Co-op's luxury Gold Seal margarine. Unfortunately, he has nothing to spread it on and does not know what vitamins are. He concludes that the audience must try it themselves.
II   Graphic card: "At Your Local Co-op. CWS Gold Seal Margarine, 1/1."

Remarks
An interesting example of an early television commercial which, unusually for the CWS, adopts a mildly comic approach. CWS Gold and Silver margarines were heavily promoted through film and television. A shorter, 15-second version of this advert was also produced. Another set of animated CWS Gold Seal margarine adverts produced in 1957, so far unlocated, and featuring the slogan, "Its fame is spreading...its fame is spreading...gold!...gold!...'Gold Seal' margarine...", received the highest award of

the independent panel of the Commercial TV News Service, indicating the innovation and quality which the CWS was able to attain with the most recent form of publicity.

NCFC 203
[CWS Margarine Advertisement 4]
(c.1957)

col · 1m 36s · sound · 16mm · NFTVA

■ A short promotional film for CWS Silver Seal margarine.

I   "What can you buy that is energy-building, is cream-like in flavour, smooth, golden and daily fresh?" – CWS Silver Seal margarine.
II   A short, three-shot sequence of the manufacture of CWS Silver Seal margarine.
III   Ideal for mealtimes: spread on bread and toast, or for cooking and baking.
IV   Graphic card: "Silver Seal Margarine, 10½d; Gold Seal Margarine, 1/-. At Your Co-operative Stores."

Remarks
An efficient cinema advertisement that manages to combine the usual promotional plugs for the product with brief industrial scenes of its manufacture. There was undoubtedly a companion film that foregrounded CWS Gold Seal margarine, but a copy has not yet been located. This print suffers from some colour-fading.

NCFC 204
A Helping Hand (c.1957)

b/w · 9m 20s · sound · Scotland · 16mm · SFA
pr CWS Film Unit *d* Nigel Byass
prod George Wynn *cam* Bert Hampson
sd Dick Smith *ed* Cath Miller *cast* Hazel Jennings, Anne Wrigg, Brian Haines.

■ A promotional film for SCWS brushes.

I   A Scottish housewife returns home to her flat. She offers advice to a neighbour who is having difficulty cleaning her doorstep.
II   A flashback to the local Co-op store where the housewife is being expertly informed by the counter assistant on the range and quality of SCWS brushes.
III   Various scenes depicting the production of SCWS brushes, and the

obtaining of the numerous materials that are required for their manufacture. Both machine and artisanal processes are detailed. A narration is provided by the counter assistant.

IV   The housewife lends her neighbour one of her new SCWS scrubbing brushes, and reminds her that they can be obtained only at Co-op stores.

Remarks
A typical "product" film, both promoting a SCWS commodity and informing about its production and Co-operative manufacturing. The film is efficient if uninspired, and relies on stock clichés and stereotypes – for example, women do the scrubbing, men are the skilled workers, and so on. The manufacture of the various brush types is presented in some detail. Interestingly and unusually, the film was produced by the film unit of the English CWS. The SCWS brush factory was situated on the Shieldhall Estate, Glasgow, and began operation in 1890.

NCFC 205
Relax with a Cogent (c.1957)

b/w · 1m 7s · sound · Scotland · 35mm · SFA

▪ A brief two-shot advertisement for SCWS Cogent cigarettes.

I   A man smokes a Cogent cigarette whilst relaxing in his armchair.
II   Graphic card: "Cogent Cigarettes – the Cigarette Masterpiece".

Remarks
A somewhat simplified version of the contemporaneous *Cogent Cigarettes* (1957; NCFC 199). This short advertising film dispenses with the brief production sequences of the brand product, and centres on the image of the relaxed male character enjoying his Cogent cigarette whilst resting in his armchair. Although the Co-operative Movement devoted the resources it could manage to the production of cigarettes, it was being drastically outpaced by the industry's leading businesses, which were capturing an ever-increasing market share. An identical situation emerged in the soap market, where leading manufacturers were substantial investors in early television advertising.
See also: NCFC 199

NCFC 206
BCS Dairy Office Xmas Party (1958)

col · 9m 23s · silent · 8mm · EAFA

▪ An "amateur" film record of this festive event sponsored by the Birmingham Co-operative Society (BCS).

I   Guests seated at table, drinking and talking; couples begin to dance.
II   A "concert party" entertains with a humorous song; close-shots of the pianist.
III   A resumption of dancing.
IV   Guests enjoying a drink and a rest; individuals are "picked out" by the camera.
V   Further dancing.

Remarks
One of a number of films deriving from the dairy department of the BCS in the late-1950s. Most of the films appeared designed for internal use and interest.

NCFC 207
Choice of Quality (1958)

col · 17m 36s · sound · 16mm · IAC, NFTVA
pr Anglo-Scottish Pictures

▪ A promotional film for CWS baking and cooking products.

I   Display of CWS cooking products – Gold, Silver and Red Seal margarines, Shortex, Hilex, Sutox; perfect pastry and cakes made with CWS ingredients.
II   The laboratory of the CWS margarine factory, Higher Irlam, Manchester.
III   The industrial processes at the CWS factory: the primary ingredient, powdered milk; the churn room where the ingredients are blended – milk, oils and vitamins; the "emulsion" is cooled on a drum; the margarine is wrapped and packed into cartons – Gold Seal margarine; an older method of production – milling; the moulding and packing machine; laboratory testing of the finished product – "spreadability"; cookery experts testing CWS Gold Seal margarine in baking an almond and cherry fruit cake (presented as a cookery demonstration); demonstration of baking a Victoria sandwich; using Silver Seal and Shortex in making flaky pastry *(Part 1)*.
IV   The manufacture of CWS Shortex:

selected oils and fats are solidified in a giant rotator; the wrapping and packing process; laboratory testing of Shortex.

V   Making flaky pastry *(Part 2)*; making a Madeira cake using Shortex; demonstration of making shortcrust pastry.

VI   The production line for CWS Hilex, the low-cost shortening.

VII   Using Hilex for shallow and deep fat frying; finishing off the flaky pastry *(Part 3)*.

VIII   The production line for CWS Sutox beef suet; laboratory tests for Sutox.

IX   Making a steam pudding with Sutox; turning the Victoria sandwich into a gâteau, using butter icing.

X   The despatch room of the CWS margarine factory; lorries loaded with CWS margarine leave the factory; a review of the delicious foods made with CWS cooking fats.

Remarks
One of several promotional films for CWS cooking fats and baking ingredients produced for the popular "Woman's Hour" show offered by the CWS Publicity Film Service throughout the 1950s. The approach of this film is slightly different in that it examines several basic brand products, their manufacture and use. The scheme of the film was detailed in the c.1963 *CWS Film Catalogue*: "Highly qualified people spend their lives seeking new ways of making life more enjoyable for you. They also keep a sharp eye on nutritional values and above all on quality." This film relied on the straight advice of experts, rather than on the gentle levity sought by its narrative counterparts – for example, *Father Takes the Cakes* (1957; NCFC 200) and *Father Holds the Fort* (1955; NCFC 163). The film unusually uses two narrators who make telling contributions: the male commentator describes the industrial and scientific processes of the factory and laboratory, whilst the female commentator is restricted to explaining the cookery demonstrations. This print suffers from some colour-fading.
See also: NCFC 159

NCFC 208
Gallons of Goodness (1958)

col · 10m 12s · sound · 16mm · NFTVA, SFA
pr Anglo-Scottish Pictures

■ An information film about CWS

Wheatsheaf milk products.

I   A dairy herd in an English pasture.

II   A lorry loaded with milk churns winds its way through country lanes to a CWS creamery; a sample of milk is taken from the delivery and tested in the laboratory; the churns are emptied into large vats.

III   The manufacture of CWS Wheatsheaf evaporated milk: the heating processes; the empty cans arrive; the cans are filled at a rate of 400 cans per minute; the cans are sealed and labelled – CWS Wheatsheaf full-cream evaporated milk; the storage room; cartons of evaporated milk pass on a conveyor.

IV   The manufacture of CWS dairy cream: cream is heated for pasteurisation; empty tins arrive at the filling machines and are sealed; a display of CWS pure dairy cream; the laboratory; a display of dishes and foods enhanced by CWS milk products – pies, pastries, cakes, tinned fruit, and so on.

V   Graphic card: "Wheatsheaf Brand From Co-operative Societies Everywhere".

Remarks
One of several films commissioned by the CWS from Anglo-Scottish Pictures, and dealing with dairy products, a product area which considerably expanded in the postwar period. The scenes at the dairy were taken at the CWS Tullygoonigan creamery, Co. Armagh, Northern Ireland. The CWS had developed substantial trade in dairy produce with Ireland, the first instance of the society extending overseas being the establishment of a purchasing depot in Ireland, and the appointment of a butter-buyer at Tipperary in 1866. Eventually, albeit in the face of certain difficulties, extensive dairy holdings were acquired by the CWS in Ireland. This print suffers from some colour-fading. An earlier film with the same subject and title had been produced for the CWS in 1937, but so far it has not been located.

NCFC 209
[Nottingham Co-op Wine Department] (1958)

b/w · 2m · silent · 16mm · EAFA

■ Celebrated jazz musician Humphrey Lyttleton opens the wine exhibition hosted by the Nottingham Co-operative Society (NCS).

I   General scenes of invited guests milling around the wine exhibition and enjoying a complimentary glass of wine.

II   Humphrey Lyttleton addresses the gathering; he enjoys a glass of wine whilst chatting to two promotion girls; Lyttleton in conversation with other guests; general scenes of guests chatting and enjoying their wine/drinks.

Remarks
An "amateur" film record of Humphrey Lyttleton's visit to the NCS to open the wine exhibition at their Central Store, Parliament Street, Nottingham. Apparently, Lyttleton was one hour late in arriving (see *Co-operative News* 19 July 1958), and the wine-tasting started without him. 200 people were in attendance for the opening ceremony, and the exhibition lasted for a week, between 12 and 19 July. Such activity by the NCS was hardly in accordance with the pioneers of the society, members of the Lenton Temperance Society. In defence, the Vice-President explained that "we are trying to popularise wines with the ordinary man in the street. There is no doubt that appreciation of wine is growing in this country." Lyttleton was a columnist for the Movement's Sunday newspaper, *The Reynold's News*, and was a celebrated bon vivant. For the NCS, the wine and spirits trade was worth about £250 000 in 1958.

NCFC 210
[Birmingham Co-op Dairy] (c.1958)

b/w · silent · 16mm · EAFA

▪ A collection of short sequences filmed at the Vauxhall Road dairy which was operated by the Birmingham Co-operative Society (BCS).

Reel 1 (1m 20s)
Milk-bottling plant: empty bottles are conveyed on tracks; bottles are rapidly filled with milk; full bottles are conveyed on tracks; close-shots of gears; distant shots of a large machine.

Reel 2 (1m 21s)
Close-shot of a meter; panning-shot of the plant; another meter; machinery and pipe-work; a large vat of milk is automatically stirred.

Reel 3 (1m 15s)
"Congress" visitors to the dairy: delegates inspecting the goods yard; inspecting the bottling plant.

Reel 4 (1m 20s)
Full milk churns entering the dairy; milk is collected into a large vat; empty churns are conveyed away from the plant; the collecting vat is emptied and the milk is piped into the dairy.

Reel 5 (1m 18s)
Full milk churns are unloaded from a lorry; their lids are removed by a special machine; an operative checks them for freshness; the churns are conveyed into the dairy, and their contents emptied into a storage vat.

Reel 6 (1m 19s)
The large pasteurisation (?) tanks; empty milk crates are conveyed across the plant; a fork-lift truck unloads crates of empties from a lorry.

Reel 7 (1m 24s)
Clean bottles are fed into a conveyor; full bottles are fed into a stacking machine; stacks of loaded milk crates awaiting collection; recently sterilised milk churns are fed along a conveyor.

Reel 8 (1m 21s)
Full crates of milk are conveyed through the plant, controlled by a "policeman"; clean empty bottles are placed onto a conveyor; loaded crates are stacked onto trolleys and pushed into the goods yard.

Reel 9 (1m 22s)
"Congress" visitors to the dairy: the party enters through the main gate; the party re-embarks on the coach; close-shots of some of the delegates; the coach departs; the pre-sterilisation machinery.

Reel 10 (1m 16s)
An operative loads crates with full bottles of milk – several views.

Reel 11 (1m 22s)
A lorry full of empty milk crates pulls into the loading bay; high-angle shot of the operation; high-angle shot of a lorry loaded with milk churns pulling into the loading bay.

Reel 12 (1m 17s)
Various views of the society's dairy herd.

Reel 13 (2m 24s)
A visit by civic dignitaries to the dairy: arrival by limousine; presentation of flowers; signing the visitors' book; inspecting the bottling plant and loading bay area; the laboratory.

Reel 14 (3m 36s)
A further visit by civic dignitaries:

arrival by limousine; signing the
visitors' book; welcome and reception;
inspecting the plant and the loading
bay area; the party's three limousines;
the laboratory; the party watches an
instructional dairy film; farewell and
departure.

Remarks
It is probable that this series of short scenes
of the BCS dairy operations at Vauxhall
Road was intended for a properly edited film
on the subject. However, there is no
indication that such a programme was ever
completed. A professionally produced film
of the dairy, *Seeing Is Believing* (NCFC
019), had been commissioned in 1929, and
provides an important record of the plant in
its early phase. By 1951, the dairy was
distributing 320 000 gallons of milk each
week, and had become a show-place for
visitors to Birmingham. I have been unable
to identify the specific congress referred to
in reel 9, but it presumably was a milk
industry event, rather than one from the
wider Co-operative Movement. A
contemporary survey commissioned by the
National Milk Publicity Council revealed that
36% of people purchased their milk from
Co-operative societies (*The Producer* March
1959).

NCFC 211
Painting For Pleasure (c.1958)

col · 11m 19s · sound · 16mm · EAFA, ETV,
NFTVA
pr Anglo-Scottish Pictures

▪ An informational film promoting CWS paint
products.

I   Various CWS brand paints pass on a
       conveyor belt.
II   A shopper is attended to by a counter
       assistant in a paint department of a
       Co-op store. She is impressed by the
       range available, and the assistant
       explains the processes behind the
       manufacture of CWS paints.
III   In a laboratory, a technician
       demonstrates the manufacture of paint
       from its constituent ingredients.
IV   The factory production of paint: resins
       are mixed with linseed oil and heated;
       after cooling, the solvent and drier are
       added, and the mixture is spun in a
       centrifuge; pigments are blended with
       the medium, and the whole passes
       through a grinder; samples are tested
       by a chemist; the canning process –

CWS enamel paint.
V   Tips on home decoration: exterior
       paintwork; the application and use of
       CWS paint and varnish-remover; the
       treatment of knots with CWS Shellac
       knotting agent; the priming coat –
       CWS genuine lead primer; the 31
       shades of CWS intermixing super high
       gloss enamel; great results from CWS
       emulsion wall finish.
VI   Weather-testing of paint samples by
       CWS laboratory staff; the viscosity
       test; the stress test.
VII   Various cans of CWS paint pass on a
       conveyor – CWS enamel paint, CWS
       emulsion finish, CWS hard gloss paint,
       CWS white ceiling paint.

Remarks
Co-operative paint manufacture was begun
in 1911 in Rochdale, at the premises
formerly used by the Pioneers as a corn
mill. Following a fire in the 1920s,
production moved to Derby, where the CWS
had an empty foundry, and the site was
developed to meet rising demand. The film
is similar to, and shares some material with,
Halcyon Days (c.1962; NCFC 253).
See also: NCFC 253

NCFC 212
Black and White (1959)

col · 6m 32s · sound · Scotland · 16mm ·
NFTVA, SFA
pr Gate Film Productions

▪ The production of SCWS Shieldhall coffee
and chicory essence.

I   Coffee beans are poured into a large
       container, from where they are drawn
       up into a storage hopper.
II   Batches of beans pass through a
       roasting machine; periodically,
       samples are checked; the beans are
       cooled by the use of cold air.
III   Beans are fed into a grinder; the finely
       ground coffee is ready for the
       percolation process.
IV   Boiling water is added to the ground
       coffee; coffee liquor is fed into huge
       vacuum pans where it is concentrated,
       leaving pure coffee extract, to which
       chicory and sugar are added.
V   The bottle-washing machine; clean,
       sterilised bottles are conveyed to the
       filling machines; bottles are filled at
       the rate of 86 per minute; full bottles
       receive their caps and labels; bottles
       are packed into cardboard cartons.

VI A bottle of Shieldhall coffee essence with two cups of coffee – one black, one white.
VII Graphic card: "Awarded The Certificate of the Royal Institute of Public Health and Hygiene for over 30 years".
VIII A promotional display of Shieldhall coffee essence.

Remarks
Coffee was one of several products handled in combination by the English and Scottish Joint CWS. The Shieldhall site, established in January 1892, was the only Co-operative coffee essence factory in Great Britain; consequently, Shieldhall coffee and chicory essence was one of a limited number of SCWS brand products marketed across the UK. The joint society reported that, for 1959, trade in canister coffee had been well-maintained, with a successful product launch of the soluble Elite brand, a budget-priced coffee aimed at an expanding market sector.
See also: NCFC 223

NCFC 213
Bladnoch Creamery (1959)

col · 8m 3s · sound · Scotland · 16mm · SFA
pr Gate Film Productions

■ An informational film promoting SCWS margarines.

I The old world village of Bladnoch, 92 miles from Glasgow, in the middle of Scotland's "Devon". Exterior of the SCWS creamery at Bladnoch.
II The manufacture of SCWS Bluebell margarine: large tankers arrive at the creamery; fats are drawn off into smaller tanks and weighed; the mixing process – "sunshine vitamins" are added; the milk room and pasteurising plant; the emulsifying process and cooling causing the liquid to solidify; the margarine is carried by conveyor to the extruder; the wrapping machine – Bluebell margarine; packing into cardboard cartons.
III Assembling the outer-wrapping for SCWS Copex cooking fat; the filling machine provides the contents and the packet is sealed; packing into cardboard cartons.
IV The laboratory.
V Display of SCWS margarines – Bluebell, Orchid and Snowdrop; display of SCWS cooking fats –

Copex, White Crest and Guild.
VI Graphic card: "SCWS. The Sign of Good Quality at your Co-op."

Remarks
The Bladnoch creamery, Wigtownshire, was established in 1899. The chief importance of the creamery was its margarine industry, which expanded ten-fold during the Great War, due to restrictions on the supply of butter. Oils for the production of margarine and cooking fats were supplied by the possessions of the English and Scottish Joint CWS in West Africa, being processed at the CWS oil mill in Liverpool. The SCWS's role in supplying milk products to retail societies in Scotland was an important one, and a major investment had been the establishment of the Ryelands milk-collecting centre in 1909. As business expanded, numerous creameries were acquired, including those at Whithorn, Stranraer, Sandhead, Drummore, East Kilbride, Coatbridge, Bathgate, Shettleston, Kilmarnock, Dumbarton and Galashiels. Other creameries were located in Ireland, which supplied high-quality Irish butter.

NCFC 214
Chemical Sundries Department (1959)

col · 10m 25s · sound · Scotland · 16mm · SFA
pr Gate Film Productions

■ An information film about a trading department of the SCWS.

I The laboratory of the SCWS Chemical Sundries Department, Shieldhall, Glasgow.
II The processing of salt: the salt is pumped into the factory from containers; the salt is fed from silo to mixing machine; the salt packing and wrapping machine; despatch of SCWS Snowdrop salt.
III The processing of Unitas oats: weighing and packaging; quality-control and inspection.
IV A wide range of SCWS products and brands are processed by the department: Jelly crystals, Pioneer custard, yellow split peas, aspirin, extract of malt with cod-liver oil.
V Stringent tests and quality-control by Shieldhall chemists.
VI The processing of wax polish, bleach, toiletries.
VII The SCWS Horticultural Section, Shieldhall. Garden seeds are tested.

VIII Colourful displays of the products of the SCWS Chemical Sundries Department.

Remarks
The Chemical Sundries Packing Department of the SCWS was inaugurated in 1892 to meet the rising demand for goods made up in packet form. The first work of the Department was the packing of cornflour and semolina. By the end of the 1950s, when this film was produced, the Department was responsible for over 2000 products. (For a complete list of the products available in 1936, see *Scottish Co-operative Wholesale Society Ltd, 1868-1936*, n.d.: 58-59.) The laboratory served the whole interests of SCWS manufacturing, and analytical work was carried out there for all departments. The SCWS Horticultural Section came into being following the expansion of allotment-tendering during the First World War, supplying the required bulbs, seeds, roots, and so on. The Department's innovative chemists developed special food products during the Second World War: emergency tea rations in tablet form, widely used by commandos, and lemon crystals, widely used to make thirst-quenching drinks by servicemen engaged in jungle warfare.

NCFC 215
[Co-op Christmas] (1959)

b/w · 12s · silent · 35mm · NFA

■ A Christmas-time television advertisement promoting the Newcastle Co-operative Society (NCS).

I   Graphic card: a still image of Father Christmas – "Everything for Christmas from the Newcastle Co-op".

Remarks
One of a series of brief advertisements sponsored by the NCS. This is the most simple in construction – indeed, it would be difficult to imagine anything more basic. It is probable that the film was used in cinemas, and that a suitable musical background was provided. By the 1960s, the NCS had over 117 000 members, and annual sales approaching £14 million.

NCFC 216
[Co-op Jewelry] (1959)

b/w · 7s · sound · 35mm · NFA

■ A television advertisement promoting jewelry sold by the Newcastle Co-operative Society (NCS).

I   A young couple relaxing at home. She models her jewelry – necklace, bracelet and ring – to the camera.
II   Graphic card: still image of the central premises – "Newcastle on Tyne Co-operative Society".
     Commentary: "Jewelry made to please and treasure. At Newcastle Co-op the store that pays the dividend".

Remarks
One of a series of brief advertisements sponsored by the NCS, suitable for use in both cinema and television advertising. Numerous Co-operative societies would have commissioned such films for local and regional promotions. However, few examples appear to have survived outside the collection from the NCS.

NCFC 217
[Co-op Menswear] (1959)

b/w · 7s · sound · 35mm · NFA

■ A television advertisement promoting menswear sold by the Newcastle Co-operative Society (NCS).

I   Two well-dressed young men and their sons meet in the street. The boys pat a dog, and one of the men models his coat and suit to the other.
II   Graphic card: still of the central premises – "Newcastle on Tyne Co-operative Society".
     Commentary: "Whatever your age you're well-dressed when you shop at Newcastle Co-op. The store that pays the dividend."

Remarks
One of a series of brief advertisements sponsored by the NCS in the 1950s: a good example of a simple local society advertising film suitable for television and cinema use.

NCFC 218
[Co-op Shoes] (1959)

b/w · 7s · sound · 35mm · NFA

■ A television advertisement promoting Co-op shoes sold by the Newcastle Co-operative Society (NCS).

I   A well-dressed family (parents, son and daughter) out on a walk. They halt at a pedestrian crossing.

II   A close-shot of their legs and feet halted at the kerb.

III Graphic card: still of the central premises – "Newcastle on Tyne Co-operative Society".
Commentary: "You can walk in comfort and fashion with the Newcastle Co-op. The store that pays the dividend."

Remarks
One of a series of brief advertisements put out by the NCS. Similar in their two-part structure, an introduction to a product range followed by the image of the society's impressive central premises, the advertisements efficiently put across their promotional message. The NCS central premises were constructed in 1932 on Newgate Street in the centre of Newcastle, and are a striking and imposing example of Co-operative architecture, dominating the city's trading district. The film would have been suitable for use in both cinema and television advertising.

NCFC 219
[Co-op Travel] (1959)

b/w · 7s · sound · 35mm · NFA

▪ A television advertisement promoting the Co-op Travel Service.

I   A young couple are being attended to at an in-store travel centre.

II   Graphic card: still of the central premises – "Newcastle on Tyne Co-operative Society".
Commentary: "For carefree travel to the four corners of the earth. Book through Newcastle Co-op Travel Bureau."

Remarks
One of a series of brief advertisements sponsored by the Newcastle Co-operative Society. Travel agencies were an important postwar growth industry amongst many Co-operative societies. Films on travel subjects were often part of the programme of CWS film shows; however, it is not possible to say whether any of those films were direct commissions by the Movement. The short commercial for NCS's Travel Bureau is the only Co-op film so far located on the subject. The film would have been suitable for use in both cinema and television advertising.

NCFC 220
[Co-op Women's Fashions] (1959)

b/w · 7s · sound · 35mm · NFA

▪ A television advertisement promoting ladies' fashions sold by the Newcastle Co-operative Society (NCS).

I   Two female models demonstrate the latest fashions: a smart dress and a tweed suit.

II   Graphic card: still of the central premises – "Newcastle on Tyne Co-operative Society".
Commentary: "You can walk in comfort and fashion with the Newcastle Co-op. The store that pays the dividend."

Remarks
One of a series of brief advertisements sponsored by the NCS. The films were efficiently constructed, managing to incorporate the product range, the society premises and the "Co-op Difference", all in seven seconds. The films were suitable for use in both cinema and television advertising.

NCFC 221
[Co-operative House, Plymouth] (1959)

b/w · 1m 12s · sound · 35mm · NFTVA

▪ Television advertisements for Co-operative House, the central premises of the Plymouth Co-operative Society.

I   Exteriors of Co-operative House, Plymouth.

II   The entrance foyer; the furniture department – a selection of chairs, bedroom furniture, three-piece suites, etc; the carpet department; the haberdashery department.

III Exterior of Co-operative House.

IV Graphic card: "Co-operative House, Plymouth".
Jingle: "There's variety on every floor,/ At Co-operative House, Plymouth's big store".

Remarks
This commercial survives in four versions. In addition to this example promoting home furnishings, alternative adverts promote the following: the fashion floor – garments and styles from various manufacturers are modelled, and the accessories department and the store's restaurant are briefly introduced (1m 12s); juvenile fashions (41s);

and the electrical department, where staff demonstrate a wide selection of appliances and brands (1m 12s). The adverts were timed to coincide with the opening of Co-operative House, Plymouth, on 12 March 1959, one year short of the society's centenary. The original central premises had been destroyed in an air attack in 1941, and the new premises were part of the enforced postwar redevelopment of the city.

NCFC 222
Dan Divi (1959)

b/w · 24s · sound · 35mm · NFA
pr Dorian

▪ A television advertisement promoting the Central Store of the Newcastle Co-operative Society.

I   A brief animated advertisement featuring a "Master of the Hounds" character, "Dan Divi", who rides his steed into the Newcastle Co-operative Department store. The character is overlaid on a series of stills of various departments within the store: the food hall; women's fashions; the furniture department; and household goods department. Dan rides off with a full basket.

II   Graphic card: "Newcastle Co-op". Jingle: "Dan Divi, Dan Divi, Dan Divi",/ Come shop at Newcastle Co-op./Dan Divi, Dan Divi, Dan Divi,/The store where the good shoppers shop."/"Yes, you get a dividend whenever you spend at the Newcastle Co-op."

Remarks
A simple advertising cartoon featuring the engaging character of Dan Divi. The film promotes the society's departmental store, rather than a brand product, and emphasises the "Co-op Difference" – the dividend payout to member-customers. It is likely that the Dan Divi character appeared across a range of publicity media. The commercial would have been suitable for both cinema and television advertising.

NCFC 223
Productive Grocery Departments (1959)

col · 9m 28s · sound · Scotland · 16mm · SFA
pr Gate Film Productions

▪ An informational film outlining the work of the Productive Grocery Departments of the SCWS.

I   Seasonal fruits are picked for despatch to SCWS preserve factories at Shieldhall and Leith; the fruit simmers in large copper "jelly" pans; the jam is piped onto cooling tanks; jars of jam moving forward on conveyors; tests are made in the laboratory to ensure quality; jars are labelled – strawberry, greengage, raspberry, marmalade, blackcurrant, damson; display of SCWS jams.

II   Display of SCWS bottled sauces; sauce bottles are filled with ketchup; bottles are capped, sealed and labelled; bottles of ketchup pass on a conveyor belt; a laden dinner table with bottles of SCWS ketchup and brown sauce.

III   Display of SCWS sweets and confectionery; boiled sweets are cellophane wrapped – Fruit Drops, Mixed Satinettes, Glucose Fruits, Caramel Butters; sweets are packed in cellophane bags, others are roll-packed; the making of Mint Imperials; a fully-loaded delivery van sets off from the sweet factory.

IV   The making of Shieldhall coffee essence: coffee beans are emptied into a container and sucked up into a roaster; a sample is tested; the beans are cooled by cold air; the coffee is ground and percolated; in large vacuum pans, the coffee liquor is concentrated into coffee extract; the bottle-washing process; bottles are filled with coffee essence, capped and labelled; the bottles are packed into cartons; display of Shieldhall coffee essence.

V   Repeat of displays of SCWS preserves, sauces, sweets and coffee essence.

VI   Graphic card: "SCWS. The Sign of Good Quality at your Co-op."

Remarks
The four departments of the Productive Grocery group at Shieldhall, Glasgow, are detailed in this film – preserves (founded 1890), confectionery (1891), pickles (1893) and coffee essence (1892). A second SCWS preserve factory was located at Leith (1922). A companion film was made in the same year, detailing the productive activities of the Chemical Sundries Department. It is possible that the film is a combination of four individual films, each dealing with a specific department. SCWS Shieldhall coffee

essence was examined in *Black and White* (1959; NCFC 212), and section IV comprises material from that film. No films on SCWS preserves, confectionery or sauces have yet been located, but it is probable that they were made.
See also: xxxii

NCFC 224
Reach for a Rocky (1959)

col · 16m 56s · sound · Scotland · 16mm · SFA
pr Gate Film Productions

▪ An information film about the production of SCWS Rocky Mount cigarettes.

I   Harvesting tobacco at Rocky Mount, North Carolina, USA: curing tobacco leaves; buying at the tobacco auction.
II   At the Shieldhall tobacco factory: processing of leaves in a vacuum chamber; cutting and cleaning the leaves; blending the tobacco; further processing into fine-cut tobacco; the rotary dryer; tipping and papering – the preparation of Rocky Mount tipped cigarettes; quality-control; packaging and despatch of cartons.
III   Operatives in the canteen.
IV   At the warehouse: making up orders for the individual Co-op shops; shipment of containers.
V   Tobacco section of a Co-op self-service shop.

Remarks
This is a blatant case of slogan-stealing – the well-known US brand of cigarette "Lucky Strike" having already established the popular slogan of "Reach for a Lucky". At the time, the SCWS tobacco factory at Shieldhall, Glasgow, produced nineteen brands of cigarettes, including Cogent, Gold Flake, Shipmate and Rocky Mount Tipped. Particularly striking to today's health-conscious viewer is the lack of regard for smoking-related health issues in the film, with the female factory operatives vigorously endorsing the product during their break at the canteen (presumably cheap cigarettes were a perk of the job!), and the housewife who buys 100 cigarettes at a time – for the family!

NCFC 225
Rocky Mountain Cigarettes (1959)

col · 15s · sound · Scotland · 35mm · SFA

▪ An advertisement for SCWS cigarettes.

I   A four-shot sequence of cowboys enjoying SCWS Rocky Mount filter-tipped cigarettes. In the third shot, a cowboy and his girl sing: "It's the smoothest smoke of them all".

Remarks
A brief advertisement that draws its iconography from the well-known Marlboro campaigns. However, unlike the American man-of-action scenarios, the SCWS had developed a more languorous approach, where smoking is an aid to relaxation. See also the advertisements for Cogent cigarettes in this respect.

NCFC 226
[Scenes at the Co-op College] (1959)

b/w · 4m 38s · silent · 16mm · EAFA

▪ Scenes with the international students during their study at the International Co-operative College, Stanford Hall, near Loughborough.

I   The front aspect of the Co-operative College. Students amble along the driveway.
II   Students take notes in a classroom seminar.
III   Chefs at work in the kitchen; mealtime in the dining room; students descend the main staircase; a class led by the principal, Mr Marshall.
IV   Students on a visit to an agricultural Co-op: plants are potted and passed into a greenhouse for forcing; the mushroom beds; demonstration of the movable greenhouse screens/sheds; free-range pig farming; exteriors of the farm dwellings; feeding the chickens; tending the vegetable beds; ploughing the fields by tractor.
V   Unidentified building.

Remarks
The material is similar in content to the earlier film, *Getting Together: A Story of Co-operation* (1955; NCFC 164), and possibly consists of out-takes not included in that original production. Alternatively, it is conceivable that an update of the original project was planned but never materialised into a completed film, and this unedited footage is what remains.

NCFC 227
The Best of Bread (c.1959)

col · 14m 37s · sound · 16mm · IAC, NFTVA
pr Anglo-Scottish Pictures

■ An information film about CWS flour-milling and bread-baking.

I   Harvesting wheat. The grain is collected and poured onto a truck.
II   The CWS flour mill, Royal Victoria Dock, London (exterior): grain is pumped into the giant silos; grain is washed and screened; the disc separator; the conditioning plant and cooling section; blending the different grains; cutting the grain – producing semolina and coarse bran; the purifier – separating the semolina from the branch; the grinding process – producing flour.
III Testing in the laboratory – the Farinograph tests the gluten content.
IV The packing of CWS Federation flour; wrapping for distribution; a CWS bulk transportation lorry; unloading sacks of CWS flour at the bakery; giant mixers make the dough; the research and quality-control department; dividing the dough; the prover and oven; the bread passing through the oven; freshly baked loaves; the slicing and wrapping machine – CWS Wheatsheaf bread.
V   English wheatfields; a family tucking into a CWS Wheatsheaf loaf; a display of CWS Wheatsheaf bread.
    Jingle: "Buy it from the Co-op man,/ Remember what he said/Where there's the Wheatsheaf/There's the Best of Bread".

Remarks
Flour-milling and bread-baking were staple productions of the CWS; for many years they made a massive contribution to the surplus. At its height, just before the Second World War, the CWS operated ten flour mills, and its largest, that at the Royal Victoria Dock, London, was under construction, its opening delayed by the war to 1945. The Movement began to lose ground in the postwar bread trade from a position of dominance, its loose federal structure proving increasingly uncompetitive in the face of the emerging combines. For instance, in 1956 it was estimated that some 300 retail societies and approximately 30 local federations were operating bakeries and selling through the Movement's 950 societies. Despite a degree of

rationalisation, the trade continued to decline, and in 1971 the radical decision was taken to merge the CWS milling and baking concerns with the Spillers Group. A new emblem for CWS Wheatsheaf bread was launched in 1959, and a high-profile television advertising campaign began in September, with the slogan, "Wheatsheaf – the best of bread". This film was clearly allied to that promotional campaign.

NCFC 228
[CWS Shirt Advertisement] (c.1959)

col · 16s · sound · 16mm · NFTVA

■ A simple animated advertisement for CWS Lestar shirts.

I   Exterior of the Plaza Theatre, where a première is about to begin.
II   Interior: a compère introduces the sensational "Lestar", the non-iron shirt.
III Graphic card: "Lestar, 32/9. At Your Co-operative Store."

Remarks
A well-produced cartoon commercial exhibiting a degree of depth and use of colour beyond the usual simple line drawings of much of the animated advertising employed by the CWS at the time. The Lestar drip-dry shirt was first marketed in 1958 to immediate success, being declared "[o]ne of the most popular CWS textile introductions of the year" (*The Producer* December 1958). More than 100 000 shirts were sold in the first three months of marketing.

NCFC 229
[Lofty Peak Cake Mixes] (c.1959)

b/w · 50s · sound · Scotland · 35mm · SFA

■ A brief advertisement for SCWS cake mixes.

I   5.00 pm. A telephone call: a housewife must prepare for some unexpected company. She decides to bake cakes with SCWS Lofty Peak prepared cake mixes.
II   6.00 pm. Her kitchen table now boasts a spread of delicious cakes.
III A display of SCWS Lofty Peak prepared cake mixes: Pancake Mix, Sponge Mix, Scone Mix, Tea-Time Fancies. "At your Local Store".

Remarks
A typical late-1950s television commercial. Lofty Peak was a long-established brand name for SCWS flour and associated products. Since the war, convenience foods had been a rapidly expanding market: this film, with its attention to the lack of available time, clearly reinforces the value of such products.

NCFC 230
[SCWS Margarine Advertisement] (c.1959)

b/w · 26s · sound · Scotland · 35mm · SFA

- A television advertisement promoting SCWS Bluebell margarine.

I   A family are at table about to enjoy tea. The mother unwraps a new pat of SCWS Bluebell margarine. Mother: "I always have Bluebell on my table. Bluebell, the economy buy with the luxury flavour."
II Graphic card: 10½d per ½lb./Full Dividend/At Your Co-op.

Remarks
A simple and to-the-point television advertisement. SCWS margarine was made at the Bladnoch and Whithorn creameries, owned and operated by the Movement. Another popular SCWS brand margarine was Snowdrop. Margarine production and consumption had massively increased during the Second World War, becoming a staple national food commodity.

NCFC 231
[Shieldhall Shoes] (c.1959)

b/w · 1m 5s · sound · Scotland · 35mm · SFA

- An advertisement promoting SCWS Triona and Morven shoes.

I   A series of shoes are conveyed towards the camera in close-ups: Ladies' shoes: the new Triona pointed toe in five exciting colours; Triona suede and calf ornamental court shoe in three colours.
Men's shoes: the Morven sports shoe with distinctive ornamental stitching; the Morven business shoe, black or brown calf.
II Graphic card: "SCWS Triona shoes for Ladies/SCWS Morven shoes for men. From your Co-op."

Remarks
The first SCWS boot factory was opened in 1885 at Shieldhall, Glasgow. The production of quality boots and shoes at prices which working people could afford was an important aim of the Movement. Many members purchased their family's footwear out of their dividend payments obtained from purchases on household goods, and, in this way, the Co-op enabled its members to "save" towards more expensive items. Made in black and white, this commercial was probably commissioned for television use, although it would have been expensive to run, lasting for over a minute.

NCFC 232
Come Shopping (1960)

b/w · 5m 25s · sound · 16mm · NFTVA
pr Television West and Wales (TWW)

- Three editions from a television advertising magazine broadcast by Television West and Wales (TWW) in the early 1960s for the South-West region.

PART 1
I   Introduction by an announcer/hostess, who suggests four good reasons to "Come Co-operative Shopping" – quality, value, service and dividend.
II   The audience are introduced to the CWS Space Plan Apollo range of bedroom furniture, available on easy terms.
III The CWS Society pyjamas for men; for women, a Pelaw housecoat, a CWS Belmont nightie or shrink-resistant pyjamas.
IV   A CWS 17" slimline Defiant television set is introduced.
V   All of the CWS products are available from the following societies: Aberdare, Bath, Bristol, Cardiff, Swansea, Swindon, West Somerset and East Devon, and Yeovil.
PART 2
I   Graphic card: "CWS Help You To Do-It-Yourself!"
II   Introduction by an announcer/host, who suggests four good reasons to "Come Co-operative Shopping" for home improvement products – quality, value, service and dividend.
III CWS Halcyon paints are introduced and recommended – 36 colours; as are CWS Invincible brushes, a CWS Society step-ladder, CWS Fiesta sweeping-brushes and brooms.
IV   CWS Unity garden tools are

introduced.
V   A CWS 17" slimline Defiant television set is introduced.
VI   All of the CWS products are available from the following societies: Aberdare, Bath, Bristol, Cardiff, Swansea, Swindon, West Somerset and East Devon, and Yeovil.

PART 3
I   Introduction by an announcer/hostess who suggests four good reasons to "Come Co-operative Shopping" – quality, value, service and dividend.
II   Graphic card: "Greet the summer in a BELMONT Dress" – a CWS Belmont dress is modelled for the camera.
III   Graphic card: "This summer you'll need a BELMONT cotton skirt" – a CWS Belmont skirt is modelled for the camera.
IV   Graphic card: "Put your best foot forward in CWS WHEATSHEAF shoes" – 3 pairs of ladies CWS Wheatsheaf shoes are modelled for the camera.
V   Graphic card: "Permanently Yours... Gaywhirl" – a permanently pleated CWS Gaywhirl skirt is modelled for the camera.
VI   A CWS 17" slimline Defiant television set is introduced.
VII   All of the CWS products are available from the following societies: Aberdare, Bath, Bristol, Cardiff, Swansea, Swindon, West Somerset and East Devon, and Yeovil.

Remarks
The first attempt at "collective television advertising" by a group of societies in the South-West region. A similar experiment was being conducted by a collection of East Anglian societies, although no film record survives for that. The programme was broadcast early in 1960. A later film survives of a collective television advertising campaign by Co-operative societies in Yorkshire, and it is reasonable to suspect that the practice was fairly widespread in the period. The programmes were broadcast live, and a telecine film was recorded for posterity.
See also: NCFC 247

NCFC 233
[CWS Biscuit Advertisement] (1960)

b/w · 41s · sound · 35mm · NFTVA
pr Anglo-Scottish Pictures cast Dora Bryan

■ A short promotional film for CWS biscuits.

I   A busy counter assistant is dealing with the high demand for CWS biscuits.
II   Glad of a break, she nibbles on a CWS Crumpsall cream cracker.
III   Graphic card: "Crumpsall Cream Crackers. From your Co-op Store!".

Remarks
Dora Bryan (born 1923), stage and screen comedienne, was well-known to the British film and theatre-going public, having played small but telling parts in such classics as Odd Man Out (1946) and The Blue Lamp (1949). Her most acclaimed role was as the mother in Tony Richardson's A Taste of Honey (1961), for which she received an award from the British Film Academy. As one critic summarised, she specialised in playing "warm-hearted tarts of the cockney or northern variety" (Leslie Halliwell, Halliwell's Filmgoer's Companion, eleventh edition, edited by John Walker [London: HarperCollins, 1995]: 95). To television audiences, she was familiar as the star of The Love Birds and Living For Pleasure. Bryan produced a total of six advertisements promoting CWS biscuits, this single long commercial, and five 15-second varieties which have yet to be traced. Bert Hampson, head of the CWS Television Section, enthused about working with her: "What an artist to work with! Not only did she immediately catch the spirit of the presentation, she was soon firing at us ideas of her own – ideas which we promptly acknowledged improved the scripts" (The Producer April 1960).

NCFC 234
Halstead Society: 100 Years of Co-operation 1860-1960 (1960)

col · 19m 39s · 16mm · EAFA
ph Richard Burn

■ A record of the centenary celebrations of the Halstead Industrial Co-operative Society.

I   Graphic card: "Tree Planting Halstead".
II   A tree-planting ceremony: a man makes an announcement to a small crowd; a tree is planted in the ground; another man (the President?) makes an address; a further address and pose for camera with a shovel.
III   Graphic card: "The New Clock, Sudbury".
IV   The unveiling ceremony of a new clock fitted to the Co-op store.
V   Graphic card: "Carnival Time".

VI A group making last-minute preparations for a parade; various tableaux waiting for the off; various floats promoting Co-op products and services; floats prepared by the nearby Braintree Co-operative Society, the Leiston Co-operative Society, and the Maldon Co-operative Society; children's fancy dress participants; the Co-operative Queen and her entourage; a marching brass band; the crowd-lined streets; exterior of the Co-operative central premises draped with the Rainbow Flag.

VII Scenes of the procession.

VIII Scenes at the gala: the busy crowd amidst the marquees; the fancy dress contest; the crowded grandstand; panning shot of the dressed vehicles; shots of the large crowd.

IX An address from the grandstand (the President?); the Co-operative Queen is crowned on her throne.

X High-angle shots of the milling crowds; men's tug-of-war; children collect their gift parcels.

Remarks

An excellently photographed amateur film. This small local society in Essex had approximately 8500 members in its centenary year, and a good proportion are evident participating in the events depicted in the film. It is interesting to note the presence of local societies in the celebrations.

NCFC 235
Newcastle Co-operative Centenary Exhibition (1960)

col · 7m 24s · silent · 16mm · NFA
pr Dorian

■ A record of the CWS Family Fare Exhibition, hosted by the Newcastle Co-operative Society (NCS) in its centenary year.

I The entrance to the Newcastle Co-operative Centenary Exhibition; a long queue waits outside the entrance to the main Family Fare Exhibition marquee; the busy crowds make their way into the exhibition.

II Civic dignitaries and guests of honour arrive in a limousine and are escorted to the exhibition.

III Interior of a marquee – an address by the Lady Mayoress; further addresses by representatives of the Board of Management – Mr J H Yeats (Chairman), Mr W H Patterson (General Manager).

IV Visitors making their entrance to the Family Fare Exhibition; various scenes around the exhibition – the busy enquiry desk; the closed-circuit television display; a CWS cookery demonstration; a pottery-making demonstration; a performance by the CWS (Manchester) Brass Band; the on-site Co-operative self-service store doing brisk trade; milling around the stalls.

V A popular fashion show with female models parading the catwalk.

VI Night-time: the visitors prepare to leave.

Remarks

The second of two films of a CWS Family Fare Exhibition in Newcastle, this time during the society's centenary celebrations. By 1960, the NCS had a membership of 116 000, and operated 250 branch stores with a turnover of £14 million. Although 13th in the list of Britain's Co-operative retail societies in terms of membership, it ranked 8th in total trade. It was fitting that the CWS Family Fare Exhibition visited Newcastle, since it was stated that the Newcastle Co-operative Society purchased more CWS products per Co-operative member than any other society, with 70% of its supplies drawn from the CWS.

NCFC 236
Biscuit Time (c.1960)

col · 15m 30s · sound · 16mm · EAFA, IAC, NFTVA
pr Anglo-Scottish Pictures

■ An information film for CWS biscuits baked at the new biscuit factory at Harlow.

I A CWS bulk Federation flour truck winding its way through Epping Forest, en route for the new CWS biscuit factory at Harlow.

II The CWS Harlow biscuit factory – exterior shots; the flour truck draws into the unloading bay; a group of visitors enjoying tea and biscuits before a tour; flour is unloaded from the truck into giant storage silos; the "space-age" control room; the huge high-speed mixers preparing half a ton of dough; the bakery floor – the dough is rolled and cut into cream crackers, and baked in large ovens; the baking of Rich Tea biscuits; the cutting of Ginger Nuts; Coconut Cookies journey to the ovens; Aladdin biscuits receive their sugar coating; the Duchess variety are pressed with their familiar stamp; Lincoln biscuits leave the ovens and samples are tested; stackers feed the biscuits into a machine for wrapping – Lincoln and Coconut Cookies; packing into cardboard cartons; cream crackers are cooled, stacked, wrapped and finally packed into cartons; digestives are wrapped; assorted creams are placed in their attractive boxes by operatives, and packed into cartons for despatch.

III   The employees clock off for lunch; the staff cafeteria and recreational area – staff play table-tennis.

IV   The making of chocolate biscuits: wholemeal biscuits receive their chocolate coating and pass onto the wrapping machines.

V   Preparing the mixture for cream biscuits; the making of custard creams, and packing into tins.

VI   Cartons of biscuits pass on long conveyors – Lincolns, Assorted Creams, Digestives; the giant storage warehouse; loading of cartons of cream crackers onto lorries which drive from the depot.

VII   Three children enjoy a CWS biscuit assortment; displays of CWS biscuits – Ginger Nuts, Rich Tea, Cameo, various.

VIII   Graphic card: "CWS Biscuits in the Varieties you like best from Co-operative Societies".

Remarks
The CWS's first productive unit had been a biscuit and confectionery factory at Crumpsall, Manchester, established in 1873. A second factory was opened at Cardiff in 1920. Such was the rising demand for biscuits after the Second World War that a third biscuit factory was planned and built at Harlow New Town in Essex. The national production of biscuits had grown from 235 000 tons in 1947, to 521 000 tons ten years later, and Co-operative production was making its contribution. The British have an unparalleled appetite for biscuits: a survey in the late-1950s showed that 98% of housewives bought biscuits. The fully automated factory at Harlow manufactured 15 million biscuits each week. A previous film with the subject of CWS biscuits, with the same title, had been released in 1936. That film has not yet been traced.
See also: xxxiii

NCFC 237
[Co-op Cartoon] (c.1960)

b/w · 32s · sound · Scotland · 35mm · SFA

▪ A brief animated advertisement for Co-operative shopping.

I   A housewife enters a Co-op store. An assistant quickly introduces the various departments: knitwear; children's wear; footwear; menswear; furniture; and groceries.

II   Graphic card: "Co-op for value. Remember the DIVIDEND".
Jingle: "Buy Co-op for value, away with your troubles and strife,/A happy shopper is a Co-oper, a well-contented wife./Forget not the dividend, everytime you shop,/At the best place of all, your Co-op, Co-op."

Remarks
As a central federal Co-operative organisation, the sponsors of the film, the SCWS had responsibility to the numerous individual retail Co-operative societies in Scotland. This advertisement, promoting the general advantages of shopping at the Co-op, was suitable for all regions, and thus was not restricted geographically – an important consideration when independent television companies broadcast over large regions. All societies would operate the departments presented in the film, and offered the inducement of dividend payments on purchases. It is important to note that, unlike its English counterpart, the Scottish Co-operative Wholesale Society had historically engaged in direct retail itself. The first SCWS retail branch store had been opened at Buckie in April 1914. At the time of this film, the society operated about 126 branch stores. The particular geographical circumstances in Scotland had led the CWS actively to establish Co-operative stores in remote and outlying areas.

NCFC 238
[CWS Cheese Advertisement] (c.1960)

col · 15s · sound · 16mm · NFTVA

▪ A brief animated advertisement for CWS Willow Vale cheese spread.

I   Six children around a table look forward to their CWS Willow Vale cheese spread; six adults can satisfy their individual tastes with Willow Vale variety cheese spread.

II   Graphic card: "Willow Vale Cheese Spread. At Your Co-op Store." Jingle: "Six at a table all of a mind,/Six in a box and all of a kind,/WILLOW VALE./Six at a table so hard to please/ Find what they like in Willow Vale Variety Cheese."

Remarks
One of a collection of CWS cinema advertisements from the period. Most animators earned their living from the industrial films sector, an aspect of film history that remains completely unresearched.

NCFC 239
[CWS Furniture Advertisement] (c.1960)

col · 15s · sound · 16mm · NFTVA

▪ A brief advertisement for CWS "Space-Plan" furniture.

I   A series of stills introduces the Jupiter dining-range of nine matching pieces designed to suit any size of room.
II   A display of the suite: "At your Co-operative Society".

Remarks
This film is a clear attempt to tie in with the interest in space travel in the late-1950s. The first Soviet Sputnik had been launched into space in 1957. The iconography of space travel exerted a considerable influence on popular culture through feature films, television programmes, comic books, and science-fiction literature – and, apparently, on furniture design and advertising. "Space-Plan" was a generic brand name for a range of household furniture, with the punning title connoting both "space-age" up-to-dateness and clinicality, and its "space-saving" design. The CWS Space-Plan range had been launched at the first National Co-operative Furniture Exhibition held at the CWS furnishing showrooms in 1956. It was part of a concerted effort to improve the Movement's performance in the dry goods trade, an area which was providing some concern.

NCFC 240
[CWS Shoe Advertisement 2] (c.1960)

col · 15s · sound · 16mm · NFTVA

▪ A brief advertisement for CWS Wheatsheaf footwear.

I   A family's feet, shod in stylish CWS Wheatsheaf footwear.
II   Graphic card: "At Your Co-operative Society".

Remarks
A typical commercial from the period. Such films lack the sophistication of most modern advertising, relying on a simple direct method of address. The late-1950s were problematic for Co-operative shoe production and retailing. The Movement's tradition of quality was making its products, across the dry goods area, relatively expensive compared with High Street multiples such as Freeman, Hardy and Willis. The difficulty was compounded in the period by unprecedented rises in world leather market prices. The Movement eventually responded with its own specialised High Street chain store, Shoefayre, which commenced trading in 1964.

NCFC 241
[CWS Soft Drink Advertisement 1] (c.1960)

col · 16s · sound · 16mm · NFTVA

▪ A brief advertisement for CWS lemon and barley drink.

I   A young boy and girl enjoy their treat of a glass of CWS lemon and barley squash.
II   Graphic card: "CWS Lemon and Barley with added glucose".

Remarks
A typical example of a cinema advert of the period, and further proof of the important soft drinks market. Until the 1960s, much of the Movement refused to engage in the liquor trade, and never brewed anything stronger than vinegar. Lemon squash had long been supplied in syphons, and the Movement's first aerated water factory was opened at Nottingham in 1937, quickly followed by plants at Middleton (Manchester), Bristol and elsewhere. The trade rapidly expanded in the postwar period.

NCFC 242
[CWS Soft Drink Advertisement 2] (c.1960)

col · 16s · sound · 16mm · NFTVA

■ A simple animated advertisement for CWS Sun-Sip orange drink.

I   A young Latin boy shoos birds away from ripening oranges on the trees – oranges used for CWS Sun-Sip orange drink.

II   Graphic card: "Sun-Sip with added glucose, from Co-op stores everywhere".

Remarks
A further example from a collection of CWS cinema commercials of the period. I have so far not traced a film dealing with the manufacture of soft drinks, which is surprising, as the trade boomed in the decades after the war. By 1947, nine Co-operative aerated water factories were in operation, five acquired since the war. As one historian comments of the relatively difficult mid-1950s period, "[i]n the CWS there were success stories to lighten the gloom. The soft drinks division's rapidly expanding trade increased by 46% in the July half-year of 1957." (Sir William Richardson, *The CWS in War and Peace 1938-1976* [Manchester: Co-operative Wholesale Society, 1977]).

NCFC 243
Halcyon Gloss Finish Paints (c.1960)

col · 16s · sound · 16mm · NFTVA

■ A brief animated advertisement for CWS Halcyon paints.

I   A variety of coloured stripes are painted across the screen; various cans of CWS Halcyon gloss paints move around the image.

II   Graphic card: "CWS Halcyon. At Your Co-op Store".
Jingle: "Halcyon, Halcyon, all so easy, brushability,/Tough resistance in sealed cans,/In the colours you want./It's New, It's Brilliant,/Wonderful Halcyon."

Remarks
An interesting film constructed to an abstract design. The colourful patterns made it suitable for cinema use, but the effect would have been lost on television, which remained standardised to monochrome at that time. The brand name of Halcyon was introduced in 1958. The Movement failed to make much of an impression in the paint market, achieving only approximately 5% of total sales at its best.

NCFC 244
Modern Miss Muffet (c.1960)

col · 11m · sound · 16mm · NFTVA, NWFA
pr Anglo-Scottish Pictures

■ An information film about cheese-making by the CWS.

I   Dairy herds in the vale of Clwyd.
II   The traditional farmhouse method of making Cheshire cheese.
III Modern cheese-making at the CWS creamery, Llandyrnog: churns of fresh milk arrive at the creamery; the pasteurisation process; the milk is introduced into large vats and the culture is added; samples are tested; rennet is added; laboratory testing; the curd is cut and the whey is drained off; the grinding process; the curd is forced into moulds and pressed; the cakes of cheese are scalded and stored to mature; in the vast storeroom, the cheeses are periodically turned; the cheeses are inspected by a grader and stamped; vacuum-sealing CWS Llan Pak brand cheese.
IV   Display of CWS Llan Pak cheeses.

Remarks
The Movement's solid position within the milk and related products industry guaranteed that the manufacture, wholesaling and retailing of cheese would feature prominently. The CWS had long been a wholesaler of cheese to retail societies, and after the Great War, important supplies were secured from New Zealand. The Movement's rapid expansion within the milk trade in the interwar period witnessed the first moves towards the manufacture of cheese, alongside the expansion of other milk products. As far as I can ascertain, this was the first Co-operative film to take cheese as its subject. It is also important in that it deals with a Welsh CWS creamery – Wales as a nation being vastly under-represented within this collection. The Llandyrnog creamery concentrated on the manufacture of Cheshire cheese, whilst Cheddar cheese was distributed exclusively out of the CWS Corwen creamery. The print suffers from some colour-fading.
See also: NCFC 249

NCFC 245
[SCWS Coffee Essence Advertisement]
(c.1960)

b/w · 25s · sound · Scotland · 35mm · SFA

▪ A short animated film promoting SCWS
Shieldhall coffee essence.

I   Two characters drag onto the screen a
     giant bottle of SCWS Shieldhall
     "Essence of Coffee and Chicory". They
     then hold up placards: "Full Dividend",
     "At Your Co-op".
     The film is accompanied by a short
     advertising jingle: "Shop, shop, at the
     Co-op,/That's what you ought to do./
     For if you want good coffee, quickly
     made,/Then Shieldhall will give it to
     you./Try Shieldhall Coffee Essence –
     Its Fine".

Remarks
A rather crude animated short, probably
intended for a regional/national television
advertising campaign. As prices of 1s 6d
and 2s 4d are flashed onscreen, the film
would have had a limited shelf-life.

NCFC 246
Back To Back (1961)

col · 18m 34s · sound · 16mm · EAFA,
NFTVA
pr Anglo-Scottish Pictures

▪ An information film about CWS Leeknit
and Lanfield knitwear.

I   In the Australian outback, sheep are
     herded to the station where they are
     sheared; the wool is baled for export –
     France, Hamburg, New York and
     London.
II   At a centre in Bradford, fleeces are
     inspected for quality and sorted; the
     fleeces are washed and dried; the
     industrial processes which create
     wool; the dying process; the drawing
     process, producing fine yarn.
III Trucks, loaded with bales of wool,
     arrive at the CWS woollen mill, Leek,
     Staffordshire; bundles are stacked in
     the receiving store; yarn is wound
     onto cones and bobbins; the circular
     knitting machines producing fabric in
     tubular form – examples of some
     fabrics; the flat knitting machines
     producing large bolts of cloth.
IV   The design department for CWS
     Leeknit and Lanfield garments –

examples of the knitwear are
displayed alongside their designs;
quality-control inspectors examining
the fabrics.
V   The pattern and cutting department –
     the expert cutters at work.
VI   Testing fabrics at the CWS technical
     research laboratories.
VII Machinists construct the various
     garments: sewing on the buttons and
     making the buttonholes; applying
     collars with the linking machine;
     stitching in the labels; the finished
     garments are examined for faults.
VIII The making-up department at the
     CWS mill, Hanley; knitwear is packed
     for despatch.
IX   CWS Leeknit and Lanfield knitwear is
     modelled by three families; further
     examples are displayed on
     mannequins/dummies.

Remarks
Two films survive on this subject, and both
draw on the literal title of "Back to Back"
(see also *From Back to Back* [1933; NCFC
030]). For this version, the production
scenes were shot at the CWS Nelson Mills
at Leek, Staffordshire. The CWS had had a
long association of purchasing in Australia
with buying activities being consolidated
there in 1897; particularly important
commodities were wheat, dairy, fruit and
wool. Leeknit fashions, available in 100
different designs, were specifically for men
and Lanfield garments for women. The well-
known Mayfair fashion designer, Matli,
created the "look" for Lanfield clothes. The
Swiss-born fashion artist was one of the
exclusive twelve who formed the
Incorporated Society of Fashion Designers,
and had previously been engaged in the
fashionable Paris salon of Premete. His
earliest connection with the Movement had
been as a fashion columnist for the Sunday
newspaper, *The Reynold's News*, and in that
role he can be viewed in the 1955 film, *Your
Sunday Newspaper* (NCFC 174). In 1957, he
was engaged to provide exclusive designs
for the CWS Lanfield label, whereby the
Co-op would "offer the couture style at
astonishingly modest prices" (*The Producer*
July 1957).
See also: NCFC 030

NCFC 247
Pounds, Shillings and Sense (1961)

b/w · 16m 8s · sound · 16mm · NFTVA
pr Granada Television *prod* Edward Joffe
presenters John Braban, Dorina Brown,

June Dawes *design* Bruce Grimes

■ An advertising magazine for the Yorkshire region promoting the Barnsley, Bradford, Brightside and Carbrook, Dewsbury, Hull, Sheffield and Eccleshall, Scunthorpe, Doncaster and York Co-operative Societies.

I   The announcer/host introduces the programme which will feature bargains at the nine featured Co-operative societies, which in the previous year had paid out £3m in dividends to their members.

II   A range of CWS Belmont dresses are modelled for the camera, with prices expressed. The fashions are described by two female announcers.

III   A range of CWS menswear is modelled for the camera: an Epsom sports jacket; trousers; a Lestar shirt; stores of the nine featured Co-operative societies are briefly presented.

IV   A range of CWS Desbeau foundation garments are presented; a range of CWS Belmont lingerie; CWS ladies shoes from the Annette range.

V   A display of CWS Wheatsheaf men's shoes from the Ardington range.

VI   A pair of CWS Salutus ladies gloves are modelled and described.

VII   The benefits of easy payment arrangements are explained, suitable for expensive items like a CWS Regal pram, which is described and presented.

VIII   The Co-op also stocks home and garden items – a deckchair and a CWS Defiant portable radio are presented.

IX   The presenters summarise the benefits of shopping at the Co-op, the "four golden rules" – quality, value, service and dividend.

Remarks
The first attempt at "collective television advertising" began early in 1960, with Co-operative societies in the South-West and in East Anglia banding together to pool resources (see *Come Shopping* [1960; NCFC 232]). The CWS Public Relations Division played an important role coordinating activities and, most importantly, national Co-operative promotions. This film was apparently the first group advertising scheme in the Yorkshire region, and was shot in London. A subsequent magazine, so far untraced, was made in 1962 and shot at the new Granada Studios, Manchester.

NCFC 248
Tomorrow Is Yours (1961)

col · 14m 25s · sound · Scotland · 16mm · SFA
pr Gate Film Productions

■ An informational film outlining the nature and extent of the SCWS.

I   A housewife strolls around a Co-op self-service store. She takes her basket to the checkout, and a counter assistant registers the total.

II   A simple animated sequence details the ownership structure of the Scottish Co-operative Movement – the members and their shops.

III   Glasgow South Co-operative Society store (exterior); Lennoxtown Friendly Victualling Society store (exterior); a Co-op mobile shop.

IV   A simple animated sequence details the ownership structure of the Scottish Co-operative Movement – the retail societies and the Wholesale Society.

V   A member draws funds from her Co-op share account, regularly swelled by her dividend payments.

VI   A simple animated sequence illustrates how customers' purchases create the chain of demand – the retail shops, the Wholesale Society, the Movement's factories – that ultimately returns benefits, in the form of dividend, to the member.

VII   The headquarters of the SCWS at Morrison Street, Glasgow (exterior); the hosiery factory, Shieldhall, Glasgow (interior); a display of SCWS hosiery products; the SCWS cigarette factory, Shieldhall (interior) – the various processes involved in the manufacture of cigarettes are briefly detailed; the SCWS shoe factory, Shieldhall (interior) – various processes in the manufacture of shoes are briefly detailed and SCWS Triona shoes are boxed; managers and buyers inspect SCWS displays of brand merchandise at special showrooms – food products, furniture and clothing is modelled, footwear in the Triona and Morven ranges.

VIII   Exterior of Co-op store; the housewife completes her purchases within the store.

IX   Graphic card: "SCWS. The Sign of Good Quality at Your Co-op."

Remarks
A general informational film about the

Movement in Scotland, useful for screening to the general public or new members. At the time of the film's production, the SCWS had 86 258 members, organised into 127 retail branches, and annual sales in excess of £7 million. The Scottish Movement was organised into 173 retail societies with sales of £87.5 million. The film efficiently surveys the history and extent of the Scottish Movement, providing interesting images of stores, and both productive and administrative premises. The extravagantly titled Lennoxtown Friendly Victualling Society, founded in 1812, had some claims to be the originator of the scheme paying dividend according to purchases, and thus holds a special place in the history of Co-operation in Scotland.

NCFC 249
Modern Cheese Making (c.1961)

col · 14m · sound · 16mm · EAFA, NFTVA

■ A promotional film for CWS Wheatsheaf cheese.

I	Dairy cows grazing on lush English pasture; cows are led into milking sheds; traditional cheese-making on an English farm.
II	Modern CWS cheese-making: a large storeroom for cheeses; the delivery of churns of milk to a creamery, which are checked, weighed and unloaded; the pasteurisation process within the plant; collection into large vats; a laboratory assistant takes a sample of the milk for testing.
III	The making of Cheshire cheese. The lactic culture is added; testing of milk samples in the laboratory; the rennet is added; rotary cutters break-up the junket into curds and whey, which are separated; the curd is cut by hand and conveyed to the peg mill where it is shredded; the broken curd is fed into drums and pressed.
IV	The making of Cheddar cheese: the cheese curd is drained from the whey; the curd is cut into blocks and stacked – the "cheddaring" process; checking the acidity level of the curd; the blocks are piled higher; the chip mill – the milling, cooling, salting and moulding of the cheese; the hydraulic press; the cakes of cheese are examined and transported to the storeroom for maturing; the cheeses are periodically turned; the cheeses are coated with wax; the grader assesses the cheese;

the cutting and wrapping of CWS Wheatsheaf cheese; display of CWS English Cheshire cheese; display of CWS English Cheddar.

Remarks
Cheese-manufacture was a growth industry in the postwar years, and modern methods of cellophane-wrapping and vacuum-sealing aided in the distribution and retailing of large quantities. Also important was the increased mechanism of the cheese-making process, and this film takes as its structure the contrast between labour-intensive traditional methods of production and the modern industrial and scientific approach. The film has many similarities with the contemporaneous *Modern Miss Muffet* (c.1960; NCFC 244), which detailed the manufacture of Cheshire cheese, whilst *Modern Cheese Making* also attends to the production of Cheddar cheese, which took place at the CWS Corwen creamery.

NCFC 250
[SCWS Margarine Advertisement] (c.1961)

b/w · 23s · sound · Scotland · 35mm · SFA

■ A simple animation based on the old nursery rhyme, "Four and Twenty Blackbirds", promoting SCWS margarine.

I	A three-shot sequence in which the Queen is baking a variety of cakes and pastries using SCWS Bluebell margarine. The King and the Knave are enjoying the fruits of her labour.
II	Graphic card: "Foil Wrapped Bluebell Margarine 10½d per ½lb. At your Co-op." Jingle: "For pastry that is tasty use Bluebell Margarine,/For cakes that are delicious use Bluebell Margarine./It mixes in a moment, creams so easily,/ For baking that is lighter Bluebell for you and me."

Remarks
A brief advertisement probably intended for a television advertising campaign. Using the story of a well-known nursery rhyme, the film puts over its message efficiently, promoting the SCWS Bluebell margarine brand.

NCFC 251
Come Co-operative Shopping [1] (c.1962)

b/w · 40s · sound · 16mm · EAFA

- A regionalised commercial for the CWS's "Come Co-operative Shopping" campaign.

I   A housewife, Mrs Moore of Cambridge, arrives outside one of her society's self-service stores.
II   Customers at the butchery counters.
III   Special offers: CWS sweet pickle, usually 1/10, now 1/6; CWS Spel washing powder, usually 1/10, now 1/8.
IV   Graphic card: "CWS. The sign of saving at your Co-op."

Remarks
One of numerous "localised" television advertisements from the long-running "Come Co-operative Shopping" campaign. It is interesting to note that each advert was distinct to the region featured; it is surprising that the cheaper method – of shooting a single scenario with the voice-over tailored to suit the chosen locality – was not adopted. This approach allowed for the presentation of the society's flagship store, an important consideration for local publicity. By the date of the film, the Cambridge and District Co-operative Society claimed a membership of 57 000.

NCFC 252
Come Co-operative Shopping [2] (c.1962)

b/w · 40s · sound · 35mm · SFA

- A television advertisement in the long-running campaign.

I   A housewife in her kitchen explains the "special offers" available at the Co-op: a free drum of Slik with the purchase of two Scot Towels kitchen rolls at 4s 11d; Orchid margarine, save 3d; CWS Pioneer custard, save 2d. Housewife: "Yes, thanks to the many special offers available, you can save when you Come Co-operative Shopping".

Remarks
An early example of a television promotional campaign wherein CWS brand loyalty had wilted. Out of the four products featured, only two – the evocatively named Pioneer custard and Orchid margarine – were produced Co-operatively. The purpose of the long-running campaign was not to build up individual CWS brand names, but to project an image of the Co-operative shop as the source of variety, quality and reasonable prices. The CWS were prepared

to increase store traffic for retail societies without materially improving the sales of CWS brand goods. Matching shop window and counter displays were made available to societies to reinforce the "Come Co-operative Shopping" marketing campaign within the store.

NCFC 253
Halcyon Days (c.1962)

col · 13m · 16mm · EAFA, IAC, NFTVA; SFA (ref)
pr Anglo-Scottish Pictures *d* Ron Brown
cam Arthur Lemming *ed* Colin Cherry
cast Keith Rogers, Pat McLoughlin

- A promotional/instructional film for CWS paints.

I   Housewife Joan gets excellent results painting a cupboard with CWS Halcyon paint.
II   Demonstration of paint-making in the laboratory – the mixing of pigments, linseed oil, resins, solvents and driers. A mixing of "Sun Yellow" accurately matches the shade card.
III   John and Joan are deciding on a colour scheme for their kitchen. They consult the range available from the CWS Halcyon brand.
IV   The CWS paint factory: resin is added to linseed oil and heated; solvents and driers are added and mixed in a centrifuge; the medium is added to the pigment; the method of grinding pigments; testing the paint for quality.
V   At home, John and Joan are progressing with their home decoration – applying undercoat, stripping old paint, treating knot-holes.
VI   A range of coloured paints flows from the machines; empty cans are filled with paint and their lids are fitted; packing of tins into cardboard cartons; the huge storage room; laboratory testing: various ingenious tests are detailed – scratch tests, impact tests, and so on.
VII   Daily life at the home of John and Joan illustrates the importance of the stringent laboratory testing.
VIII   Further testing: painted panels are exposed to wind, rain and sun on the roof of the paint factory; the "weatherometer" – exposing CWS paints to months of weather in a fraction of the time; the salt spray cabinet; humidity tests.
IX   John and Joan are pleased with their

- 128 -

labours and with CWS Halcyon paints.

Remarks
CWS paint-manufacture commenced in Derby in 1924, and a large, modern plant was established on the eve of the Second World War. That remained the Movement's sole paint factory for many years. During the period of drastic rationalisation in the late-1960s, it was closed, together with other single factories that had been losing money (such as the Tyseley cycle factory, Birmingham), and arrangements were made with another manufacturer to ensure continued supply of the product as a Co-op own-brand. This film has many similarities with the contemporaneous *Painting For Pleasure* (c.1958; NCFC 211).
See also: xxii, NCFC 211

NCFC 254
Time For Toys (c.1962)

col · 3m 50s · silent · 16mm · ETV

■ A simple record of a charitable campaign by the Women's Co-operative Guild (WCG).

I   Graphic card: "Thousands of toys, collected by branches of the Women's Co-operative Guild for the 'Save the Children Fund'".
II A large pile of toys – mainly soft toys; a Guild woman with a toy doll; a Guild woman with "Big Ears", the popular children's character; Guild women checking toys.
III The arrival of Father Christmas; Father Christmas fills his sack with toys.
IV The official presentation: "British toys were taken by decorated trailer to be distributed".
V   Further sacks are filled with toys; Santa plays on a rocking-horse.

Remarks
The WCG had been founded in 1883 and proved a particularly progressive force within the Movement. Around the time of this film (and 80 years after its inception), it rearranged its name to the Co-operative Women's Guild (CWG). By the 1960s, the Guild was in decline and particularly so in terms of its influence. The film details a typical campaign which the organisation engaged in, and probably deals with Guild women sponsored by the RACS. Between 1955 and 1970 at that society alone, 33 branches were closed as against the opening of eight new ones. In 1969, the average age of a member within those

branches was 67, and it was proving difficult to attract younger women. A surprising lack of attention was paid to the CWG in the Movement's film work.

NCFC 255
Come Co-operative Shopping [3] (1963)

b/w · 40s · sound · 16mm · EAFA

■ A regionalised commercial for the CWS's "Come Co-operative Shopping" campaign.

I   Mrs Henwood of Swansea enters a local Co-op supermarket.
II Special offers: CWS orange marmalade, usually 1/7½, now 1/4½; CWS Silver Seal margarine, 4d per 1lb off.
III Graphic card: "CWS Centurywise, 1863-1963. The Sign of Saving at Your Co-op."

Remarks
One of two surviving advertisements from the campaign which additionally mark the centenary of the CWS. The store featured is the society's main department store on Oxford Street, Swansea, which incorporated a supermarket. By the time of the film, Swansea Co-operative Retail Services claimed a membership of approximately 30 000.

NCFC 256
Come Co-operative Shopping [4] (1963)

b/w · 40s · sound · 16mm · EAFA

■ A regionalised commercial for the CWS's "Come Co-operative Shopping" campaign.

I   Mrs Clarke of Plymouth enters Co-operative House, Plymouth, and proceeds through the grocery department.
II Special offers: Reddish Made sweets, usually 1/6, now 1/-; CWS Excelda and Federation flours, 3d off.
III Graphic card: "CWS Centurywise, 1863-1963. The Sign of Saving at Your Co-op."

Remarks
The Plymouth Society was a leading regional Co-operative society, with a membership of c.100 000. The Co-operative House department store, Derrys Cross, was a recent building, part of the postwar reconstruction of the town following the

devastation of the Blitz.

NCFC 257
It's In the Can (1963)

col · 12m 40s · sound · 16mm · EAFA,
NFTVA; SFA (ref)
pr Anglo-Scottish Pictures

▪ An information film about CWS Waveney
canned goods.

I   A pre-credit sequence shows cans of
CWS Waveney products moving
around the CWS Lowestoft canning
factory – garden peas, baked beans,
processed peas, beetroot.
II   A model of a fishing drifter, symbol of
the CWS canning factory, amidst a
display of Waveney canned goods.
III The harvesting of garden peas; the
vining of peas on the farm; inspecting
the freshly picked peas on a conveyor;
empty cans are transported on
overhead conveyors, and filled; the
giant hydro-static cookers; samples
are tested by the quality inspectors –
the "tenderometer" tests the
tenderness of the peas; inspecting
sun-dried process peas; cans of
baked beans are filled and then pass
into the giant cookers; scientific testing
in the laboratory, and tests for taste;
the making of cream of chicken soup
– cans of Waveney cream of chicken
soup; filling jars of savoury meat paste
and fixing the caps; loading a carton
of Waveney fish and meat paste; the
making of Willow Vale cheese spread;
further checking by the quality
inspectorate; fresh carrots are topped,
tailed and washed; the grading of
carrots for size; the labelling of
Waveney whole carrots; cans are
packed into cartons and the cartons
into lorries.
IV A display of CWS Waveney canned
products – beans in tomato sauce,
garden peas, processed peas, etc.

Remarks
The CWS first established its canning
operations at Lowestoft in 1930, and an
untitled film from that period survives
detailing the productive activities there. A
further film on CWS canned products,
Kitchen Capers (NCFC 058), was produced
in 1937, and a print survives in part. With
the increase in demand for convenience
foods, the Lowestoft factory expanded in the
postwar period, eventually becoming the
Movement's biggest manufacturing unit, with
nearly 1000 employees engaged in canning
vegetables, meat products, puddings,
soups, and so on, with some of the produce
coming from the society's own farms. The
brand name of Waveney is derived from the
river which runs through Lowestoft and by
the factory. This print suffers from some
colour-fading.
See also: xxii, NCFC 191

NCFC 258
Season of Agricultural Co-operation
(1963)

col · 20m 52s · sound · 16mm · EAFA,
NFTVA
pr Cygnet Films

▪ An informational film about CWS African
Oil Mill (AOM) farm foods and the CWS.

I   General scenes of agricultural work –
harvesting, milking, battery hens,
feeding livestock, etc.
II   The nature and function of agricultural
Co-operative societies – the suppliers
of foodstuffs, fertilisers and other vital
materials: the premises of the
Worcestershire Farmers Ltd; the
mechanic and maintenance van of the
South Western Farmers Ltd,
machinery and farm equipment
services; the McBain Peacutter
manufactured by Eastern Counties
Farmers Ltd; the provision of chicks by
Eifionydd Farmers' Association Ltd; an
agricultural Co-operative shop (exterior
and interior); a fuel tanker of the South
Shropshire Farmers Ltd; a
representative of the Staffordshire
Farmers Ltd calls on a member
farmer. His order is delivered by lorry.
III A simple animated sequence outlines
the structure of farmer Co-operatives.
IV An executive meeting of
representatives of farmers'
Co-operatives and the CWS.
V   A lorry of the Preston Farmers leaves
the CWS Sun Mill; exterior shots of
various CWS mills which provide
animal feed, including the CWS mill at
Royal Victoria Dock, London; scenes
within a mill; arrival of ingredients at
the dock; samples are tested in the
laboratory; the processing of farm
foods within the mill; the bagging of
bulk quantities of farm foods and its
collection by farmers' Co-operatives.
VI Research and development at the
Manchester Research Department of

the CWS.

VII Aerial views of the CWS farm at Stoughton, Leicestershire; various scenes around the farm – feeding cattle, milking, the sheep herd.

VIII Statistical research using a modern electronic computer.

IX The CWS farm at Hetton, Berwick-upon-Tweed – the celebrated sheep herds, beef raising, the piggery. Trials using AOM foodstuffs – pigs and poultry.

X The CWS seed trial grounds at Derby – the plots, laboratory testing.

XI A CWS packing station (interior) – the packing of potatoes.

XII Milk is collected from a farm and delivered to a CWS creamery; a CWS tanker leaves the creamery for London and the bottling plant; the production of cheese.

XIII Interior shots of a CWS egg-packing station.

XIV Interior shots of a CWS bakery.

XV Exteriors of Co-operative stores; a busy checkout counter of a Co-operative store.

XVI A general summary of the points made by the film, cut with appropriate shots.

Remarks

Although the "back to the land" sentiments of many early Co-operative societies dissipated, ownership of farming land had become a substantial fact of consumer Co-operation by the middle of the 20th century. The Agricultural Department of the CWS was established in 1914 to coordinate trade with agricultural societies. At the time of the making of this film, over 39 000 acres were operated. The society's agricultural holdings were affected by the general rationalisation undertaken by the Movement in the late-1960s, when, for instance, the Hetton estate featured in the film was sold. Nevertheless, the CWS Farms Group continued to be Britain's biggest farming business. The first trip of CWS representatives to West Africa to assess oil-palm supplies was in 1913. Eventually, the substantial bulk of the trade was carried on in Nigeria. The CWS African Oil Mill was established in Liverpool in 1916. The seed-packing factory and trial grounds, long situated at Derby, were promoted to a Horticultural Department in 1937. At the time of this film, farm Co-operatives claimed 325 000 members in 319 societies, engaged in £168 million worth of business annually. The CWS bought £152 million of produce from them each season, illustrating the integrated nature of the farmers' Co-operatives with the consumer Movement.

NCFC 259
Symbol of Success (1963)

col · 21m · sound · 16mm and 35mm: NFTVA / 16mm: EAFA, IAC, WFSA
pr Aspect Productions Ltd d John Spencer
prod Guy Howarth cam Kenneth Talbot
ed Mike Gascoyne mus Johnny Johnson, Alex Mortimer sc Brian De Salvo
comm Russell Napier

▪ A presentation on the CWS in its centenary year.

I Co-operation in nature – the case of ants.

II Scenes at a busy Co-op self-service store (interior and exterior). The "Come Co-operative Shopping" promotional campaign is featured on display cards and window bills.

III A housewife is interviewed in her home about her thoughts on the Co-op.

IV A village Co-op store of the Brington Industrial and Provident Co-operative Society (exterior); the construction site of a new modern store for the Manchester and Salford Co-operative Society; CWS delivery lorries leave a depot; the CWS grain warehouse, London docks (exterior); manufacturing sequence – CWS Excelda flour; CWS farm scenes – cattle, pigs, hens, sheep; Co-op brand products displayed in-store.

V "Mrs Brennard" enters New Century House, Manchester, the headquarters of the CWS, to attend a shareholder's meeting. She provides an explanatory commentary; the meeting in the New Century Hall; Brennard gives her views to a journalist.

VI A sequence of images detailing the activities of the Movement – store fronts, store interiors, advertising posters, delivery vans, milk roundsmen, etc.

VII The original CWS premises, Cooper Street, Manchester (exterior and interior).

VIII "Mrs Cole" is interviewed in her own home and explains how, after deciding to purchase a CWS Defiant radiogram, she became a member of the local society.

IX The CWS Manchester Brass Band in

performance, cut with various manufacturing activities at CWS factories – Stanley Matthews playing for Stoke City; a young boy being fitted with a pair of Stanley Matthews Football Boots; scenes at a CWS farm; a dog eating its CWS meat nuggets; ceramic painters; pottery-making; CWS delivery lorries; a milk float; a bottling plant, etc.

Remarks

The film was one of a number of items commissioned for the centenary celebrations of the CWS. The most evident and lasting achievement of 1963 was the opening of the new Co-operative office complex of the Co-operative Insurance Society and CWS in Manchester – the CWS building being appropriately named New Century House. The New Century Hall featured within the film was a replacement for the Mitchell Memorial Hall which had been destroyed during the war. Other centenary celebrations included a "Centurywise" Exhibition at Belle Vue, Manchester, enjoyed by three quarters of a million visitors; a commemorative book; functions for employees; and a national competition for members of retail societies. The film is interesting for its concentration on the democratic rather than the productive aspects of the CWS, and for focusing attention on the housewife/female member, which – admittedly, rather patronisingly – unusually takes the focus away from men as the decision-makers. The CWS Manchester Band was established as the CWS Tobacco Factory Prize Band in 1907. After featuring in several CWS films, legendary footballer Stanley Matthews makes his final appearance here, having moved clubs from Blackpool to Stoke. Matthews continued professional football until the unprecedented age of 50.
See also: xxxiii, NCFC 134

NCFC 260
Trentside Story (1963)

col · 37m 29s · sound · 16mm · EAFA

▪ A film produced for the centenary of the Nottingham Co-operative Society.

I   Scenes at Nottingham Castle, including the famous Robin Hood statue.
II   Nottingham, "Queen of the Midlands": views of the city from the castle; the old Market Square; Trent Bridge;

Wollaton Hall; Nottingham University; the Lace Market; the Raleigh, Players and Boots factories; busy Nottingham streets; the Co-operative Central Store, Parliament Street (exterior and interior).
III 19th-century Nottingham: photographs contrasting rich and poor in the city in the 1860s; the development of Nottingham during the Industrial Revolution; a woman making lace; the shop of a food adulterer; the notorious inns and alehouses; a meeting of the Lenton Temperance Society, 1863, hears of developments in Co-operation at Rochdale. A resolution to form a local Co-operative society is carried – the Lenton Industrial and Provident Society.
IV   The development of Co-operation in Nottingham: a recreation of the first store; good news at the first general meeting – a profit of £27.00; branch store no. 2 (exterior); the first dividend payout; the society's growing turnover; the society's temporary decline after 1880 discussed by Mr W J Douse, pioneer committee man; regained prosperity after 1886; combatting price inflation during the Great War – the greed of private interests; June 1915, laying the foundation stone of Co-operative House, the new central premises – interior scenes of Co-op House in 1963; the commencement of milk retailing, 1923 – scenes at the modern dairy, Meadow Lane (interior and exterior), and milk floats making their deliveries; the model bakery opened in 1927 now operated by the CWS; the Chief Executive Officer, Mr C T Forsyth is made a Freeman of the City of Nottingham; a scene from a performance of L du Garde Peach's *Co-operative Century: A Pageant of the People*, 1944; the opening of the Co-op Arts Centre, 1948 – the choir rehearsing Bizet's *Les Pêcheurs de Perles*; the Co-op Education Centre – Broad Street; educational groups – the Nottingham Film Society, the Camera Club, etc; the centenary publication, *Co-operation in Nottingham*, by F W Lehman; centenary events – the Co-op sports ground, Lenton; at the Co-op Arts Theatre; scenes within Co-operative stores, exteriors of the central premises.
V   Aerial views of Nottingham; scenes of modern Nottingham; a balloon ascends from the grounds of Nottingham Castle.

Remarks
A richly detailed film of the history and development of Co-operation in Nottingham. The society represents a good example of the often close relationship between the Victorian values of temperance, self-help and providence, and the establishment of mutuality associations. NCS had long supported dramatic activities, and the Arts Centre Drama Group is competently used in this film to render the historical sequences. The Co-op Arts Centre was opened in 1948 for use by the group. The stimulus for that purchase came during the Movement's centenary celebrations of 1944 with the production of L du Garde Peach's centenary play, *Co-operative Century: A Pageant of the People*, at the Theatre Royal, Nottingham, with the lead taken by Wilfred Pickles. A film record of the production was commissioned from the Workers' Film Association, and a brief extract appears in this production. Unfortunately, the original film now appears to be lost. At the time of the making of the film, the NCS had 177 000 members, annual sales of £17 million, and over 5000 employees.

NCFC 261
Value for Money (1963)

b/w · 38m 22s · sound · 16mm · EAFA
pr Trent Film Productions

▪ A presentation on consumer issues and rights to a meeting of the Boston branch of the Women's Co-operative Guild.

I   Miss Elizabeth Gundrey, consumer rights activist, explains the background to the "Value for Money" campaign. She is standing in a Co-operative self-service store.
II A meeting of the Boston branch of the Women's Co-operative Guild to discuss and consider consumer issues arising from the campaign: opening address by the branch secretary, cut with shots of a busy Co-operative store interior, advertising hoardings, etc. She demonstrates some of the concerns with regard to packaging, hygiene, weights and measures.
III Mr Hicks, Chief Inspector of the Boston Weights and Measures Department, makes his presentation, which is cut with appropriate shots to illustrate the point being made: the situation with regard to packaging; aspects of the law with regard to weights and measures; things to be

aware of when buying coal; he demonstrates issues of packaging and weights – soap, paraffin, aerosols, detergents.
IV Mr Butler, National Organiser of the Co-operative Party, puts forward the Movement's position on consumer rights, and its historical responsibility towards the consumer, cut with shots of Co-operative House, the central premises of the Nottingham Co-operative Society (interior and exterior).
V   Miss Gundrey summarises the lessons of the film and the recent development around the formation of local consumer groups.

Remarks
An important film since it deals with two subjects under-represented in the collection: the Women's Co-operative Guild (of which the film records of the WCG Congress at Hull in 1939 [NCFC 086] and at Newcastle in 1955 [NCFC 173] are the only other extensive film coverage), and the postwar developments in consumer rights legislation and organisations, which saw the formation of the Consumer Advisory Council in 1954, and the Consumer Association in 1957. The Co-operative Movement, primarily an organisation of consumers (the one aspect that most schoolchildren recall about the original Rochdale Co-operators is their defence of pure unadulterated food), has continued to fight the corner of the consumer, and consumer education has played an important part in the cultural work of retail societies, especially in the 1960s and 1970s. This film thus provides a valuable insight into both the workings of a WCG branch meeting, and the role played by the Movement in encouraging discussion about consumer issues. It is worth noting that the Co-operative Party was formed in 1917 to represent the consumer in Parliament. The film's presenter, Elizabeth Gundrey, was the founder and editor of the *Shopper's Guide*.

NCFC 262
Blackheath Bank Holiday (c.1963)

b/w and col · 26m · silent · 16mm · ETV
pr RACS Education Department/Woolwich and Plumstead Institute

▪ A study of South London's Blackheath Common by students of the film class of the Woolwich and Plumstead Institute.

I   A fairground is constructed.
II Scenes of Blackheath at dawn; model
    boats on the pond; distant views of
    the funfair; a lunchtime drink;
    snapshots of people enjoying
    themselves on the heath; three
    generations of a family on an outing;
    relaxation and refreshments; sheltering
    from the rain; a St John's Ambulance
    tent *(colour)*.
III Scenes at the funfair; fast food; the
    gondolas; the ghost train; the rockets;
    the waltzer; the busy turnstiles; the
    donkey rides; the big horses *(colour)*.
IV Further scenes at the boating lake;
    scenes of the heath at dusk; night-
    time at the funfair – the dodgems,
    children's rides, darts *(colour)*.

Remarks
A second student film in the collection
sponsored by the RACS, and companion to
Educational Pleasures (c.1956; NCFC 195).
In contrast, this film has no overt
Co-operative subject, it being a film study of
a local park and recreational amenity.
Blackheath was situated within the trading
area of the RACS. As to be expected, the
film is largely undistinguished as a work of
art, and is somewhat stodgy in construction.
Of course, the tradition of the cinematic
study of a specific geographic location was
well-established both within the silent film
form, and, more contemporaneously, with
Free Cinema productions such as *O
Dreamland* (1953) and *Every Day Except
Christmas* (1957), but the students of the
Woolwich and Plumstead Institute fall short
of that standard. However, some of the
images are of historical and sociological
interest.

NCFC 263
The Handy Manns (c.1963)

col · 10m 13s · sound · 16mm · EAFA,
NFTVA
pr Anglo-Scottish Pictures *d* Peter
Crowhurst *sc* Bob Monkhouse, Denis
Gifford *cam* Eddie Earp *ed* Ron Brown
mus Malcolm Mitchell *cast* Michael Howard,
Valli Newby

■ A promotional film for CWS household
cleaning products.

I   Mr and Mrs Mann (Andy and Mandy)
    prepare for Monday washday chores.
    She obtains perfect results with CWS
    Spel washing powder; using more
    traditional techniques, he experiences

disaster.
II Mandy demonstrates how to achieve
    successful results for delicate fabrics
    with CWS Crysella soap flakes; Andy
    experiences disaster with his
    grandmother's traditional "recipe".
III A handy hint on how to make candles
    fit their holders.
IV Mandy introduces CWS Olive soaps –
    white, pink and green.
V   Following Andy's disaster with the
    cheese fondue, Mandy demonstrates
    how to clean stubborn pans with CWS
    Pulvo pan scourer.
VI A handy hint on how to prevent the
    ice-tray from sticking in the freezer.
VII Mandy demonstrates the virtues of
    CWS Newsheaf soap and CWS
    Miracle Mil washing-up liquid.
VIII Stop press – CWS Nap washing
    powder.

Remarks
Perhaps the most striking aspect of this
publicity film is the co-scripting credit of
celebrated British comic, Bob Monkhouse.
The humorous approach adopted by the
film is a welcome contrast to the rather dry
and informative style of the majority of the
Co-operative Movement's product
promotional films of the 1950s. An
advertisement for the CWS Film Library
emphasised the film's entertaining nature,
describing it as a "lighthearted film in full
colour with bright music" (*The Bulletin for
Co-operative Educationalists* April 1964).
Judging from the tone of the film, it would
have been aimed at the Co-operative
housewife, and likely screened at special
"women's shows" provided by the film units
of the CWS Publicity Department. With its
approach of "women know their domain
best", the film appears resolutely
anachronistic in today's politically correct
society.
See also: xxii

NCFC 264
Christmas Cheer (1964)

b/w · 1m 3s · sound · 35mm · NFTVA; SFA
(ref)

■ A Christmas-time television advertisement
promoting the CWS's "Come Co-operative
Shopping" campaign.

I   A close-up of a large mixing bowl, in
    which a Christmas pudding is being
    made; a display of CWS baking
    ingredients – all you require for your

Xmas baking!
II   A mother and daughter busily at work
      on their Christmas baking.
III   Details are stressed of the £43 million
      dividend payout in 1963.
IV   The mother and daughter purchasing
      their Christmas food items at a Co-op
      store.
V   Graphic card: "Come Co-operative
      Shopping. Where the Profit comes
      back to You!".

Remarks
This seasonal edition of the CWS's long-lasting "Come Co-operative Shopping" promotional campaign was broadcast throughout December 1964. Longer commercials in the series, such as this one, tend to promote the general virtues of shopping at the Co-op, whilst shorter 30-second variants are more focused on publicising specific brand products, typically presented as special offers. It is interesting to note the importance given in the 60-second commercials to the extent of the dividend payout, the most apparent benefit of being a member of a retail Co-operative society, and the central tenet of the "Co-operative difference".

NCFC 265
Come Co-operative Shopping [5] (1964)

b/w · 1m 3s · sound · 35mm · NFTVA

■ A television advertisement promoting the CWS's "Come Co-operative Shopping" campaign.

I   What makes a good grocer? A Co-op
      grocer is shown examining his stock
      room – correct storage of his CWS
      Avondale butter, CWS cheeses and
      bacon.
II   The Co-op grocer is seen helping and
      advising his customers with tea, eggs,
      bread, and so on.
III   Details of the £43m dividend payout in
      1963 are stressed.
IV   The grocer helps a customer load her
      basket at the checkout and to the exit.
V   Graphic card: "Come Co-operative
      Shopping. Where the Profit comes
      back to You!".

Remarks
The longer 60-second commercials from the CWS's "Come Co-operative Shopping" promotional campaign, in contrast to the more widespread 30-second commercials, do not publicise monthly special offers. As

evident here, the longer version is more concerned with the experience of Co-operative shopping than with brand promotion. This particular example was broadcast throughout November 1964, the commercials being changed on a monthly basis.

NCFC 266
Come Co-operative Shopping [6] (1964)

b/w · 13s · sound · Scotland · 35mm · SFA

■ A television advertisement sponsored by the SCWS. A sequence of two graphic titles with matching voice-over narration.

I   "SCWS – Come Co-operative
      Shopping".
II   "Australian Canned Pears and
      Wheatsheaf Cream, 3/6 for 2/11½ –
      Double Offer This Week".

Remarks
See entry for NCFC 267.

NCFC 267
Come Co-operative Shopping [7] (1964)

b/w · 13s · sound · Scotland · 35mm · SFA

■ A television advertisement sponsored by the SCWS. A sequence of three graphic titles with matching voice-over narration.

I   "SCWS – Come Co-operative
      Shopping".
II   "Extra Special This Week".
III   "Creamery Butter 3/3 per lb".

Remarks
The "Come Co-operative Shopping" advertising campaign began in 1962, and coordinated a range of print and broadcast promotions: press advertising; television spot advertising; point-of-sale promotions; window bills; prize tie-ins. As well as the short and basic type of brand advertisement represented here, longer commercials of 30 and 60 seconds were also produced which contained brief acted sequences. The "Come Co-operative Shopping" campaign slogan was retained well into the 1960s. This example from Scotland, like NCFC 266, is simpler in structure than typical examples commissioned by the Manchester-based CWS.

NCFC 268
[CWS Canned Goods Advertisement]
(1964)

b/w · 1m 2s · sound · 35mm · NFTVA

■ A television advertisement for CWS canned products.

I   A sequence of cans rolling along chutes in a factory.
II   CWS Wheatsheaf brand – evaporated milk, rice pudding, Australian apricots; CWS Waveney brand – chicken soup, baked beans, processed peas; CWS Lokreel brand salmon, pears, peaches.
III A can of CWS Lokreel peaches is opened and its contents poured into a fruit bowl; a can of CWS Wheatsheaf evaporated milk is poured into a jug; a can of CWS Waveney tomato soup is poured into a saucepan; a family enjoying their meal of CWS canned products.
IV A housewife purchasing cans of CWS products in a Co-op store. Details are stressed of the £43m payout during 1963.
V   A display of Lokreel, Waveney and Wheatsheaf products.
VI Graphic card: "Come Co-operative Shopping".

Remarks
One of three surviving examples from the extensive "Come Co-operative Shopping" promotional campaign lasting a longer one minute, as against the typical 30 seconds. The extra time is clearly used to explore in a little more detail a broader product range – in this instance, CWS canned goods within the Wheatsheaf and Lokreel brands. It is fortunate that each of these three films survives with its date of transmission. This film was the basis of the "Come Co-operative Shopping" campaign for October 1964.

NCFC 269
Proof of the Pudding (1964)

col · 17m 28s · sound · 16mm · EAFA, NFTVA
pr Cygnet Films

■ An informational film promoting CWS milk products.

I   English village scenes; a dairy herd; a CWS milk lorry collects churns of milk.

II   An aerial view of a CWS milk product factory; the lorry arrives with its load of milk; the milk is checked for freshness and weight; the churns are sterilised and returned to the lorry; the milk is cooled and stored; the milk separators; cream is canned; churning of cream into butter; the making of evaporated milk; the making of dried milk powder – CWS Sunsheaf brand; testing and quality-control; the Movement of cans around the factory; the making of tinned rice pudding – loading, sealing and cooking the cans, adding the labels, packing into cartons – CWS Wheatsheaf brand; the giant warehouse.
III Display of Wheatsheaf butter, Wheatsheaf condensed milk, Wheatsheaf semolina, Wheatsheaf evaporated milk, Wheatsheaf sago, Wheatsheaf macaroni, Wheatsheaf tapioca, Wheatsheaf macaroni cheese, Wheatsheaf dairy cream and Wheatsheaf rice pudding.

Remarks
Being such an important concern in the milk trade, it is not surprising that the CWS became involved in related milk products. Their manufacture took place at a variety of CWS creameries and factories – such as the canning factory at Lowestoft – but three specific centres emerged at Manchester, London and Newcastle. The CWS Wheatsheaf brand label became particularly widespread in the postwar period – the Wheatsheaf, of course, long being something of an icon for the Labour Movement, and widely appropriated by Co-operative societies.
See also: NCFC 270

NCFC 270
The Selling Side (1964)

col · 6m 3s · sound · 16mm · NFTVA

■ A "postscript" to the film, *Proof of the Pudding* (1964; NCFC 269), detailing the supporting publicity materials for CWS Wheatsheaf milk products.

I   A sales executive outlines the themes of the promotional film, *Proof of the Pudding*, and stresses the need to push CWS own-brand products above those of competitors. He introduces the attractive point-of-sale publicity materials to aid in the campaign – posters, display units, window

II   Store interiors with the display materials clearly evident.
III   How the counter assistant can help in the campaign – always offer a Wheatsheaf brand, unless asked otherwise. A sales assistant is shown helping a customer who purchases a can of Wheatsheaf rice pudding.
IV   In-store product placement and shelf allocation – various shots of customers making purchases in a self-service store. The siting of "gondola ends", "dump displays" and "Today's Specials", and their usefulness in the campaign.
V   The sales executive summarises the presentation, stressing the value of selling CWS products, which returns more profit to the Movement, society and member than competitors' products.

Remarks
An innovative film, produced specifically for the CWS Milk Products Department, which aimed to reinforce the promotional intentions of that year's publicity film, *Proof of the Pudding*. Both films would have been screened to retail staff, making them aware of CWS Wheatsheaf milk products and their production, as well as of the attendant publicity media to aid sales. It is the only example of such an "associated" training film so far located.

NCFC 271
Come Co-operative Shopping [8] (c.1964)

b/w · 42s · sound · 35mm · NFTVA

■ A regionalised advertisement for the CWS's "Come Co-operative Shopping" campaign.

I   A housewife, Mrs Sheila Pullen of Walsall, making her purchases in a Co-operative self-service store. She selects a can of CWS Waveney tomato soup and a box of CWS Spel washing powder.
II   It is explained that the customer owns the Co-op, and that the profits are returned to her/him.
III   Special offers: CWS marmalade, 1/6d; Miracle Mil 2/7d.
IV   Mrs Pullen reaches the checkout with her basket full.
V   Graphic card: "CWS. The sign of saving at YOUR Co-op."

Remarks
"Come Co-operative Shopping" was "the biggest national advertising campaign ever undertaken by the CWS to boost grocery sales in Co-operative Shops" (*The Producer* June 1962). It began on 1 July 1962 with an initial trial period of six months. Costing £250 000, it included extensive television coverage on all independent channels, as well as national newspaper advertising on a large scale. The whole expense of the campaign was met by the CWS, which was prepared to continue the scheme indefinitely with an allocation of £500 000 a year if it proved a success. The "Come Co-operative Shopping" theme continued to be the basis of the Co-op's national advertising well into the 1960s. A surviving film, *What's So Important About a Window Bill?* (1966; NCFC 296), helped explain the integrated nature of the campaign to retail societies and branch managers. Some television commercials promoting the campaign have survived from the mid-1960s, and are distinguished by their regional specificity.

NCFC 272
Come Co-operative Shopping [9] (c.1964)

b/w · 42s · sound · 35mm · NFTVA

■ A regionalised advertisement for the CWS's "Come Co-operative Shopping" campaign.

I   A housewife, Mrs Pamela Whitbread of Slough, making her purchases in a Co-operative self-service store.
II   The distinct ownership structure of the Co-op is explained.
III   Special offers: CWS Excelda and CWS Federation self-raising flours, 3d off; Wheatsheaf pork luncheon meat, 2/3.
IV   Mrs Whitbread reaches the checkout with her basket full.
V   Graphic card: "Save Now, Save Always. Come Co-operative Shopping."

Remarks
One of a series of surviving commercials from the extensive "Come Co-operative Shopping" campaign of the 1960s. It is instructive to note that the promotions sponsored CWS brands exclusively. However, the period of loyalty to Co-op productions was drawing to an end and future campaigns such as "This Week's Super Savers" and "The Co-op's Big Six Savers" would be attentive to market-leaders manufactured by competitors, signalling in

the Movement a major shift of emphasis towards profitable retailing.

NCFC 273
Come Co-operative Shopping [10]
(c.1964)

b/w · 30s · sound · 35mm · NFTVA

■ A regionalised television advertisement in the CWS's "Come Co-operative Shopping" campaign.

    (Introduction missing)
I   Housewife Mrs Esme Green of Colchester and her daughter enter a Co-op store and commence their purchases.
II   The distinct ownership structure of the Co-operative Movement is briefly explained.
III   Special offers: CWS Silver Seal margarine, save 4d; CWS Excelda and Federation self-raising flours, 3d off.
IV   The pair are buying a chicken at the cold meat counter.
V   Graphic card: "CWS. The Sign of Saving at YOUR Co-op."

Remarks
A further example from the long-running series of television commercials. Featured promotions were organised on a monthly basis, with each promotion – in this instance, CWS margarine and flour – commencing on the first Monday in the month. The following month would witness a different special offer promotion, and associated publicity media and point-of-sale displays would reinforce the message in-store.

NCFC 274
Come Co-operative Shopping [11]
(c.1964)

b/w · 40s · sound · 35mm · NFTVA

■ A regionalised advertisement for the CWS's "Come Co-operative Shopping" campaign.

I   A housewife making her purchases in a Co-op self-service store at Ripley.
II   The distinct ownership structure of the Co-operative Movement is explained.
III   Special offers: CWS Crysella soap flakes, 4d off; CWS custard powder, save 4d; CWS Sun-Sip, save 5d.
IV   The housewife is helped to the door

with her basket full of CWS brand products.
V   Graphic card: "Come Co-operative Shopping".

Remarks
One of several surviving commercials from the "Come Co-operative Shopping" promotional campaign. Structured identically, the spots featured "a selection of attractive price cuts [which] continue to hammer home the advantages of shopping at the Co-op to millions of viewers" (*The Producer* June 1964). Various commercials were produced at varied lengths – 60 seconds, 45 seconds, 30 seconds, and shorter 15-second and 7-second reminder spots. Mainly examples from the 30-second mid-range group have been located, with a few of the one-minute variety. This example includes an innovative travelling shot from within the customer's basket, giving a clear view of the CWS brand purchases already made, and this was used regularly within the series.

NCFC 275
Come Co-operative Shopping [12]
(c.1964)

b/w · 42s · sound · 35mm · NFTVA

■ A regionalised advertisement for the CWS's "Come Co-operative Shopping" campaign.

I   A housewife, Mrs Jean Gott of Middlesborough, enters her local Co-op store and commences her purchases.
II   The distinct ownership structure of the Co-op is briefly explained.
III   Special offers: CWS Silver Seal margarine, save 6d; CWS Waveney beans, now 10½d.
IV   Exterior of Co-operative store.
V   Graphic card: "Come Co-operative Shopping".

Remarks
A surviving example from a series of advertisements broadcast in 1964 and 1965, which conformed to a particular structure of "30-second television spots [which featured] selected special offers slotted into commercials introducing Co-operative housewive's" (*The Producer* February 1964). Themed point-of-sale advertising was made available to societies, and the whole package funded by the CWS. It was concluded that "the combined special offers

programme and supplementary campaign amount to the most powerful advertising boost ever undertaken for the Co-op Shop" (*The Producer* June 1964).

NCFC 276
[CWS Margarine Advertisement 5] (1965)

b/w · 34s · sound · 35mm · NFTVA

- A brief advertisement for CWS Silver Seal margarine.

I	A bar of CWS Silver Seal margarine: "Silver Seal is Superb".
II	Silver Seal is easy to spread, delicious to eat. Ideal for sandwiches and cooking. The sequence is cut to appropriate shots.
III	The range of CWS margarines – Silver Seal, Gold Seal, Red Seal and Gala.
IV	A sequence of Co-op store fronts – "Come Co-operative Shopping".
V	A bar of CWS Silver Seal margarine: "Silver Seal is Superb".

Remarks
A variant within the extensive "Come Co-operative Shopping" promotional campaign which commenced in 1962 and ran well into the decade. A series of 30-second television commercials was commissioned promoting CWS Silver Seal margarine and broadcast in the North of England over a twenty-week period beginning in June 1965. Retail societies were informed that "[a] minimum of seven 30-second spots a week will take the message that 'Silver Seal's Superb' into millions of homes" (*The Producer* June 1965).

NCFC 277
[CWS Margarine Advertisement 6] (1965)

b/w · 35s · sound · 35mm · NFTVA

- A brief advertisement for CWS Silver Seal margarine.

I	A bar of CWS Silver Seal margarine: "Silver Seal is Superb".
II	Silver Seal is ideal for home cooking – for cakes, for puff pastry, for super good taste!
III	The range of CWS margarines – Silver Seal, Gold Seal, Red Seal, and Gala.
IV	A sequence of Co-op store fronts – "Come Co-operative Shopping".
V	A bar of CWS Silver Seal margarine:

"Silver Seal is Superb".

Remarks
"For 20 weeks this summer and autumn hard-selling 30-second television commercials are giving a boost to sales of Silver Seal margarine in the Northern (Lancashire and Yorkshire) area. Seven spots a week – for the most part at peak viewing times – are hammering home the advantages of this spread-easy, mix-easy margarine, and introducing the slogan 'Silver Seal's Superb'. An estimated total of 208 million 'home impressions' will be made during the whole campaign, which is the biggest ever in the North for Silver Seal margarine" (*The Producer* July 1965). The commentators give no indication as to why special devotion was given to the north of England in the promotion of Silver Seal.

NCFC 278
[CWS Margarine Advertisement 7] (1965)

b/w · 35s · sound · 35mm · NFTVA

- A brief advertisement for CWS Silver Seal margarine.

I	A bar of Silver Seal margarine is displayed on a revolving pedestal under a spotlight.
II	The margarine's ease of spreading is demonstrated.
III	The margarine's ease of creaming is demonstrated – so good for cakes and pastries.
IV	A housewife selects Silver Seal margarine from the cold counter of her Co-op store.
V	Graphic card: "Come Co-operative Shopping".

Remarks
One of four surviving television commercials promoting CWS Silver Seal margarine, which were broadcast between June and October 1965. Presumably to help distinguish between them, this one was nicknamed "Spotlight" by the CWS Publicity Department staff.

NCFC 279
[CWS Margarine Advertisement 8] (1965)

b/w · 34s · sound · 35mm · NFTVA

- A brief advertisement for CWS Silver Seal margarine.

I   "What spreads like margarine? Mixes like margarine? But tastes Mmmm – much better! Silver Seal." The statements are linked with appropriate shots.
II   A housewife selects Silver Seal margarine from the cold counter of her Co-op store.
III Graphic card: "Come Co-operative Shopping".

Remarks
One of several surviving television commercials from 1965 promoting CWS Silver Seal margarine, contained within the broader generic campaign of "Come Co-operative Shopping". To help distinguish the 30-second commercials, CWS publicity staff referred to this example as "Much Better!".

NCFC 280
[CWS Tea Advertisement 1] (1965)

b/w · 12s · sound · 35mm · NFTVA

■ A brief animated advertisement for the Co-op's celebrated 99 tea.

I   Three young girls on a stage sing the jingle.
II   Graphic card: "Ninety Nine Tea 99 from Co-op Shops".
     Jingle: "For quality tea buy 99".

Remarks
One of a surviving series of television commercials promoting 99 tea. Apparently, the brand name for this remarkably successful product refers to the cumulative number of the actual blend, it being the 99th attained by the CWS tea department over the years. An alternative anecdote relates that the name of the tea derives from the address of the English and Scottish CWS London tea warehouse, number "99" Leman Street. Each commercial of the series attempted a slightly different rendition of the simple jingle, in this instance being inspired by the popular puppet show, *Pinky and Perky*.

NCFC 281
[CWS Tea Advertisement 2] (1965)

b/w · 11s · sound · 35mm · NFTVA

■ A brief animated advertisement for Co-op 99 tea.

I   An Indian dancer performs an exotic routine.
II   Graphic card: "Ninety Nine Tea 99 from Co-op shops".
     Jingle: "For quality tea buy 99".

Remarks
A further addition to the series of commercials promoting 99 tea, and distinguished by their simplicity and brevity. This one gives an Indian theme, the jingle being sung over appropriate Eastern music.

NCFC 282
[CWS Tea Advertisement 3] (1965)

b/w · 12s · sound · 35mm · NFTVA

■ A brief animated advertisement for Co-op 99 tea.

I   A male opera singer walks onstage and delivers the jingle.
II   Graphic card: "Ninety Nine Tea 99 from Co-op stores".
     Jingle: "For quality tea buy 99".

Remarks
This example, from the series of commercials promoting 99 tea, exists in two forms. In a variation of the above, a large box of 99 tea, effectively the final graphic card, falls on the head of the opera singer. Both prints are held at the NFTVA.

NCFC 283
[CWS Tea Advertisement 4] (1965)

b/w · 12s · sound · 35mm · NFTVA

■ A brief advertisement for Co-op 99 tea.

I   A tartan caddy is lifted from a packet of 99 tea.
II   Graphic card: "Ninety Nine Tea 99 from Co-op Shops".
     Jingle: "For quality tea buy 99".

Remarks
A further edition in the series of television commercials promoting 99 tea. This example is given a Scottish flavour – to be broadcast in Scotland? – with the jingle being performed over bagpipes.

NCFC 284
[CWS Tea Advertisement 5] (1965)

b/w · 11s · sound · 35mm · NFTVA

- A brief advertisement for the Co-op's celebrated 99 tea.

I   Letters spelling Nine Tea Nine dance around the screen.

II   Graphic card: "Ninety Nine Tea 99 from Co-op Shops".
Jingle: "For quality tea buy 99".

Remarks
Another example from a series of television commercials promoting 99 tea.

NCFC 285
[Opening of Denton Burn Co-op] (1965)

b/w · 3m 35s · silent · 16mm · NFA
pr Dorian

- A film record of the opening of a new food store by the Newcastle Co-operative Society.

I   Exterior of the Denton Burn supermarket of the Newcastle Co-operative Society. It is 8.50 am, and a large crowd waits to gain admittance.

II   An address is made to the waiting crowd by members of the Board of Management – Mr J H Yeats (Chairman) and Mr J M Sanderson.

III   The doors are officially opened and the crowd floods in.

IV   Interior of the store – the patient shoppers are addressed by representatives of the society.

V   Scenes around the self-service food store as local shoppers familiarise themselves with the new facilities – the provisions aisles, the giant freezers, the butchery counter, the delicatessen counter, etc.

Remarks
The opening of a new branch store was an important occasion for a local Co-operative society, and invariably was conducted with some ceremony. This film record provides some excellent images of the interior of a self-service supermarket which might very well have been a relatively new shopping experience for the residents of the locality. The store was closed by the society in the late-1980s, and it was reckoned to be the last Co-operative building to be constructed by the society with a Guild meeting room above the premises.

NCFC 286
Come Co-operative Shopping [13]

(c.1965)

b/w · 41s · sound · 35mm · NFTVA

- A regionalised advertisement for the CWS's "Come Co-operative Shopping" campaign.

I   Exterior of a Co-operative store. Housewife Mrs Jean Bartlett of Darlington has made her purchases, and leaves the store for her car.

II   The distinct ownership structure of the Movement is explained.

III   Special offers: Wheatsheaf pork luncheon meat, only 1/8; Sun-Sip canned drinks, any 3 for 2/6.

IV   The Bartlett family enjoying their Co-op brand foods on a picnic.

V   Graphic card: "Come Co-operative Shopping".

Remarks
This example from the series of commercials promoting the "Come Co-operative Shopping" campaign is distinct in that the character's existence outside the store is explored. It derives from August 1965, when customers were reminded that "it's picnic time" – with suggestions of CWS goods that were guaranteed to make any picnic a success.

NCFC 287
Come Co-operative Shopping [14]
(c.1965)

b/w · 41s · sound · 35mm · NFTVA

- A regionalised advertisement for the CWS's "Come Co-operative Shopping" campaign.

I   A housewife, Mrs Janet Cosgrove of Sheffield, enters her local Co-op store and begins to make her purchases.

II   The distinct ownership structure of the Co-op is explained.

III   Special offers: Crumpsall cream crackers, save 2d; Wheatsheaf Australian tinned fruit, peaches 2/5 and pears 2/6.

IV   Mrs Cosgrove reaches the checkout with her basket full.

V   Graphic card: "Come Co-operative Shopping".

Remarks
All the adverts in this series feature a housewife as the typical customer of the Co-operative store. Husbands or single

men/women are apparently unconsidered, suggesting an acquiescence on the part of the Movement to the powerful dominant ideology which stresses women's role as home-maker, wife and mother. It is to the Movement's shame that it failed to break from convention and explore alternative gender roles, and to acknowledge consumers other than the typical housewife with the basket.

NCFC 288
Come Co-operative Shopping [15]
(c.1965)

b/w · 48s · sound · 16mm · EAFA

▪ A regionalised advertisement in the CWS's "Come Co-operative Shopping" campaign.

I   A housewife, Mrs Pickering of Birmingham, one of the many owners of Birmingham Co-operative Society. The sequence shows us her children and home, and various Co-op store fronts.
II Interiors of a Co-op self-service store.
III Special offers: Wheatsheaf rice pudding, now 10½d; CWS Spel washing powder, now 1/8.
IV Graphic card: "CWS. The Sign of Saving at your Co-op Shop".

Remarks
One of a series of surviving advertisements in the popular "Come Co-operative Shopping" campaign. In the tradition of the series, Mrs Pickering, the featured housewife in the commercial, was an actual member of the Birmingham Society, which at that time claimed a membership of 411 000.

NCFC 289
Come Co-operative Shopping [16]
(c.1965)

b/w · 42s · sound · 35mm · NFTVA

▪ A regionalised advertisement for the CWS's "Come Co-operative Shopping" campaign.

I   A housewife, Mrs Verina Morgan of Cheltenham, enters her local Co-op store and begins to make her purchases.
II The distinct ownership structure of the Co-op is explained.
III Special offers: CWS Silver Seal

margarine, save 6d; CWS Excelda and Federation self-raising flours, save 3d. At your Co-op now!
IV Mrs Morgan reaches the checkout with her basket full.
V   Graphic card: "Come Co-operative Shopping".

Remarks
One of a series of television adverts for the "Come Co-operative Shopping" campaign, which introduced money-off special offers, altered each month, and commented on the "Co-operative difference" – whereby "the profit comes back to you when you shop at the Co-op".

NCFC 290
Come Co-operative Shopping [17]
(c.1965)

b/w · 33s · sound · 35mm · NFTVA

▪ Regionalised advertisement for the CWS's "Come Co-operative Shopping" campaign.

I   A housewife, Mrs Veronica Jackson of Leicester, enters her local Co-op store and begins to make her purchases.
II The distinct ownership structure of the Co-op is explained.
III Special offers: Wheatsheaf tinned peaches and pears, 3/2 the two; Crumpsall cream crackers, save 2d.
IV Mrs Jackson reaches the checkout with her basket full.
V   Graphic card: "Come Co-operative Shopping".

Remarks
To help marshal retail staff into the spirit of the "Come Co-operative Shopping" promotional campaign, the CWS inaugurated a selling competition for branch employees. At stake was a new Morris Mini car for the successful branch manager with the best window display on the theme, and £10 each for his counter staff. The first winner was Ronald Allen, manager of the Caerau Road branch of Maesteg Co-operative Retail Services. Of the overall campaign, he remarked: "The 'Come Co-operative Shopping' campaign in mass circulation newspapers and on independent television had achieved some spectacular results in terms of increased sales of products featured as special offers" (*The Producer* September 1965).

NCFC 291
Come Co-operative Shopping [18]
(c.1965)

b/w · 41s · sound · 35mm · NFTVA

▪ A regionalised advertisement in the CWS's "Come Co-operative Shopping" campaign.

(Introduction missing)

I   A housewife, Mrs Hutchinson of Caldwell, near Richmond, Yorkshire, discovers she is out of marmalade.
II   A mobile Co-operative grocery van pulls up outside her home; from inside the van we see Mrs Hutchinson purchase a jar of CWS marmalade.
III Interior of a Co-op store: another shopper purchases a jar of CWS marmalade, 1/6.
IV Special offers: CWS Crysella soap flakes, save 4d; CWS White Olive beauty soap; save 3d; CWS Scentol disinfectant, save 11d.
V   Graphic card: "Come Co-operative Shopping".

Remarks
This example from the series of surviving films promoting the "Come Co-operative Shopping" theme is structured somewhat differently from the others. Here, the housewife is located at home, rather than at the Co-op store, allowing for the appearance of a mobile Co-operative grocery van, an important and successful service provided by retail societies in rural districts. In addition, the commercial places less emphasis on the "Co-operative difference", a structured feature of all other surviving examples.

NCFC 292
Come Co-operative Shopping [19]
(c.1965)

b/w · 42s · sound · 35mm · NFTVA

▪ A regionalised advertisement for the CWS's "Come Co-operative Shopping" campaign.

I   A housewife, Mrs Margaret Mather of Swindon, makes her purchases in a Co-operative self-service store.
II   The distinct ownership structure of the Movement is explained.
III Special offers: 99 tea, 1/6; Wheatsheaf dairy cream, 11½d.
IV Mrs Mather reaches the checkout with her basket full.

V   Graphic card: "Come Co-operative Shopping".

Remarks
A further addition to the extensive "Come Co-operative Shopping" advertising campaign financed by the CWS throughout the mid-1960s. Parallel television advertising by the CWS continued throughout the period; for instance, Wheatsheaf bread, 99 tea and CWS shoes were all vigorously promoted in 1965, independent of the "Come Co-operative Shopping" campaign.

NCFC 293
Come Co-operative Shopping [20]
(c.1965)

b/w · 42s · sound · 35mm · NFTVA

▪ A regionalised advertisement for the CWS's "Come Co-operative Shopping" campaign.

I   A housewife, Mrs Joan Hope of Letchworth, making her purchases in a Co-op self-service store.
II   The distinct ownership structure of the Movement is explained.
III Special offers: CWS custard powder, save 4d; CWS Sun-Sip, save 5d.
IV Mrs Hope reaches the checkout with her basket full.
V   Graphic card: "Come Co-operative Shopping".

Remarks
Unusually, this example from the series of commercials broadcast in the mid-1960s exists in two forms. A second, virtually identical version, replaces the CWS Sun-Sip drink with a special offer on CWS Nice biscuits. The series as a whole was considered innovative in that it used actual housewives, not actresses. The first choice for the Letchworth commercial had to be replaced when it was learned that her name was Mrs Bird – unsuitable for a film advertising CWS custard powder, since Bird's was a rival custard manufacturer!

NCFC 294
Come Co-operative Shopping [21]
(c.1965)

b/w · 42s · sound · 35mm · NFTVA

▪ A regionalised advertisement for the CWS's "Come Co-operative Shopping" campaign.

I   A housewife, Mrs Sheila Leakey of Taunton, enters her local Co-op store and begins to make her purchases.
II   The distinct ownership structure of the Movement is explained.
III   Special offers: CWS mincemeat, save 9d; Waveney beans, save 2½d.
IV   Mrs Leakey has finished her shopping and unloads her basket of Co-op brand products.
V   Graphic card: "Come Co-operative Shopping".

Remarks
A further example in the CWS's "Come Co-operative Shopping" campaign. The series was unusual in featuring a specific location for each commercial, although the films were not restricted to regional broadcasts, and each edition was broadcast nationally. The films were honest in that they did feature a regular customer, correctly designated and visiting the actual retail society specified. The producers were probably exaggerating when they claimed to have travelled 100 000 miles in preparing the series.

NCFC 295
Woodcraft Folk (miscellaneous) (c.1965-69)

col · 91m 36s · silent · 8mm · PC

▪ A collection of six standard 8mm "home-movies" of Woodcraft Folk gatherings and activities in the mid-1960s.

I   A small group of WCF at the seaside: scenes at camp, rambles, recreation on the beach, day-trips, boat trips, coach trip (15m 27s).
II   An international camp involving youth contingents from Poland, Switzerland, Malta and Great Britain – Newham and Mitcham WCF; scenes around camp, sports and games, presentations from a large stage, music and dance performances, scenes at the coast, rambles, town visit, camp-fire, scenes at zoo, scenes around London (19 minutes).
III   A village festival: a large party enters a church, scenes around the village, morris dancing, ramble, countryside scenes, scenes at an old mine, scenes at the coast, scenes at an old abbey, further scenes at the village festival (15m 28s).
IV   Scenes at a small WCF camp: sport and games, general activities.

V   "Our Holiday". General scenes at an international camp in England: various views of the camp-site, fancy dress parade, camp-fire, mealtime, fun and games, ramble, fun at a park, day-trip, further scenes around the camp-site, games of skill and judgment, a parade in costumes by the campers, dancing displays and performance, a camp-fire, presentations from a large stage, breaking camp, onboard a train (26m 30s).
VI   The WCF in France: scenes at a WCF camp, fancy dress parade, building the camp-fire, scenes around a French town, Paris – the Eiffel Tower, a French village, a French cathedral, a French château, the French countryside, mealtime, further châteaux, the White Cliffs of Dover from the ferry, English fauna (15m 11s).

Remarks
These amateur films were made for "personal" consumption, and conform to the typical aesthetics of "home-movies" – numerous brief action sequences, undeveloped continuity, unsteady camerawork, variable lighting and compositional quality, and so on. They are interesting in their revelation that for families committed to the ideals of camaraderie and the Folk, an annual holiday meant a WCF camp. So far, this is the only film material detailing Folk activities in the 1960s.

NCFC 296
What's So Important About a Window Bill? (1966)

col · 8m · sound · 16mm · EAFA, NFTVA
pr Cygnet Films

▪ A film detailing the "Come Co-operative Shopping" promotional campaign.

I   A young couple are watching a television commercial, "Come Co-operative Shopping", and are impressed by the Co-op's bright new image and smart new stores.
II   Allied to the television commercials is a variety of themed promotional materials: full-page "Come Co-operative Shopping" advertisements in daily newspapers – stressing the advantages of Co-operation, special offers and competitions; full-page colour advertisements in women's magazines.

III   A montage of print media advertising from the "Come Co-operative Shopping" campaign.
IV   Other promotional sites: hoardings; strip-advertising on public transport.
V   A housewife on a shopping trip is drawn to the window displays, themed to the "Come Co-operative Shopping" campaign, at her own local Co-op store; a montage of examples of window bills supporting the scheme.
VI   Interior of Co-op store. A range of display advertising linked to the scheme is evident.
VII   Examples of each of the promotional sites – television, daily press, colour magazines, hoardings, buses, in-store displays.

Remarks
A film aimed at branch store managers to elicit their support of the national "Come Co-operative Shopping" marketing scheme, originally launched in 1962. The Movement, based on numerous independent retail societies, had found it difficult to mount a meaningful national advertising campaign. The film gives a good indication of the CWS's attempts to overcome that difficulty with an extremely well-resourced scheme utilising the whole range of promotional media. It was claimed that the "Come Co-operative Shopping" campaign was the biggest ever advertising campaign by a retail organisation. The location used for the store sequences was Colchester and East Essex Co-operative and Industrial Society's Culver Street branch.
See also: xxxii, NCFC 271

NCFC 297
The New Co-op (1967)

b/w and col · 17m 44s · sound · 16mm · EAFA, NFTVA

■ A film explaining to retail societies some of the structural changes and promotional strategies adopted by the CWS in 1967.

I   New Century House, HQ of the CWS (exterior, night).
II   Store fronts of the Movement's competitors – Sainsbury's, Tesco, Safeway, Fine Fare, Spar.
III   Philip Thomas, Chief Executive Officer (CEO) of the CWS, outlines the circumstances of the late-1960s and the objectives for future success.
IV   The New Co-op symbol – appearing on various vans, trucks and lorries,

uniforms, stationery, etc; displays of established CWS brands – Wheatsheaf, Lokreel, Waveney, etc, to be dispensed for a unified Co-op brand.
V   Market research: canvassing housewives; stock-checks in stores; food-testers; quality-control; expert tasters; in-store taste-tests; large-scale testing, utilising volunteer consumers *(b/w)*.
VI   Display of Co-op brand products utilising the new logo.
VII   Putting the message across to housewives – advertising.
VIII   An example from the new television advertising campaign – "It's All At the Co-op Now!" *(b/w)*.
IX   Coordinated promotional campaigns taking in magazines, window bills, and so on.
X   The "Big Six Savers" campaign – an example of a television advert *(b/w)*.
XI   Thomas outlines the role of the local society and the necessity of their vital support for the campaign.
XII   The campaign's opening "It's All At the Co-op Now!" television commercial.
XIII   Another example of an advert from the campaign – "Big Six Savers".

Remarks
Philip Thomas began his duties at the CWS on 1 February 1967, and tragically died in a plane crash on 20 April 1968. An historian of the Movement has written of his tenure: "In the 445 days between the two dates he had revolutionised the CWS and had profoundly influenced the operations and the morale of the retail Movement" (Sir William Richardson, *The CWS in War and Peace 1938-1976* [Manchester: Co-operative Wholesale Society, 1977]). The trading figures of the Movement were alarming, with food sales by retail societies down by 2%, compared to a 7% increase by the multiples. 1967 can be seen as a retreat from certain historical practices, with a rationalisation of the structure of the CWS, the introduction and expansion of contemporary marketing and promotional methods, the enlargement of the banking and financial operations (the Banking Department was renamed the Co-operative Bank), and an attempt to improve the image of the Movement. The film contains a valuable collection of promotional materials, including the inaugural commercial in the successful "It's All At the Co-op Now!" series, and, of course, a presentation by the new CEO, whose tenure was so tragically cut short.

NCFC 298
[CWS Operation Facelift] (1968)

col · 19m · sound · 16mm · EAFA, NFTVA, WFSA

■ A film explaining the contemporary attempts to improve and modernise the Co-op's image, a strategy know as "Operation Facelift".

I   A sequence contrasting aspects of the Co-op's old and dowdy image with modern efforts at revitalisation.
II   Strategies for change: training of the sales force; fact-sheets for retail staff; dispensing with traditional CWS brand names – Waveney, Wheatsheaf, Lokreel – for a unified Co-op brand identity. Considerable visual emphasis is placed on the new Co-op logo – on vans, store fronts, products, etc.
III   A sequence of competitor's store fronts – Tesco, Boots, Sainsbury's, Burtons, and Marks and Spencer.
IV   A sequence on the "improved" Co-op image: store fronts; delivery vehicles; store interiors; brand-labelling; national advertising campaigns; agreed marketing style, utilising a new national logo.
V   An executive salesman discusses the recent advances made by the Co-op: the sequence includes various scenes of Co-op production, retailing, research testing, and so on.
VI   The Co-op's "Big Six Savers" campaign. Spokesmen for Nestlé and Oxo provide their endorsement of the Co-op's new direction.
VII   Improved point-of-sale designs: products; gondolas; promotional signs.
VIII   Executives discuss the Co-op's improved sales performance.
IX   The Chief Executive Officer of Plymouth Co-operative Society endorses the changes, and demonstrates his society's advances in a tour of the trading district.
X   A final exhortation to societies to accept the changes.

Remarks
In an attempt to attract the "modern shopper", "Operation Facelift" was launched in November 1968. The CWS offered to societies an economically priced package for refurbishing older stores, and a target was set of 2500 "facelifts" in the first twelve months. 1300 were carried out in the first six months, and the target was attained two months within schedule.

To create a stronger public awareness of the Movement, and to establish a more clearly defined corporate identity, a new national symbol was sought. Thankfully, it was recognised that a universally recognised "brand name" already existed – the Co-op – and the familiar Co-op on blue background was created. It would become arguably the best known logo and trade name in the country. An alternative, "Gold Mark", was wisely rejected.

At the time of the campaign, there were 400 individual retail societies, and the issue of a single national identity had become acute with the rise of giant multiple chains. The Co-op's share of the retail market was 16%, down from 22.5% ten years previously. Although still claiming to be Britain's biggest business, all the trends were downwards and a fight back was under way. The film indicates some of the major changes in emphasis in Co-operative trade and production. "Universalism", the Co-op as a self-sufficient provider, was no longer a major structuring force, and profitable retailing was the main concern. This is evident in the appearance of spokesmen from "competitor" companies, and in the use of "outside" design experts to revamp the Co-op image. "Profit" and not "commonwealth" was becoming the operative term within the Movement.

NCFC 299
I'm a Member of a Family (1968)

col · 12m · sound · 16mm · EAFA
pr Worldwide Pictures

■ The international youth camp at Normanby Hall, near Scunthorpe, 1967.

        Pre-credit sequence:
        Two young boys in military outfit fight each other. The Woodcraft Folk aims to dispel aggression and militarism.
I   Panning shot of the WCF camp; a large gathering of campers and supporters; delegates from different countries in conversation.
II   The "morning circle", symbol of democracy, is taken beneath the various flags of participating nations and groups; a group sing a Folk song; close-shots of some of the younger children.
III   A diagram explains the age-group structures of the WCF: Elfins, 6-9; Pioneers, 10-13; Venturers, 14-17; leaders.

IV The origins of the WCF, out of the Scouts and Kibbo Kift Movements, are explained over shots of contemporary news clippings.
V The gathered campers enjoy songs and performance from the grand stage; fancy dress parade; sports day in a nearby stadium; parents' visiting day; folk-dancing; preparing food and mealtime; sitting out the storm under canvas.
VI Basil Rawson, President of the WCF, exchanges tokens of friendship with the delegates from abroad.
VII Torches are lit from the pagoda – the ceremonial fire; "The Envoy" is recited – a convention that starts and ends group meetings of the Folk; "Youth and Maiden" is sung; fireworks spell out "Friendship"; a campfire; campers asleep in their tents; a boy recites "The Pioneer Creed".

Remarks
One of only two surviving professionally recorded films for the WCF; the substantial body of film material relating to the Folk was recorded by "amateurs" – members of Folk groups – since it was difficult for the voluntary organisation to fund professional-quality sound colour productions. An earlier commissioned film, *The Republic of Children* (1939; NCFC 382), produced by the WFA, is believed lost. The film here is of particular interest in its clear presentation of Folk rituals, such as the "morning circle", the ceremonial fire, and the reciting of "The Envoy".

NCFC 300
[Co-op Tottenham] (1969)

b/w · 11m 8s · silent · 16mm · NFTVA

■ A film record of the official opening of a LCS food store.

I Staff make the final preparations to a food store, its fixtures and displays, before the first customers are invited in: the shelf displays, the freezer cabinets; fruit and vegetables; the cold meat counter.
II The customers waiting outside greet the arrival of the celebrity, Bruce Forsyth.
III Bruce is greeted by management and staff inside the store; he is fitted with a large "It's All At the Co-op Now!" badge; Bruce chats with one of the waiting customers; he cuts the ribbon.

IV A second celebrity arrives – the Brooke Bond PG Tips chimp. He poses with Bruce for a publicity shot.
V Bruce tours the store and chats with some of the staff. He is introduced to the Mayor.
VI Store exterior – the waiting shoppers observe proceedings through the windows.
VII The first customers make their selections and purchases inside the store; a marketing assistant engaged in an ice-cream promotion.

Remarks
An interesting example of the use of celebrities for the opening of a new store. Bruce Forsyth's renowned ease and familiarity with the general public are evident in the scenes where he chats and jokes with waiting customers and staff members – although he does appear rather unsettled when his co-celebrity appears on the scene! The film provides a valuable observation of a late-1960s store, a period which witnessed numerous refittings and refurbishments to help enhance and modernise the Co-op's image.

NCFC 301
Co-operative 3rd National Marketing Conference (Edited Highlights) (1969)

b/w · 42m · sound · 16mm · EAFA, NFTVA; SFA (ref)
compère Cliff Michelmore

■ An edited record of a conference organised by the CWS to inform executives of retail Co-operative societies regarding strategies for modernisation.

I Introduction by compère Cliff Michelmore.
II Opening address by Alfred Wilson, Chief Executive Officer of the CWS; a brief edited sequence involving a sales promotion girl at a Co-op department store cut to contemporary pop music – updating the Movement's image!
III Cliff Michelmore discusses with CWS Executive, Keith Willoughby, strategies to update and standardise the Movement's image and market identity.
IV An address by Denis Greensmith, Deputy Chief Executive Officer, and departmental colleagues of the CWS on five activities to update Co-operative retailing: "Operation Facelift"; site assessment; architectural

services; dividend stamps; and computerisation. Each of the activities is discussed in some detail.

V An address by Ken Medlock and colleagues from the Non-Food Division on strategies to improve operations: electrical "best buys" for 1970; issues of non-food are discussed in some detail, including plans for national advertising; the latest Co-op fashions are demonstrated to the delegates by six models.

VI An address by Arthur Sugden and three colleagues of the CWS Food Division outlining the present position and strategies for future progress: four contemporary adverts in the "It's All At the Co-op Now!" and "Co-op Super-Savers" series; Sugden sums up the position of food retailing.

VII Alfred Wilson summarises the aims of the conference.

Remarks
This national conference to aid the dissemination of "progressive" trading practices, under the slogan "Co-op At Your Service", was held in Manchester and shot as a television production. (This edited version is a telecine of the original recording.) Several films were produced to push the campaign, most notably an untitled film about "Operation Facelift" (1968; NCFC 298), a campaign which the historian of the postwar CWS has summarised as "plans, plans, plans. Plans for the now well-known 'Co-op' symbol, for restyling about 2500 food packs and labels, for helping retail societies to smarten up their shops, for the appointment of the firm of Masius Wynn-Williams as the society's advertising agents, for a massive advertising campaign to promote store traffic, for the rationalisation of office methods and working space, for new factories and products, for increasing computerisation, for the establishment of regional grocery warehouses, and for a possible Co-operative dividend stamp scheme to counter the increasing popularity of stamps." (Sir William Richardson, *The CWS in War and Peace 1938-1976* [Manchester: Co-operative Wholesale Society, 1977]).

NCFC 302
Save in 1969 (1969)

b/w · 40s · sound · 35mm · SFA

▪ A television advertisement promoting "special offer" purchases.

I A mother and daughter have returned from a shopping trip at the Co-op, and unload their basket in the kitchen. They have purchased a number of "special offers": Del Monte pineapples only 1/-; Heinz tomato soup only 1s 2d; Chieftain cream crackers only 1/-; Batchelors packet soups only 10d; Golden Ball marmalade only 1s 9d.

Remarks
The Movement's shift away from CWS brand loyalty is complete in this television advertisement, which exclusively promotes non-Co-op brands. The Movement underwent immense changes in the 1960s, as it responded to major shifts in national culture and retailing. However, such a publicity exercise which promoted competitor's (and capitalist's) products would have horrified a previous generation of Co-operators. The film heavily features the new national logo (1968): "Co-op" on a blue background.

NCFC 303
[Birmingham Society Cultural Activities]
(c.1969)

b/w and col · 6m 7s · silent · 16mm · EAFA
pr Birmingham Co-operative Society

▪ Sports and cultural activities sponsored by the Birmingham Co-operative Society.

(b/w sequence)
I A quick succession of finishes of sprint races – men's, women's and children's.
II Women's egg and spoon races; men's obstacle races.
III Men's tug-of-war; the finish of men's sprint races.
IV Women's sack races; mixed three-legged race.
V The amused spectators.
VI The prize-giving ceremony.
(colour sequence)
VII Mountain scenery from a coach.
VIII The day-trippers enjoy the view, strolling by their coaches.
IX Strolling on the promenade at the seaside; a group portrait on the sea front; a tripper enjoys a bottle of beer.
X Groups and individuals stroll on the promenade.
XI The beach and seashore; portrait of a group on the sea front.

Remarks
Material probably shot by a member of the Birmingham Co-operative Society, and

recording two annual events of the society: sports day, and a staff/members (?) outing to the seaside.

NCFC 304
[CWS "Big Six Savers"] (c.1969)

b/w · 33s · sound · 16mm · NFTVA

▪ A brief television advertisement for the Co-op's "Big Six Savers" campaign.

I   This week's Co-op "Big Six Savers": Ambrosia creamed rice, now 11d, Pedigree Chum, now 1/8, Kleenex tissues, now 1/6, Daddies tomato ketchup, now 10½d, Co-op baked beans, now 10½d, Robertson's jams, now 1/11.
II   Customers, with prominent Co-op shopping bags, leave in a variety of vehicles.
III Graphic card: "Co-op. It's all at the Co-op now!".

Remarks
The CWS negotiated with prominent manufacturers to feature popular brand products in national advertising campaigns, and to retail as special offers. In this example, only one item is Co-operatively-produced. The campaign was embraced within a broader scheme to improve the Movement's retail image and performance, of which the generic promotional slogan was "It's All At the Co-op Now!". A variant on this "Big Six Savers" campaign was "This Week's Super Savers", for which a television advertisement survives.

NCFC 305
[CWS Carpet Products Advertisement] (c.1969)

b/w · 33s · sound · 16mm · NFTVA

▪ A brief television advertisement for Co-op carpets and carpet cleaners.

I   A family in their living room: a beautiful carpet – for mother; a soft carpet – for baby; a tough carpet – for father.
II   A range of Co-op carpet cleaners: a display of sweeping appliances; a display of vacuum cleaners.
III Graphic card: "Co-op. It's all at the Co-op now!".

Remarks
A further example in the successful "It's All

At the Co-op Now!" promotional campaign.

NCFC 306
[CWS Christmas Advertisement 1] (c.1969)

b/w · 33s · sound · 16mm · NFTVA

▪ A brief Christmas-time television advertisement for shopping at the Co-op.

I   A shopping basket full of Co-op brand products.
II   A mother and daughter make a Christmas pudding with Co-op brand ingredients.
III A table laden with Co-op food items.
IV Graphic card: "Co-op. It's all at the Co-op now!".

Remarks
A further example from the "It's All At the Co-op Now!" series of television adverts. This food commercial is in contrast to another surviving Christmas-time example from the series, in that it exclusively promotes Co-op brand products. Viewers are reminded of all the excellent Co-op brand foodstuffs ideal for Christmas festivities. By the late-1960s, this was an increasingly rare occurrence. All the surviving films from this campaign were produced in black and white. Within a short period, after the coming to dominance of colour television in the early 1970s, all television commercials would be produced in colour.

NCFC 307
[CWS Christmas Advertisement 2] (c.1969)

b/w · 42s · sound · 16mm · NFTVA

▪ A brief Christmas-time television advertisement.

I   Two Santas promise to give back at least two shillings for every pound spent on certain gifts: Philips foodmixer, Carmen rollers, Morphy Richards toaster, Viners carving set, Black and Decker drill, Co-op Agincourt coffee set.
II   Graphic card: "Co-op. It's all at the Co-op now!".

Remarks
One of two surviving examples of Christmas-time advertisements from the

influential "It's All At the Co-op Now!" series. This one promotes dry goods, amongst which only one item is Co-operatively-produced.

NCFC 308
[CWS Cream Advertisement] (c.1969)

b/w · 33s · sound · 16mm · NFTVA

▪ A brief television advertisement for Co-op dairy cream and associated products.

I	A young boy and his kitten eagerly anticipate teatime; Co-op tinned peaches are poured into a fruit bowl; Co-op dairy cream is poured into a jug; the boy and the kitten enjoying their treat.
II	Co-op dairy cream is also ideal with Co-op fruit salad, Co-op pears, Co-op strawberry jam, Co-op mandarin oranges.
III	Display of the six Co-op food items featured.
IV	Graphic card: "Co-op. It's all at the Co-op now!".

Remarks
In 1967-68, the Movement began a broad campaign to improve its image and halt the decline of its share of the retail trade. A new logo was introduced, CWS packs and labels were redesigned, and some products reformulated to improve quality. Massive advertising sustained the campaign under the slogan, "It's All At the Co-op Now!" (later altered to "It's All At YOUR Co-op"). Provided with a dramatic and memorable tune, the slogan was probably the Co-op's most effective. The advert heavily features the new logo, brand packaging and slogan.

NCFC 309
[CWS Ladies' Wear Advertisement] (c.1969)

b/w · 33s · sound · 16mm · NFTVA

▪ A brief television advertisement for ladies' wear.

I	Four models demonstrate the varieties of a fully-fashioned pure new wool or Courtelle cardigan. 21 exciting colours in both short or long-sleeve jumper styles.
II	Also available – stockings, panty-tights, skirts and super knitwear.
III	Graphic card: "Co-op. It's all at the

Co-op now!".

Remarks
A typical example of a late-1960s television advert, one of a surviving number in the "It's All At the Co-op Now!" series.

NCFC 310
[CWS Menswear Advertisement] (c.1969)

b/w · 33s · sound · 16mm · NFTVA

▪ A brief television advertisement for menswear.

I	In a sequence with a male model, the virtues of a good shirt are demonstrated – freedom of the fit, the quality of the material, and so on.
II	Graphic card: "The Co-op Lestar de luxe – 46/6".
III	Socks, ties, suit and overcoat are modelled in a sequence of stills.
IV	Graphic card: "Co-op. It's all at the Co-op now!".

Remarks
At its height in 1939, the CWS operated five shirt factories, employing 2128 workers – Broughton, Sheffield, Pelaw, Upminster and Cardiff. Three CWS cotton mills provided the raw material for an annual output in excess of 3 million shirts. This simple advert, largely constructed of stills, was part of the well-known "It's All At the Co-op Now!" promotional series.

NCFC 311
[CWS Shoe Advertisement 3] (c.1969)

b/w · 33s · sound · 16mm · NFTVA

▪ A brief television advertisement for Co-op shoes.

I	A young woman admires her "3 styles in one" pair of Co-op shoes: plain shoes, with clip-on bow or clip-on buckle, for just 69/11.
II	Display of fashion shoes; display of men's shoes; display of family shoes.
III	Graphic card: "Co-op. It's all at the Co-op now!".

Remarks
A typical example of a television advertisement within the "It's All At the Co-op Now!" campaign.

NCFC 312
[CWS "This Week's Super Savers"]
(c.1969)

b/w · 33s · sound · 16mm · NFTVA

■ A brief television advertisement for the Co-op's "This Week's Super Savers" campaign.

I Roman cavalry charge across a desert.
II Graphic card: "Co-op. This Week's Super Savers".
III Jeyes Parozone, Now 2/3, Kennomeat, Now 1/3, Co-op 99 tea, Now 1/4½, Coca-Cola, Now 9d, Ambrosia creamed rice, Now 1/6, Heinz baked beans, Now 1/-, Co-op garden peas, Now 1/-.
IV A Roman soldier with his fully laden Co-op shopping bag: "It's All At the Co-op Now!".

Remarks
Another example of a special television promotion linked to prominent brand manufacturers. Here, two Co-operatively-produced products are featured out of seven.

NCFC 313
[Dividend Stamp Scheme] (c.1969)

b/w · 47s · sound · 16mm · NFTVA

■ A brief television advertisement explaining the Co-op's new dividend stamp scheme.

I A series of stills details a Co-op store interior, cashiers, checkouts, Co-op brand products, promotional displays, Co-op dividend stamps and books. A commentary provides a general background to the scheme – each book can be refunded for 10/-.
II Graphic card: "Co-op. It's all at the Co-op now!".

Remarks
By the mid-1950s, retail societies were beginning to face difficulties and dividend payouts were falling. There was a general feeling that, with full employment and relatively high incomes, the dividend was ceasing to be a strong inducement to shop at the Co-op. Trading stamp schemes had generally proved extremely popular, and the CWS introduced a Co-operative variant in 1968. It was well-timed to coincide with a comprehensive campaign to restore the image of the Movement. The new dividend stamp scheme proved popular with societies: 92% of the trade of the Movement was involved by 1976, but less so with the traditional membership, who now had to share their dividend with all customers.

NCFC 314
Not So Much a Warehouse... (1972)

col · 22m 52s · sound · 16mm · NFTVA
pr British Films Ltd *d* David Cons
prod George Buckland-Smith *cam* Ron Bicker *anim* Brian Stevens *ed* Michael Crane

■ An information film about the Regional Distribution Centre established by the CWS at Birtley.

I A general exposition on the automated CWS Regional Distribution Centre (RDC) at Birtley, Co. Durham, played over various scenes of the site.
II Stills of old, traditional warehouses.
III Simple diagrammatic sequence of the inefficiencies of conventional chains of distribution as compared with a modern, automated, regional distribution centre; diagrammatic breakdown of the RDC. Some live-action sequences are included for illustration.
IV A diagrammatic sequence of the problems of goods handling within distribution. Some live-action sequences are included for illustration.
V Details of the computer room and its operations.
VI A diagrammatic sequence detailing the computerised distributive process – receipt of orders, order assembly, stock control, despatch; completing orders for despatch; stock control procedures; loading of trailers for despatch to stores; a fully-laden lorry commences its journey. Some live-action sequences are included for illustration.

Remarks
Plans for the more efficient organisation of product distribution and handling were initially discussed by the CWS Board in 1963. The Regional Distribution Centre (originally known as a regional grocery warehouse) replaced the great number of retail warehouses operated by individual societies, and was a modern, more efficient centre, capable of handling the grocery requirements of a regional group of societies. The cost of new technologies

could only be met by large retail societies, and, therefore, a federal scheme backed by the CWS offered the advantages and efficiency gains to the whole Movement. The prototype warehouse was opened at Birtley in June 1966 to serve the north-eastern societies. The project, considered "a significant advance in the technology of distribution and materials handling" (Sir William Richardson, *The CWS in War and Peace 1938-1976* [Manchester: Co-operative Wholesale Society, 1977]), received an award of £150 000 from the Department of Technology, the first-ever innovation grant. The film was sponsored by a government department, the Department of Trade and Industry, and commissioned by the COI. It would have been widely circulated within the distributive industry. This print suffers from some colour-fading.

NCFC 315
"Co-operation" (c.1972)

col · 30m · sound · 16mm · EAFA
pr Abacus *d* Doug Aitken *prod* Ron Trainer *sc* John Pitt *ph* Bruce Parsons *ed* Jack Baldwin *mus* Chris Downing *cast* Alan Hart, George Irving, Clare Clifford, Judy Elrington, Lee Fox, Stuart Sherwin, Eric Francis, William Simons, Josh Bamfield.

▪ A dramatic film about a young man regaining his faith in the efficacy of the Co-operative Movement.

I   On a car journey, a father berates his son, Harry – and the younger generation in general – on his lack of aspirations; Harry is reluctant to get a job, which he sees as acquiescing to the "system".
II Harry gets a job at the Co-op, but his father is far from elated; the Co-op store manager explains the philosophy of the Co-op to his new staff member, and the young man is a quick and eager learner; the small local society is preparing to merge with a larger one, and the store manager is a little reluctant.
III Harry enlists on a course at the Co-operative College to train to become a retail manager: exteriors of the Co-op College, Stanford Hall; classroom lectures on the retail Co-operative Movement; various scenes of recreation and study; Harry begins to lose his enthusiasm and becomes disruptive; the students visit Co-op factories and stores.

IV Harry, becoming increasingly disillusioned with the Movement's competitive attitude, is given a dressing down by his Chief Executive Officer. The CEO explains the reasons for the Movement's need to adopt the modern methods of its competitors, but hopefully not at the cost of losing the original ideals.
V   Preparing to leave the College, Harry has second thoughts and returns to pursue his studies, his faith in the Movement rekindled.

Remarks
This film serves two basic purposes. Most obviously, it uses the drama of the situation and the characters to put over general information about the Co-operative Movement, and the plot device of the formal lectures is crucial in that respect. Its subtext, however, is concerned with confronting the traditionalists in the Movement with the necessity for modernisation, and for the engagement with competitors and their commercial methods. This debate is played through the character of Harry, whose initial scepticism is overcome when he realises that Co-operative ideals and modern commercial trading are compatible. During the early 1970s, the CWS was making great efforts to convert numerous local retail societies to that way of thinking. The film uses professional actors apart from the character of the tutor who is played by Josh Bamfield, a serving tutor at the Co-operative College.

NCFC 316
[CWS Fashion Show] (1973)

col · 5m 56s · sound · 16mm · NFTVA

▪ A film record of a Co-op fashion show in the early 1970s.

I   Female models parade a variety of fashions on a stage and catwalk.
II Two modern business suits are modelled by men in a city centre location.

Remarks
This film is hardly a production, but rather a crude recording of a fashion show with a brief sequence promoting men's clothes tacked onto the end. The film is replete with jump cuts and jarring sound-joins. It does not include any details of the makes, styles or manufacturers of the garments, and was most likely produced for internal CWS

purposes. This print suffers from some colour-fading.

NCFC 317
Our World (1975)

col · 22m · sound · 16mm · EAFA
pr Worldwide Pictures *d* John Peter Samson
cam Les Johnson, Graham McKinney

■ A story film explaining the aims and ideals of the Woodcraft Folk.

I   Panning shot of rooftops strewn with television aerials, over which is played a sound montage of "voices of the world"; a young boy and girl sit transfixed in front of a television set – are today's young being conditioned by the violent images of television?
II   Tranquil rural scenes – the two children and their parents on a country walk; the children join in the activities of a local WCF group; the Folk leader explains the nature of the WCF to the parents.
III   The parents visit a Folk meeting, and the Movement's ideals and activities are explained and demonstrated; a circle dance; the parents meet with local organisers to hear more about the Folk – some of the ideals are discussed.
IV   The parents become Folk leaders themselves: scenes of Folk activities and meetings – camps, dancing, discussion groups, and so on.
V   A WCF camp – "morning cry" awakens campers; breakfast; hiking; group singing.
VI   The family, shopping at the Co-op, tackle their neighbour about her racism.
VII   The WCF Annual Delegate Conference – an address by Tony Raines, National Chair.
VIII   Snapshots of an International Falcon Movement camp, Austria (?).

Remarks
The second of two surviving films produced by Worldwide Pictures for the WCF. Although professionally produced, the scenario was written by officials within the Movement, and acted by actual members. The film's director was married to a prominent member of the Folk. The film reflects the views of a modernising tendency within the WCF, and was filmed around Milton Keynes.

NCFC 318
GNCS Opening of Carlton Superstore November 1980 (1980)

col · 2m 58s · silent · 16mm · EAFA

■ A film recording the opening ceremony of a new superstore by the Greater Nottingham Co-operative Society.

I   Members and officials inspect the new store; various shots of the displays and counters; the arrival of the Mayor and Lady Mayoress; the line of cash registers and checkouts.
II   The waiting customers; a speech by the Mayor, followed by his cutting of the tape; the store's first customers are let in; busy scenes within the store; promotions assistants dressed as Beefeaters; brisk trade at the checkouts; store exterior; the staff canteen.

Remarks
A modest film recording the opening of a superstore by the Greater Nottingham Co-operative Society in a Nottingham suburb. At the time, Greater Nottingham was one of the largest of the independent retail societies, its trading district stretching from parts of Derbyshire in the west, to Skegness in the east. In the event of the society's expansion, numerous local societies had been absorbed. The film was probably shot by a society member simply as a record of the event.

NCFC 319
[Beehive Stores] (c.1980)

col · 1m · 35mm · EAFA

■ A brief television advertisement promoting Beehive shopping centres.

I   A woman pushes her trolley through the aisles of a supermarket: the food aisles; the dry goods section.
II   A woman and son inspect items in the non-food section.
III   Graphic card: "Beehive Shopping Centres. Cambridge, Coldham's Lane and Bedford, The Howard Centre."

Remarks
The "Beehive" trading name was introduced in the late-1970s by the Cambridge and District Co-operative Society for their revamped superstores. During that period, numerous Co-operative societies began

experimenting with trading names according to store types, few of which had any relevance to a specific Co-operative identity. This example, of course, utilises a traditional icon of the Left, the industrious beehive, a symbol of community.

Unlocated Films

The detailed Catalogue presented in this book comprises all the films relating to the British consumer Co-operative Movement which have so far been traced. The 319 films listed represent a significant advance on the research position of only a few years ago, when the work of tracking down Co-op films commenced. No one had contemplated the great extent of the Movement's investment in film, nor could have hoped for the astounding success in locating prints, bringing the films once again within the domain of the research community, and making possible a far more extensive and complete history.

However, the nature of this project is such that some important titles, referenced in the press and promotional literature of the time, remain elusive. The fear is that copies may no longer exist; film is, after all, a perishable material and simply disintegrates in time.

Numerous films giving views of CWS productive works, farms and estates were taken between 1898 and 1914. Subjects included: the Irlam soap works; the Leman Street tea warehouse; the fruit farms at Denia, Spain; the Crumpsall biscuit factory; the CWS English fruit estates at Roden, Morden and Wisbech; the Sun Mill; the CWS tobacco works; the Longsight printing works; and the Wheatsheaf boot factory. None of these films, made without titles, has so far been located – if they have survived, they await identification.

The earliest CWS film in this catalogue is *The Magic Basket* (1928), which inaugurated a series of films detailing CWS factories and promoting popular Co-operative products. Commencing with *Her Dress Allowance* in 1930, the films were produced in both sound and silent versions. Unfortunately, only silent prints have been traced for *Her Dress Allowance, From Back to Back* (1933) and *Partners* (1933), and locating the sound versions would be an important discovery.

The following untraced films were made or commissioned by Co-operative bodies, and are listed with the intention that future researchers in the field of the non-fiction film will be prompted to continue the work commenced here; that the information will enable the identification of unknown films already in the possession of film archives; and that a fuller picture will eventually emerge of the use of film for political and/or commercial purposes. In some instances, copies of original release prints are held by archives and await funds for preservation and the making of viewing prints. Those films are listed herein as *Reference prints*, and as such I have been unable to view them.

NCFC 320
[Stratford Parade] (c.1905)
Record of a Stratford Society procession.

NCFC 321
[Lowestoft Publicity Film] (1914)
A promotional film for the Lowestoft
Co-operative Society, and featuring its
trading premises.

NCFC 322
Clothing a Statue (1921)
CWS garment manufacture. Produced for
the CWS.

NCFC 323
**Economic Power: The Power of
Possession** (1921)
Promoting Co-operation. Produced for the
CWS.

NCFC 324
**Manufacturing Goods for Use, not for
Making Profit** (1921)
Promoting Co-op manufacturing. Produced
for the CWS.

NCFC 325
Money in the Wrong Place (1921)
The CWS Bank. Produced for the CWS.

NCFC 326
The Penny: What Can be Done with it?
(1921)
Promoting Co-operation. Produced for the
CWS.

NCFC 327
Delivering the Goods (1928)
The activities of the Leeds Industrial
Co-operative Society.

NCFC 328
Footsteps (1929)
Boots and shoes. Produced for the CWS.

NCFC 329
What the Diary Told (1929)

Soap. Produced for the CWS.

NCFC 330
Teaching Him a Lesson (1930)
Soap. Produced for the CWS.

NCFC 331
Jammy (c.1930)
Preserves. Produced for the CWS.

NCFC 332
Three Great Questions (c.1930)
Propaganda film. Produced for the SCWS.

NCFC 333
[Birmingham Jubilee] (1931)
The Jubilee celebrations of the Birmingham
Co-operative Society.

NCFC 334
Harvest of Sea and Field (1931)
Lowestoft canning factory. Produced for the
CWS.
See also: NCFC 25

NCFC 335
Milk: Life of a Nation (1931)
Stockport Co-operative Society's dairy
operations.

NCFC 336
Shopping at the Co-op Shop (1931)
A promotional film for the Leeds Industrial
Co-operative Society.

NCFC 337
**Better Health: The Story of Co-operative
Milk** (1932)
Made by Gaumont for the Co-operative Milk
Trade Association.

NCFC 338
Song of the Shirt (1933)
Shirt-making. Produced for the CWS.
See also: NCFC 30

NCFC 339
Co-operation in Industry (1934)

Co-operative Co-Partnerships. Produced for the CWS.

NCFC 340
CWS Manchester Male Voice Choir (1934)
Musical performance. Produced for the CWS.

NCFC 341
CWS Manchester Tobacco Factory Prize Band (1934)
Musical performance. Produced for the CWS.

NCFC 342
CWS Newsreel (1934)
Various. Produced for the CWS.

NCFC 343
The Elevation of Labour (1934)
Produced by Pathé for the Co-operative Productive Federation.

NCFC 344
Hospital Carnival (1934)
Local community film. Produced by J H Poyser and the Long Eaton Co-operative Society.

NCFC 345
International Festival Camp, Männedorf (1934)
The Woodcraft Folk: an international camp hosted by the Swiss Red Falcon Movement.

NCFC 346
The Town's Municipal Works (1934)
Local municipal film. Produced by J H Poyser and the Long Eaton Co-operative Society.

NCFC 347
Happy Schooldays (1935)
Education in Long Eaton. Produced by J H Poyser and the Long Eaton Co-operative Society.

NCFC 348
Hospital Carnival (1935)
A second instalment of the carnival event. Produced by J H Poyser and the Long Eaton Co-operative Society.

NCFC 349
If the Shoe Pinches (1935)
A training film for shoe salespeople. Produced by the Dalziel Co-operative Society.

NCFC 350
Spending the Divi (1935)
The advantages of the Co-op divi. Produced by J H Poyser and the Long Eaton Co-operative Society.

NCFC 351
Biscuit Time (1936)
Biscuits. Produced for the CWS.

NCFC 352
Cavalcade of Co-operation (1936)
Produced for the CWS.

NCFC 353
[Co-op Shoes] (1936)
A promotional short for shoes. Produced by J H Poyser and the Long Eaton Co-operative Society.

NCFC 354
LECS Newsreel (1936)
Various local newsworthy events. Produced by J H Poyser and the Long Eaton Co-operative Society.

NCFC 355
LECS Newsreel (1936)
Various local newsworthy events. Produced by Reginald Denny and the LECS.
See also: NCFC 057

NCFC 356
Merry Mondays (1936)
Soap. Produced for the CWS.
See also: xxi, NCFC 63

NCFC 357
Neighbours (c.1936)
Lutona cocoa and chocolate. Produced for the CWS.

NCFC 358
Ask the Ladies (1937)
Ladies wear. Produced for the CWS.

NCFC 359
Clothes Make the Man (1937)
Menswear. Produced for the CWS.

NCFC 360
Fruit on the March (1937)
Fruit growing and canning. Produced for the CWS.

NCFC 361
Gallons of Goodness (1937)
Milk. Produced for the CWS.

NCFC 362
Mannequin Parade (1937)
A display of fashions. Produced by J H
Poyser and the Long Eaton Co-operative
Society.

NCFC 363
Old Friends Meet (1937)
A cartoon promoting bread and milk.
Produced by the Leicester Co-operative
Society.

NCFC 364
Radio Favourites (1937)
Biscuits. Produced for the CWS.

NCFC 365
Sweets of Victory (1937)
Lutona chocolate (cartoon). Produced for
the CWS.
See also: xxi

NCFC 366
Magic Letters (c.1937)
Subject unknown (cartoon). Produced for
the CWS.

NCFC 367
The Awakening of Mr Cole (1938)
The story of a modern-day Scrooge.
Produced by F H W Cox and the LCS
Political Committee.

NCFC 368
Co-op Congress, Scarborough (1938)
The first Congress film. Produced by A
Booth and the Bolton Co-operative Society.

NCFC 369
Fashion Parade (1938)
A promotional film for LCS fashions.
Produced by F H W Cox and the LCS
Political Committee.

NCFC 370
Holidays With Pay (1938)
How the divi could provide funds for a
holiday. Produced by J H Poyser and the
Long Eaton Co-operative Society.

NCFC 371
Playway to Co-operative Knowledge
(1938)
The Co-operative Union's junior class work.
Produced by Reginald Denny.

NCFC 372
Utopia (1938)

A satire on contemporary society. Produced
by F H W Cox and the LCS Political
Committee.
See also: NCFC 62

NCFC 373
WCG Congress, Southampton (1938)
The first film record of a WCG Congress.

NCFC 374
Each For All (c.1938)
Propaganda for Co-operation. Produced by
F H W Cox and the LCS Political
Committee.

NCFC 375
Odds and Ends (c.1938)
A concert party sponsored by the Guildford
and District Co-operative Society.

NCFC 376
Camberwell Is Prepared (1939)
A WFA production for the London borough.

NCFC 377
Co-op Union Education Convention (1939)
A record of the Newcastle Convention of the
Co-operative Union.

NCFC 378
**Manchester and Salford Society Pageant
at Bellevue, Manchester** (1939)
A rare colour film. Produced by A Booth and
the Bolton Co-operative Society.

NCFC 379
A New Recruit (1939)
Propaganda for the Co-operative Party.
Produced by F H W Cox and the LCS
Political Committee.

NCFC 380
Potter's Clay (1939)
Children and education. Produced by F H W
Cox and the LCS Political Committee.

NCFC 381
The Rape of Czecho-Slovakia (1939)
A documentary on events in Central Europe.
Produced by F H W Cox and the LCS
Political Committee.

NCFC 382
The Republic of Children (1939)
The Woodcraft Folk's international camp at
Liège. Produced by the Workers' Film
Association.
See also: NCFC 299

NCFC 383
WFA News Reel No.1 (1939)
The Workers' Film Association's only newsreel.

NCFC 384
Various [titles unknown] (1930s)
Several films relating to Eccles Co-operative Society.

NCFC 385
The Folk Go Camping (c.1930s)
The Woodcraft Folk: how to organise a camp.

NCFC 386
Various [titles unknown] (c.1930s)
Several films produced by the Education Department at Derby Co-operative Society.

NCFC 387
ARP Film, Bolton (1940)
One of several local community films. Produced by A Booth and the Bolton Co-operative Society.

NCFC 388
The Builders (1940)
The Amalgamated Union of Building Trade Workers. Produced by the Workers' Film Association.

NCFC 389
Co-op Congress, Glasgow (1940)
First film produced by the CWS Film Unit.

NCFC 390
The Home Front (1940)
An attack on profiteering. Produced by F H W Cox and the LCS Political Committee.
See also: xxvii

NCFC 391
It Must Not Happen Here (1940)
An attack on Nazism. Produced by F H W Cox and the LCS Political Committee.

NCFC 392
Mr Smith Wakes Up (1940)
The political awakening of an ordinary man. Produced by F H W Cox and the LCS Political Committee.
See also: xxvii

NCFC 393
Opening of Dairy (1941)
For Manchester and Salford Co-operative Society. Includes guest of honour, A V

Alexander. Produced by A Booth and the Bolton Co-operative Society.

NCFC 394
[Untitled] (1942)
Subject unknown. Film produced by Charles Christmas at the Birkenhead Co-operative Society.

NCFC 395
Golden Harvest (c.1942)
The manufacture of CWS Silk Cut cigarettes. Produced by the CWS.
See also: NCFC 98

NCFC 396
Machines and Men (c.1942)
A Ministry of Information film. Produced by the CWS Film Unit.

NCFC 397
Tobacco (c.1942)
The CWS tobacco factory. Produced by the CWS.
See also: NCFC 98

NCFC 398
The Rochdale Centenary Pageant (1944)
A record of Nottingham Co-operative Society's performance of L du Garde Peach's pageant. Produced by the Workers' Film Association.

NCFC 399
Gung Ho! (1945)
Chinese industrial Co-operatives. Produced by F H W Cox and the LCS Political Committee.

NCFC 400
The Precious Stone (1946)
A record of a pageant drama for the Guildford and District Co-operative Society. Produced by the Workers' Film Association.

NCFC 401
Co-op Congress, Brighton (1947)
Apparently the only postwar congress filmed. Produced by the CWS.

NCFC 402
Call to Action (1949)
A CWS film for the Operative Bakers' Union.

NCFC 403
From Cow to Customer (1949)
Film made by schoolchildren for the Bishop Auckland Co-operative Society.

NCFC 404
[St Cuthbert's] (1949)
Film for the St Cuthbert's Co-operative
Association.

NCFC 405
Profit Without Honour (1940s)
Co-operation contrasted with capitalism.
Produced by F H W Cox and the LCS
Political Committee.

NCFC 406
Keeping Up Appearances (c.1940s)
CWS goods complete a happy marriage.
Produced by the CWS.

NCFC 407
Mrs Feather Explains (c.1940s)
A comedy produced by the CWS.

NCFC 408
One of Those Days (c.1940s)
Produced by the CWS, and featuring Vera
Pearce and Denier Warren.

NCFC 409
Beauties of Britain (c.1954)
Public relations film, in colour. Produced by
the CWS.

NCFC 410
Fresh Approach (c.1957)
Publicity film for soap. Produced for the
SCWS.

NCFC 411
Meat for the Millions [2] (1958)
The CWS trade in meat.
See also: xxxii, NCFC 60

NCFC 412
Play with the Best (c.1950s)
A short promotional film for CWS Stanley
Matthews football boots. Produced by the
CWS.
See also: NCFC 151, NCFC 177

NCFC 413
Thirst Come, Thirst Served (c.1950s)
Soft drinks. Produced by the CWS.

Reference Prints

The following titles are held as reference prints at the stated film archives. Such prints are awaiting funds for preservation and, until that time, are presently unavailable for viewing.

NCFC 414
CWS Aldgate (1924)
b/w · silent · NFTVA
Newsreel item from *Topical Budget*.

NCFC 415
[Shieldhall Factories] (c.1930)
b/w · silent · SFA
Industrial film.

NCFC 416
Keeping Step With the Times (1933)
b/w · silent · SFA
Shoe manufacture.

NCFC 417
[International Co-operators' Day] (1936)
b/w · silent · NFTVA
Newsreel.

NCFC 418
Wishaw Co-operative Society Outing
(1939)
col · silent · SFA
Cultural.
See also: NCFC 1

NCFC 419
[Co-op Congress in Glasgow] (1940)
b/w · silent · SFA
Newsreel.

NCFC 420
A Radio Address by Neil Beaton (1943)
b/w · sound · SFA
Newsreel.

NCFC 421
Beyond the Sunset (1944)
b/w · sound · SFA
Flour milling.

NCFC 422
Youth Looks Ahead (1947)
b/w · sound · NFTVA

The Co-operative Youth Movement.

NCFC 423
[Wheatsheaf Bread] (c.1947)
b/w · sound · SFA
Promotional film.

NCFC 424
**Glasgow and District Co-operative
Association** (1953)
b/w · silent · SFA
Cultural.

NCFC 425
[Creamery, Wishaw] (1954)
b/w · silent · SFA
Milk products.

NCFC 426
[Co-op Advertisement 1] (c.1955)
b/w · sound · SFA
Promotional film.

NCFC 427
[Co-op Advertisement 2] (c.1955)
b/w · sound · SFA
Promotional film.

NCFC 428
[Cogent Cigarettes] (1956)
b/w · sound · SFA
Promotional film.

NCFC 429
[Co-op Butter] (1956)
b/w · sound · SFA
Promotional film.

NCFC 430
Knitwear Without Tears (1956)
col · sound · SFA
Promotional film.

NCFC 431
Co-operative Shopping (1957)

b/w · sound · SFA
Promotional film.

NCFC 432
Are Sales Lost on Saturdays? (1958)
b/w · silent · SFA
Training film.

NCFC 433
[99 Tea] (1959)
b/w · sound · SFA
Promotional film.

NCFC 434
[Glasgow Co-op Shoes] (1959)
b/w · silent · SFA
Promotional film.

NCFC 435
[Staff Recruitment] (1959)
col · sound · SFA
Training film.

NCFC 436
[Strawberry Jam] (1959)
b/w · sound · SFA
Promotional film.

NCFC 437
[Bluebell Margarine 1] (1960)
b/w · sound · SFA
Promotional film.

NCFC 438
[Facts and Figures 4] (1960)
b/w · sound · SFA
Promotional film.

NCFC 439
[Lofty Peak Cake Mixes 2] (1960)
b/w · sound · SFA
Promotional film.

NCFC 440
[Co-op Cheese] (c.1960)
b/w · sound · SFA
Promotional film.

NCFC 441
[Co-op Sauce] (c.1960)
b/w · sound · SFA
Promotional film.

NCFC 442
[Co-op Sugar] (c.1960)
b/w · sound · SFA
Promotional film.

NCFC 443
[Jelly Crystals] (c.1960)

b/w · sound · SFA
Promotional film.

NCFC 444
[Lemon Curd 1] (c.1960)
b/w · sound · SFA
Promotional film.

NCFC 445
[Lofty Peak Flour 1] (c.1960)
b/w · sound · SFA
Promotional film.

NCFC 446
[Lofty Peak Offer] (c.1960)
b/w · sound · SFA
Promotional film.

NCFC 447
[Marmalade 1] (c.1960)
b/w · sound · SFA
Promotional film.

NCFC 448
[Orchid Butter] (c.1960)
b/w · sound · SFA
Promotional film.

NCFC 449
[Orchid Margarine 1] (c.1960)
b/w · sound · SFA
Promotional film.

NCFC 450
[Pineapple and Rice] (c.1960)
b/w · sound · SFA
Promotional film.

NCFC 451
[Spring Sale] (c.1960)
b/w · sound · SFA
Promotional film.

NCFC 452
Made to Measure (1962)
b/w · sound · SFA
Training film (possibly not a Co-operative
subject)

NCFC 453
[Marmalade 2] (1962)
b/w · sound · SFA
Promotional film.

NCFC 454
Come Co-operative Shopping [22]
(c.1962)
b/w · sound · SFA
Promotional film.

NCFC 455
Come Co-operative Shopping [23] (1963)
b/w · sound · SFA
Promotional film.

NCFC 456
Royal Visit Co-operative Centenary
(c.1963)
col · silent · SFA
Newsreel.

NCFC 457
Come Co-operative Shopping [24] (1964)
b/w · sound · SFA
Promotional film.

NCFC 458
[Copex Cooking Fat] (1964)
b/w · sound · SFA
Promotional film.

NCFC 459
[Margarine – Cartoon 2] (1964)
b/w · sound · SFA
Promotional film.

NCFC 460
[Shieldhall Coffee] (1964)
b/w · sound · SFA
Promotional film.

NCFC 461
[Orchid Margarine 2] (1965)
b/w · sound · SFA
Promotional film.

NCFC 462
[Bluebell Margarine 2] (c.1965)
b/w · sound · SFA
Promotional film.

NCFC 463
[Lemon Curd 2] (c.1965)
b/w · sound · SFA
Promotional film.

NCFC 464
[Orchid Margarine 3] (c.1965)
b/w · sound · SFA
Promotional film.

NCFC 465
Come Co-operative Shopping [25] (1966)
b/w · sound · SFA
Promotional film.

NCFC 466
[Lofty Peak Flour 2] (1966)
b/w · sound · SFA

Promotional film.

NCFC 467
Divided We Stand (1968)
b/w · sound · NFTVA, SFA
Documentary.

NCFC 468
HM the Queen Visits Centenary House
(1968)
col · silent · SFA
Newsreel.

NCFC 469
[Co-op Advertisement 3] (1969)
b/w and col · sound · SFA

NCFC 470
[SCWS Special Offers] (1969)
b/w · sound · SFA
Promotional film.

NCFC 471
The Clan Has Arrived (c.1969)
b/w · silent · SFA
Promotional film.

NCFC 472
[Co-op Advertisement 4] (1960s)
b/w · silent · SFA
Promotional film.

NCFC 473
[Co-op Advertisement 5] (1960s)
b/w · sound · SFA
Promotional film.

NCFC 474
[Co-op Advertisement 6] (1960s)
b/w · sound · SFA
Promotional film.

NCFC 475
[Co-op Advertisement 7] (1960s)
b/w · sound · SFA
Promotional film.

NCFC 476
[Strathclyde Schoolwear] (c.1972)
col · sound · SFA
Promotional film.

NCFC 477
**[Opening of New Co-op Hypermarket,
Glasgow]** (1977)
col · silent · SFA
Newsreel.

Appendices

The British Co-operative Movement, comprising many hundreds of societies and millions of members, had to ensure that adequate channels of communication were in place so that its varied and numerous constituents remained appraised of important developments and decisions. Moreover, the ethos of democracy demanded an easy and widespread flow of information, thereby facilitating participation and debate. Correspondingly, the Movement engaged in extensive publishing activities in the attempt to communicate with societies and members: newspapers, journals, pamphlets, magazines and leaflets were all conscripted into that task. Of course, the cinema and films also offered an invaluable means to inform and educate regarding Co-operative issues of the day.

Accordingly, the historian of Co-operation has access to a wealth of written testimony and evidence concerning the emergence and development of Co-operative practice and policy. The month-to-month debate of members and officials is recorded in the minutes of the democratic structures, the meetings of the local, regional and national committees of Co-operation, which provided the arena for the decision-making process. The Co-operative press guaranteed a wider constituency for that debate and, furthermore, offered a platform for propagandists of a multitude of causes. The nature of cinema and its potential for publicity, propaganda and education were subjects that attracted considerable interest and attention amongst Co-operators. In harmony with the dominant attitude of the times, film was thought to be immensely influential, and much effort was expended in arguing for its mobilisation to help persuade the public to recognise the virtues and benefits of Co-operative trading and ideals. The fine detail of a satisfactory cinema policy was discussed at length, and the varied experiments and strategies in production, distribution and exhibition were reported to an interested readership.

The following appendices present a selection of articles and reports which appeared in the Movement's contemporary press, and its publications, revealing the genuine concern to bring the cinema to aid in the task of "making Co-operators".

By the eve of the First World War, the Co-operative Movement's weekly newspaper, *The Co-operative News, had a circulation of approximately 80 000. This article represents the first detailed discussion of the potential of cinema to inform the masses about Co-operation. By that date, the CWS had been offering film displays on behalf of member societies for sixteen years, and this anonymous publicist is suggesting an intensification and expansion of that work. It is important to note that this recognition of the propaganda value of cinema by the Co-operative Movement predates any comparable discussion of the subject either by the trade union Movement or by the Labour Party.*

*   *   *

THE CINEMA.

Should It be Used for Co-operative Purposes?

How to Reach the Masses

[BY OUR SPECIAL COMMISSIONER.]

THE magic-lantern slide has doubtlessly played an important part in the educational work of co-operative societies. But its day is now over; it has been killed by the moving picture, which cinematographic art, invention, and enterprise have now brought to a high state of development. At any rate, if it has not been killed, it is, contrasted with the "living" picture, a rather tame object, and one that would never touch the imagination, or convey the real facts of life, like its ingenious rival. The possibilities of the cinema for entertaining and instructive purposes are tremendous. Unfortunately, its use is sometimes abused.

The object of this article, however, is not to criticise, or eulogise, the picture palace, but to suggest that the cinema might be used, with much advantage, for spreading a knowledge of co-operative activities. We are always looking about us for features that will not only bring people into our ranks, but that disseminate information about our great undertakings, and by that means convey something of the extent of our operations and their possibilities in the near and the distant future. Why not bring the cinema to aid? Why not make use of it in all parts of the kingdom for attracting the masses—young and old—in a way that would enable them to obtain knowledge, and, at the same time, be vastly entertained?

I am one who believes that the people should do everything for themselves in a collective capacity. Co-operators should do everything for themselves in their co-operative capacity. We have the men and the women; we have the money; we have the brains and the talent; we have a vast and an increasing number of people on our side. We are the force that is capable of transforming the industrial and economic conditions into that state in which we would like to see them and know them, and live them, when we think of what mankind should be, and might be, and ought to be. But we should do everything for ourselves; we should grow and manufacture our food, our clothes; we should build our own houses, our own factories, our own schools, our own colleges. The ultimate object of our activities should be that we should not be dependent upon anybody except ourselves. We should have our own colleges, our own educational institutions of every character. We should provide our own amusements, our own forms of social enjoyments. And our amusements and social enjoyments should be as pure as should be the food and the clothes we supply for our material needs.

Why, then, not bring in the cinema? We are extremely well organised for its use; we have our buildings in which it could be utilised. Its purpose would be that of entertainment, education, and social contact. If we do not make use of it, it will remain in the hands of other people to detract from our own forms of entertainment. I do not suggest that there should be cinema shows in every co-operative hall every afternoon and evening. But we might have something in the shape of a central body, or committee, to organise the feature, to arrange for films, to control the machinery, and send out the living pictures here and there, as we now send out lecturers, &c. However, all this would be a matter for consideration, if it were decided to carry out the idea.

What should the pictures be? Co-operative, principally, with general ones intervening—educative and humorous. We should not keep out humour—in fact, we would do with a little more humour in the co-operative movement; it would certainly not make us any less human, nor any less divine, nor less serious. But there is no end of scope for pictures of our own work. We could have "living" scenes from our workshops and factories, from our offices, from our warehouses, and from our C.W.S. market days. We could have topical scenes that occur from time to time—such as distressed people being fed by co-operative food during strikes and lockouts, or industrial disasters. In fact, the more we went into the idea, and on with the idea, features would open out before us. We could touch with them incidents connected with the life, work, and habits of the whole of the world's workers.

We could show how our boots are made, how our clothes are made, how our soap is made, how our biscuits are made, how our newspapers are printed, how our jams are made, how our flour is manufactured; and so on, and so on. Take the great "Sun" mill at Manchester. There would be the ship bringing the raw material into the Canal siding, the wonderful grain elevators greedily devouring it (as it were) from the hold of the vessels and carrying it to the capacious silos. And we could see it conveyed by marvellous automatic means to the machinery, see it being turned into flour, and see the flour being loaded for the retail store. That is just one feature. We could see our mills at work—the machinery running and the operatives labouring—in all parts of the kingdom; in all the Co-operative Wholesale Societies' works in England, Wales, Scotland, and Ireland. We could see moving crowds of co-operative workpeople going to, or coming from, the great industrial establishments we now own, not to speak of similar scenes in connection with retail societies, such, for instance, as the iron-ore miners of the Desborough Society. We could see our looms at work at Bury and Radcliffe.

In fact, you will realise for yourselves what could be seen and enjoyed. I am mentioning only one or two things that come in my mind as I write. We could get pictures from sources of raw material that are manufactured into articles that we buy from our societies. There are, for instance, the raw cotton fields of Georgia, the coalfields of Yorkshire, the tobacco fields of old Kentucky, the sheep farms of Australia, the flax fields of Belgium, the wheat fields of Canada. We could get scenes from Manchester, London, Glasgow, Belfast, Newcastle, Bristol, Cardiff, and Aberdeen, where we have great co-operative properties. We could secure films depicting human, industrial, and picturesque scenes in and about our tea plantations in Ceylon, from butter depôts in Denmark and Ireland. We could describe, in living detail, Spanish life at Denia, whence we get our Valencia raisins; in Greece and in Asiatic Turkey, whence we procure the chief supplies of our Christmas dried fruits. We could bring living pictures from Sydney (Australia), where we have our tallow works. Or we could have interesting pictures from places nearer home, not forgetting the Potteries, where we have something to do with the manufacture of pots. And what of the strange and fascinating scenes we could procure from West Africa, where the Wholesale Society is now negotiating for the establishment of co-operative works—to wit, in Sierra Leone. Indeed, the co-operative movement is now so big, the operations of the two Wholesale Societies so wide, that we could carry living pictures, directly and indirectly associated with our co-operative enterprise, from most parts of the world, in addition to sights of human interest from our own islands—England, Ireland, Scotland, and Wales.

The cinema would lend itself to a splendid means of propaganda, an attractive means of propaganda, and at the same time it would be a fine educational feature in both co-operative and general subjects. The great advantage to us would be its spread of a knowledge of co-operative activities in a way that the rank-and-file of the movement would come to see and learn. We are always talking about the necessity of reaching the masses and bringing the masses together. The cinema would do this for us. At present, our conferences about the movement, including co-operative production, are attended mostly by the same people—what I mean is, that one nearly always meets the same people there, the same faces, and hears the same speeches again and again. This is all right, in a way, because all movements are kept going, are kept knitted together, by the constant attention of a comparatively few people. It is necessary that these people should meet together and discuss things. It is very important, however, that the mass of members outside these persistent workers should be touched in some way or other. This is where the cinema would be useful. Is it not a matter that is worthy of consideration by our educational authorities in joint action, perhaps, with the two Wholesale Societies? The uses to which it could be put may be perceived by any reader, according to his or her knowledge and imagination. The object of this article is merely to introduce the idea, and vaguely suggest its uses and importance.

Beginning in 1928, a series of expensive advertising films was commissioned by the CWS for screening to general audiences in public cinemas. This report introduced the scheme to a Co-operative readership whom in the following period were informed of the weekly playdates of The Magic Basket, *the first film in the series. The further titles in preparation, alluded to in the article, were as follows:* Round the Clock *(1930; biscuits),* What the Diary Told *(1929; soap),* Jammy *(1930; preserves),* Footsteps *(1929; boots and shoes);* The King and the Cakes *(1930; flour) and* Her Dress Allowance *(1930; drapery). [The production company referred to in the penultimate paragraph was, in fact, Publicity Films Ltd.]*

*   *   *

A FILM WITH A STORY INTEREST.
DEPICTING CO-OPERATIVE FACTORIES AND SHOPS.
TO BE SHOWN AT 1,000 CINEMAS.

During the next twelve months the picture-goers of this country will see a new film entitled "The Magic Basket." It takes four to five minutes to show, and depicts processes in C.W.S. factories, and emphasises the advantages of joining a co-operative society.

Commencing at the end of January, this film is to be shown at 1,000 cinema halls in this country, in the industrial towns during the winter and autumn, and at seaside places in spring and summer. It is the first time the C.W.S. has had a film prepared for public exhibition in this way. Local societies will be acquainted of the fact when the film is appearing in their districts.

The letters of the main title will be made of wicker. They fly apart and the pieces of wicker build themselves into a real shopping basket. Then follows this screen title:—

Has it ever occurred to you that behind the brains and capital by which great businesses are founded, behind the labour by which goods are produced, in actual effective control of the world of Industry, is the housewife's shopping basket?

A huge factory fades in. Then follow a series of spectacular snapshots filmed in selected C.W.S. factories. The scenes dissolve one into the other, and so far as possible are taken from unusual viewpoints, the idea being to express the whirl and might of industry. The last scene of the series dissolves back to the shopping basket.

The scene changes to the interior of a co-operative store. A bright little woman is chatting to the smiling, white jacketed shop assistant who is packing her various purchases into her shopping basket, "The Magic Basket." The customer remarks:—

And to think that I am part owner of the factories where all these are made!

The assistant replies:—

Same here, ma'am—I 'm a member myself. The "divi's" very handy.

After showing the exterior of a fine co-operative store the picture re-opens in a cashier's office. In some cases members are withdrawing dividend, and we see our friend enter. Then this screen title follows:—

It's my birthday—I'm going to treat myself to a new frock.

The cashier chats cheerily as he pays her out.

The next scene is the interior of a drapery department. She is buying her frock. We see a representative display of goods as, with the aid of a courteous assistant, she makes her choice. She also buys her husband a handsome scarf.

The picture re-opens in a middle or good working-class living-room. She takes the C.W.S. products out of the basket one by one, and goes into another room, where she puts on the new frock. Delightedly she looks herself up and down, and is in the midst of a pirouette of feminine satisfaction when her husband comes home from work. When he sees the present he asks:—

But how did you manage it?

She produces her share book, opens it, and in a close-up we see the entries denoting accumulation of dividends.

This film has been produced for the C.W.S. by Films Publicity Limited, London, who are also filming at the present time six C.W.S. factories, including Crumpsall biscuit works, Irlam soap works, Middleton jam factory, Northampton boot and shoe works, Avonmouth flour mill, and a textile mill.

These films are being made according to the latest methods, and there will be an attractive story in connection with each. The films are to be used in connection with C.W.S. lectures, but copies will be lent to societies that desire to show them in their own premises or in local picture houses.

Influential elements within the Movement recognised negative as well as positive attributes in the film medium. It was widely appreciated on the Left that cinema was a powerful instrument of persuasion in the control of capitalist interests. Beginning as early as 1928, members of the Women's Co-operative Guild (WCG) mounted a campaign against the overt militarism of war films. This report represented the opening salvo in a long-running debate concerning the evils of the war film, and many further articles and readers' letters were published in subsequent issues. The WCG played a significant part in the interwar pacifist Movement.

* * *

DANGER OF WAR FILMS.

THINGS WE WOMEN SHOULD WATCH.

HOW PEACE WORK IS THWARTED.

There is scarcely a reader of these "Pages" who does not take some interest in films. It is impossible to disregard the part played by them in the leisure hours of the nation.

It may be, however, that the increasing number of war films has not yet been realised either by our readers or the public generally. "Zeebrugge," "The Prince of Wales' Tour in the 'Renown'," "Britain's Birthright," "Life on the Ocean Wave," "Flag Lieutenant," and "The Luck of the Navy" are a few well-known names given to war films. And it is a fact that peace-loving people are beginning to be alarmed at the popularity of these pictures.

German Professor's Regrets.

A German professor engaged in educational work in this country has shown his very genuine regret on this matter in the following words:— "Is there no way to stop the war-film business altogether? Here we are, men and women who try to bridge the gulf opened between England and Germany by the war, who attempt to heal the wounds done by war, we work hard to bring about an atmosphere averse to that of the years of the war and after, to create a mutual feeling that lets us forget the hostile feeling of war and after-war time. But what is the good of it if the mass of the people are always again reminded of the war superiority of one nation over the other, if our atmosphere again and again gets poisoned by, as it seems to me, partial memories of times we all would do better to be ashamed of?"

Sinister Moves.

There is a very sinister side to the question which all guildswomen would do well to watch. In the House of Commons on December 13th, Commodore King (Financial Secretary to the War Office), in reply to a question by Commander Kenworthy, said: "There are at the present moment three films for which military facilities are being given or have been promised, and three other cases are under consideration."

Again, Mr. Baldwin has declared that "it is the policy of the Board of Admiralty, the Army Council, and the Air Council to give assistance, by way of loan of personnel and material, to approved British film companies engaged in making war films, with certain business provisions safeguarding the secrecy of military operations and financial arrangements."

The Federation of British Industries is also concerned with the business of war films. They inform us that under the auspices of the Navy League, the Battles of Coronel and Falkland Islands are to be made the subject of a great national film, in the production of which the Admiralty are giving their wholehearted support.

Women to the Rescue.

The Women's International League are taking up the question, and are exposing the danger which is close upon us.

"This question of war films has been engaging our attention for some time," said Miss Dorothy Woodman the secretary. "Lovers of peace, as we are, we are not necessarily against war films as such. They are inevitable, and even necessary, if the future is to learn from the history of the past. What is bad about them is that children are in danger of being taught to love and admire war in itself, for it is too often made attractive to them on the screen. We of the older generation have memories which correct this, but the younger generation must not, through the influence of some of these films, be made to think that war is the normal and in fact a glorious way of settling international difficulties. It is this mentality alone which will bring the recruiting sergeant his response, if and when he again makes his appearance."

War Office Congratulates.

Miss Woodman said that so effectively had one recent film glorified war that the manager of one of the largest cinemas in London has been congratulated by the War Office for its great patriotic effort of helping to raise recruits. "We are actively engaged in arranging a conference in London on February 21st," said Miss Woodman, "dealing with this very question of the influence of the war films. At the afternoon session a prominent M.P. and a well-known film critic are being invited to speak on 'Why and by Whom are War Films Being produced?' At the second session, to which teachers will be specially invited, the subject will be 'How Do War Films Affect the Public?' A leading psychologist and other speakers well known to the film public will take part, and Miss Agnes Dawson will, we hope, take the chair. Such a conference, to which the film trade, the War Office, Admiralty, and Air Force, as well as political, social, and educational associations will be invited, should do much to bring into the open the whole question of war films."

Like many businesses, local Co-ops sought publicity from the visit of and endorsement by well-known celebrities. For the Co-operative Movement no one was more suitable – or popular – than Gracie Fields, herself a native of Rochdale. This report of her visit to a Birmingham Society store indicates the star's genuine ease with her adoring public. In 1929, "Our Gracie" recorded the popular "Stop and Shop at the Co-op Shop", to which the article refers.

* * *

A LOVELY "CO-OP."

SHOPPING AT THE "CO-OP. SHOP."

MISS GRACIE FIELDS VISITS BIRMINGHAM'S EMPORIUM.

MISS GRACIE FIELDS, the most popular comedienne of the day, spent half-an-hour in a homely atmosphere on Tuesday, when she experienced the pleasure of bargain hunting at a sale at Birmingham's excellent "Co-op. shop."

Mr. J. McDowall (secretary of the Birmingham Society) and Mr. H. Johnson (drapery manager) welcomed Miss Fields in the Grand Louvre premises, in which many thousands of Birmingham women find their wants are so well supplied. That their choice is good was confirmed by the famous visitor.

"It is a lovely co-op.," she said. "I didn't think you had such a wonderful shop. Your display is wonderful and your goods are exceptionally cheap."

As a native of the birthplace of modern co-operation, Miss Fields naturally knows much about the co-operative movement. "We were always keen about 'co-ops.' at Rochdale," was her remark. "In fact, whenever there were funerals we always went to the 'co-op.' for teas!"

By this time her presence in the shop had become known, and hundreds of women crowded round to get a glimpse of her. They were delighted with her naturalness, her homely comments and cheerful repartee.

For a minute or two Miss Fields became businesslike, and after turning up the sleeves of her woollen jumper endeavoured to sell "a nice bit of stuff" from the artificial silk counter.

She then visited the lingerie section and the millinery and mantle sections, trying on a beret and a coatee, and also examining with interest the evening gowns.

A Colleague from Wigan.

Her natural and unassuming demeanour captivated everyone. When introduced to Mr. J. W. Whatmough (the assistant secretary of the society), who hails from

Wigan, Miss Fields greeted him with "Hello! I have a brother-in-law who comes from Wigan." Assistants, customers, and officials were all treated in the same friendly manner.

At the end of her tour Miss Fields signed the visitors' book of the society, and accepted a souvenir of her visit from Mr. Johnson. There was traditional cautiousness in her response to Mr. Johnson's suggestion that he should forward the souvenir to her. "I had better take it with me," she said. "You might forget to send it."

Miss Fields is appearing at the Birmingham Hippodrome this week, and one of her principal hits is "The Co-op Shop." For this now famous song Birmingham has provided an additional verse, composed by Mr. J. Scurrah (Birmingham Society's publicity department), which Miss Fields agreed to sing on Wednesday, Thursday, Friday, and Saturday evenings this week. It runs:—

But it's more than a shop, the "Co-op." shop;
    It's more like a home from home.
There's Women's Guilds each week;
For the ailing and the weak
    There's a Convalescent Home;
Playing fields and a kiddies' gala day,
And the old man's insured wi' nowt to pay.

In addition Miss Fields makes reference to the local society in her amusing patter.

Appendix E: from *The Millgate* September 1934

Throughout the 1930s, activists for Labour cinema published regularly and widely. This article, which appeared in a popular Co-operative monthly journal, argues for expansion in the Movement's film work and suggests some of the advantages offered by film in terms of publicity and propaganda. Some of the recommendations were adopted by some societies at various times, but a national policy along the lines indicated never came to be. There was a film about the Rochdale Pioneers (1944); many Co-operative film shows were enlivened by entertaining cartoons (the News Theatre of the Blackpool Society had exclusive rights in the district for Mickey Mouse cartoons!); and A V Alexander, a Co-operative parliamentarian, appeared in several films, most notably Advance Democracy *(1938). It is interesting to note the acknowledgement of the activities of the Conservative and Unionist Film Association – a threat, it is recognised, which should be met.*

* * *

A FILM PLAN.

Why Not News Reels of Co-operative Events?

By A. S. Graham.

AT long last co-operation is to launch a Press push, and plans for a new newspaper are nearly settled. But I can find no mention of the film push–which is as badly needed. Only a month or two ago large vans complete with daylight screens, canned speeches, and excellent documentary films set out from London to spread Conservatism. Each week another institution is added to the list of those using the screen to get information and propaganda home. More and more it is being realised that films, hitting through the eyes and making people actually see for themselves, are the most forceful weapon in the hands of advertisers, educationists, and propagandists alike. But do the leaders of the "Co-op." yet realise it? A few advertising films have been made, and there are others featuring such C.W.S. news as the visit of the Duke of York to Higher Irlam. But the full extent of the field open has never been considered. There is no reason why the halls of all local societies should not be fitted up with apparatus, and treated for some nights in the week as miniature news theatres on the model of those now operating successfully in London. The shows could be advertised in the ordinary way by placard and thrown open to non-members. Provided that the films shown had been well chosen for their interest value, a small sum might be charged for admission.

Should this plan seem too ambitious to start with, apparatus might be shared among several societies in the same area, films hired in common, and the show given one night per fortnight in each hall.

Nothing can be done, however, until the films themselves are provided, until in fact the movement realises what a chance is waiting to be taken. The 1933 year book contains the sentence: "If the 6,000,000 co-operative members had been *conscious* consumers the penal Tax would never have been imposed," and states that though the Co-operative Party has the highest membership of any in politics, the average member knows nothing of its programme or policy.

The easiest way to remedy this lamentable ignorance of the rank and file, and lack of solid party feeling, is through educational films made by experts. The subjects for them are not difficult to find. One should be historical, starting with the Rochdale pioneers, and emphasising not so much how factory has been added unto factory as the movement grew, but how the dividend principle has led to prosperity. Methods of organisation might be compared with those of similar capitalist concerns. Another film should be made on workers' conditions in the C.W.S. A third would treat of the national aspect of the movement, based perhaps on the "Britain Reborn" pamphlets, with a commentary by Mr. A. V. Alexander. The work of co-operative officials in government service is another likely angle.

It would not be too hard a matter to draw up a full programme of such films and, shown in the halls, they could not fail to make the average member politically and movement conscious in a shorter time than almost anything else.

Apart from the propaganda there is material in the movement for two other classes of film. The news theatres could hardly keep going without news. Every conference provides this, and so also does the opening and building of new factories at home and abroad. How many members have seen or heard their leaders or know the kind of questions which are settled at conferences? Very few. Yet the questions are often vital, and the speeches sometimes of real interest. New factories are opened regularly, and there are sports meetings, choir festivals, and other recreational activities worth the camera's attention. There should easily be material throughout Great Britain for a first-rate news film each week.

"Drifters" was an example of the final class of film–the documentary. In this field the available material is immense. Apart from factory processes in this country which should provide many hundred thousand feet of celluloid, there are co-operative endeavours throughout the world that simply ask to be filmed. Methods of training in Siam, South Africa, or Iceland, are full of novelty. And a series of travel films could be undertaken. Using these three kinds of films, and hiring others of the Mickey Mouse type to give the lighter side–or perhaps even making those–the Co-operative Movement should be able to put itself across as never before.

If the films were technically up to a good standard they would hold attention and attract audiences. There would have to be no suggestion that propaganda was being pushed down people's throats, merely, instead, a persistent stream of accurate information presented in a palatable way. Co-operation's great enemy is ignorance, not misconception. The film is the best weapon to banish it.

Co-operative societies expended considerable resources on providing leisure and cultural activities for their members. Here is a particularly striking example: the provision of commercial cinemas, mainly by societies in north-west England, to help meet the recreational needs of Co-operators and the local community. It is apparent that such a resource offered various benefits to a local society in terms of trade and publicity, yet it is important to stress its real innovatory nature at a time when influential elements in the Labour Movement were hostile to commercial popular culture and American influences.

* * *

CO-OPERATIVE CINEMA ENTERPRISE.

ONLY a few co-operative societies have ventured to provide facilities for the leisure hours of their members and the public generally. This is a matter that should have some attention from societies that seek a complete and comprehensive service both in the daily routine and in the evening hours.

One of the most successful examples of the co-operative cinema is at Dewsbury. Mr. E. B. Wright, the general manager and secretary of the society, has given us the impressions of the cinema manager, whose views are based upon actual knowledge of the business. In his opinion, the two chief assets conferred upon any co-operative society which include a cinema among its activities are, firstly, the purely commercial. The second is more subtle and none the less valuable. Can a Co-operative Cinema be made to pay? Given sound and enterprising management, it quite definitely can. One has only to examine the accounts of Dewsbury Pioneers' Industrial Society to find one instance of how profits can be made. There is probably no reason why several more societies should not augment their income by supplying the entertainment needs of the townspeople just, for example, as they supply their grocery needs.

There are, however, other benefits besides financial ones. A cinema on the society's own premises has a very real social value for the members. It is, so to speak, their own entertainment rendezvous. Managers will tell you that there are certain co-operator-patrons who attend on the same day with almost clockwork regularity—often meeting to exchange a few words in the lounge before going in to enjoy the show. To be successful, however, it is necessary to aim far beyond one's own members for patronage. The cinema has to meet opposition on a purely competitive basis. The best programmes draw the people . . . that is the indisputable fact which the managers have to face.

A successful co-operative cinema is constantly attracting potential members into the building. In time many of these potential members become actual members.

In Lancashire, the Billington and Whalley Society, near Blackburn, and that at Clitheroe have provided cinemas with diverse results. That of the Billington and

Whalley Society is known throughout the district as the "Co-op. Cinema, Whalley." It seats 500 people and provides a first-class two hours' show, the highest price being only 7d., including tax. The lowest charge for admission is 4d., while children are give a half price advantage from Monday to Friday evenings, Saturday being the only exception to this concession to juveniles. The cinema has the support of all classes in the locality, both members and non-members, and is generally full at its one-show nightly performances. On Saturday two shows are given.

During the days of silent films the cinema showed a substantial profit for many years. Since the advent of "talkies" this has declined somewhat, but even now the profits are quite satisfactory. Moreover, the cinema provides a splendid opportunity for advertising co-operation. Occasionally the C.W.S. films are shown, and more often slides announcing changes in prices at the stores, various meetings of the society, and other local matters are exhibited. The whole of the business of the cinema is conducted by the management committee, Mr. A. Brooks (the secretary and manager) also acting as the cinema manager. During the winter months they arrange for a free afternoon for adults on the first Thursday in each month. This consists of pictures for an hour, and a 15 minutes' talk on the Society by the manager, who is thus able to keep 500 adults well informed of the progress of their local society.

The experience of the Clitheroe Equitable Society has not been quite so rosy, probably owing to the fact that there are two other cinemas in the town and that they all have a seating capacity of 800 each. This seems rather much for a population of only 12,000. The Clitheroe Society has a membership of 2,400, so that the members might well do a little more to support their own enterprise as they have the most attractive hall and a cinema which gives as much comfort as any in the town. Certainly the Clitheroe co-operators have shown enterprise, and the committee deserve the support of their people in maintaining it on a successful financial basis.

The Mossley Society has a cinema, which, after some experience of running it as a departmental venture, has been let to a company which runs three other cinemas. In that way it is becoming a useful asset. Horbury Society also has a cinema to which we shall make reference in an early issue.

The Scunthorpe Society has a cinema which is greatly appreciated throughout the district. It is on a paying basis and always secures good audiences. The co-operative cinema has the best talking apparatus in the town, and its popular programmes, introducing the newest films, prove the contention that it is doing something for the organisation of the leisure hours of the people. During the past half year the attendance at the Jubilee Cinema of the Scunthorpe Society exceeded 107,000. A popular feature of the week's entertainment is the matinee on Monday, Thursday and Saturday afternoons. Sometimes, when pictures by George Arliss or other stars are shown, morning programmes at 10-30 a.m. are given, so that the shift workers at the local steelworks may have opportunity of enjoying the performance. This is an innovation by Mr. Alfred Wyld, the general secretary, which contributes to the success of the cinema. When the society holds mannequin parades, the matinee shows are suspended so that the parades can be held under the most pleasing conditions. This, of course, does not interfere with the evening "two houses nightly" arrangements.

This little review of co-operative cinema enterprise may be regarded as supplementary to the paper on the Co-operative Use of Leisure, given at the International Congress. We shall be pleased to have news of any other co-operative cinemas in this country—and also the views of readers on the development of co-operative pleasures for the people.

Appendix G: from *The Producer* August 1935

Throughout the 1930s, several societies experimented with amateur ciné equipment, and the results were broadly discussed in the Movement's press. A leading propagandist was J H Poyser of the Long Eaton Society, Derbyshire, and here is an early report of his film activities. Note how he advocates a balance between entertainment and propaganda in film displays, a situation that was being grappled with by Co-op publicists throughout the Movement. Poyser was an important innovator of local Co-op films; as well as staging fictional subjects, as related here, he worked with some of the early amateur colour film stocks and sound-recording equipment. The CWS Greater Nottingham region has recently situated its main hypermarket at Toton, the east Derbyshire village mentioned in the text of the article.

* * *

Local Co-operative Films
"Something Different" in Propaganda, Education, and Entertainment
Review of a successful experiment

By J. H. POYSER

MUCH of my leisure during the summer of 1934 was spent in the pleasant voluntary task of taking a number of 16 m.m. silent films for the education committee of the Long Eaton Society. These included "Urban District Council Activities," "Long Eaton, 1934, Hospital Carnival," and "Co-operative Milk"—a film showing the progress of milk from the cows grazing on the society's farm, through the dairy processes and distribution, to the members' tea-table.

A Popular Medium

Subsequent experience has proved convincingly that the sub-standard film is a popular and most fruitful medium of co-operative propaganda, education, and entertainment. Actually, about 80 per cent of the programme is "what the audience wants"; the remaining 20 per cent is made up of co-operative education and propaganda. The programme constitutes an approximately two-hour show. Over sixty shows were held last winter, with gratifying success, the producer giving a running commentary, sometimes serious, often flippant, and occasionally humorous.

Admittance was free to the shows, for which the committee were responsible. When shows were given under the auspices of such organisations as social clubs, chapel bazaars, women's institutes, Wesley guilds, and so on, the responsible organisation was free to charge or not as it pleased. The committee were satisfied with the 20 per cent propaganda reaching people to whom the society could not otherwise appeal.

The advantages of 16 m.m. films are that the film itself is not too costly and is non-inflammable; the cine-camera is handy and manageable, and the projecting apparatus portable and easily fixed. Within eight minutes of arrival at a village in an ordinary car, the operator and commentator have fixed up the apparatus and started the show before a crowded audience in the village hall.

Committee asked for more

Prompted by their experience during the past twelve months, the committee have asked for four more local films for next season's showing. They will deal with "Co-operative Bread," "Spending the Divi.," "Educational Facilities in Long Eaton," and the "Hospital Carnival" again. In reserve is "Building Long Eaton's Biggest Shop," a film showing how the C.W.S. Building Department has demolished the society's old central premises and built a £40,000 emporium in its place. On the screen, building operations extending considerably over a year are condensed into half-an-hour.

The new films are in various stages of production. For the bread film "shots" have been taken of ploughing, cultivating, drilling the seed, harrowing, rolling the growing wheat, and the wheat in ear on the society's Toten Farm. The bread-baking will probably be filmed before the wheat is harvested, threshed and milled into flour from which the bread will appear to be made!

Readers may be interested in the progress of the educational film, especially as it gives opportunities for touches of propaganda, all the more effective because unexpected, though not out of place. Permission to film was readily obtained from the authorities, as well as the approval and assistance of head teachers. First to be filmed was the elementary and advanced evening continuation classes.

"Shots" at the Classes

Here arose the difficulty of getting sufficient light, as there was a limit to the floodlights to be borrowed and the tension the schools' electric wiring would stand. However, this problem was overcome, and a co-operative bookkeeping class and the women's physical culture class were among the "shots." Elementary schoolgirls sipping their co-operative school milk, another class of girls in the school swimming baths, infants at "nose drill," elementary schoolboys doing woodwork, and an Easter week-end school at Trent College are other typical scenes.

One of the "high spots" of the film is the Jubilee Day holiday. On that occasion a *colour film w*as taken of hundreds of children in procession and scores of schoolgirls in country dances on the local park, as well as some of the four thousand children enjoying a picnic tea in the park—drinking their tea out of Jubilee beakers made by the C.W.S. and presented by the Long Eaton Society, and eating food prepared by the society's café department! This film will carry the audience from infants' school to college in half-an-hour. Incidentally, the stodgy title, "Educational Facilities," has been replaced by "Happy Schooldays."

The "Sumbodies"

"Spending the Divi." is intended to show the trials and troubles of "The Sumbodies "—an unemployed man, his wife and family—and how the co-operative dividend proved a godsend. Propaganda will be introduced for the new emporium by arranging that the "Sumbodies" spend their dividend in its allied departments. It was found that the average dividend did not provide enough money for the purpose; but this problem was solved and publicity given to yet another of the society's benefits, by arranging for Mrs. Sumbodie to receive the collective life insurance money due on the convenient death of her aunt!

A suitable council house could not be found for the interior scenes, so the choir room was converted into a film studio, with two walls improvised from lath and cardboard, and with some old furniture. Mrs. Sumbodie (played by Mrs. A. Styles, a director of the society) was asked to borrow a baby, and turned up at the studio with a borrowed baby which was less than a week old, but acted the part excellently.

If this film fulfils expectations it will prove valuable in drawing attention to the advantages of cooperation, the dividend, collective life insurance, and the new emporium.

The eight-day hospital carnival, with its crowds, processions, bands, fancy dresses, its life, movement and colour, is ideal for film work, if favoured by sunshine. A minor feature of the carnival is the co-operative cinema, which proved very popular last year. The choir room will be the cinema, at which the Saturday and Sunday events will be shown on the Tuesday, and so on through the week. Three shows a day will be given, with a charge for admission, the money going to carnival funds.

So much for the productions in hand at Long Eaton. Now a word about costs. The projector and screen, &c., cost £60, the cine-camera £30, the film for a two-hour show is estimated at £50, but varies with the type of film used. With the exception of the services of the full-time education secretary, who has done much of the humdrum work of cutting, splicing, and operating the projector as part of his ordinary duties, all the work has been done voluntarily. Costs of shows vary from one shilling, covering dispatch of apparatus to a local schoolroom or club, to £2, covering hire of village hall, chair rent, travelling and advertising.

Handling the Cine-camera

Little difficulty has been found in handling the cine-camera. Any fair amateur photographer can manage this. Developing occasions no worry; the film makers see to this, and make a charge which includes processing. As regards actors, there is a general pleasure—with few exceptions—in "being on the films" and in doing precisely what is asked. No doubt experience as stage manager to amateur operatic and dramatic groups assists in the work of visualising a picture in advance and handling people to produce the desired effect. Apart from the limits of finance and subject imposed by the committee, the producer has an absolutely free hand.

A Comparison

One outstanding point is the large amount of time involved in filming. On one occasion three hours were spent in making and taking a tricky title that appears only five seconds on the screen. On another, three hours on Jubilee Day provided enough film for six minutes' screen time. The running commentary can be absorbing and interesting. Lecturing to lantern slides is child's play by comparison. One has to know the film thoroughly, and every word has to be timed to a split second.

Any society or education committee looking for an effective means of propaganda, advertising, or education would be well advised to consider the appeal of the "movies." These will appeal to all types of audiences: the Long Eaton shows have attracted young people between 18 and 25 years old, as well as others above and below this age. There are difficulties, but they can be surmounted; mistakes will be made, but they need not appear on the screen.

Again, local production is better than buying cinemas and using films produced in Hollywood or Elstree, considering the amount of money involved. Local scenes with local people in local activities have been the secret of success with films at Long Eaton.

Then there is the value to the trading side of the society to be considered. Here are comparative figures for the society's dairy trade during the period the co-operative milk film was being made and shown:—

Cash sales, quarter ending April 14th, 1934, £12,391.

Cash sales, quarter ending April 13th, 1935, £13,399.

An increase of over £1,000 per quarter.

Here is something refreshingly and successfully different from standing on a platform bleating for loyalty.

As this example shows, Co-operators kept themselves appraised of the wider debates on the nature and influence of film. Culturally, the suspicion and denigration of popular commercial cinema crossed ideological lines, and both reactionaries and Labour groups tended to demand more uplifting films. The statistics cited in the article are derived from Simon Rowson's famous survey, "A Statistical Survey of the Cinema Industry in Great Britain in 1934" (1936).

* * *

The World Around Us

The Influence of the Cinema

SOME astounding figures of the size of the cinema industry in Great Britain were given before the Royal Statistical Society a month ago. There are 4,304 cinemas with a total seating capacity of 3,872,000. In 1934 957 million persons visited cinemas and paid a total of £40,950,000 for admission. The average weekly attendance was 18,500,000. The average attendance of children, youths, and adults is about twenty-six times a year. Every British film is shown nearly 7,500 times, and every foreign film about 7,000 times.

These astonishing figures give some indication of the influence of the cinema in our modern social life. If all the films that are shown to the people could be made to conform to a good standard in story, acting, and production, we should not need to worry about the influence of the cinema. But far too many films are questionable in their appeal to human emotions.

How far the cinema moulds opinions is a matter which has not yet been discussed, but it is clear that it can be made into a potent force. As things are, most of the films produced concern themselves with false values, extolling the rather improbable lines of impossible people. What a marvellous opportunity exists for films portraying the lives of real people in adventure, comedy, work, play, even in imagination, and in their struggles to accomplish great achievements.

The co-operative movement has so far produced only advertising films. They have their place and serve a useful purpose, but Co-operation is a subject which deserves to be filmed. Its history is a thrilling story, its day to day work contains many scenarios of absorbing interest.

Internationalism is a central tenet of Co-operative philosophy. Films circulated freely between national Co-operative Movements, exchanging views on practices and achievements. The International Co-operative Alliance facilitated that process, and kept a catalogue and library of films. The British consumer Movement was seemingly most active in film work, and its films were widely disseminated. The British and Swedish Movements, two of Europe's largest and most successful, had close relations; ideas and information were constantly exchanged – in this instance through film. I have been unable to trace the source film detailing the African chieftain's visit to a CWS factory.

* * *

"Our English Friends"

Presenting C.W.S. Films
to Co-operators Abroad

An Interesting Example of
Swedish Enterprise

THE transformation of extracts from several English co-operative films into a new film specially for a foreign audience is the latest example of international co-operation in which the C.W.S. has played a part.

The idea of adapting British films to suit a foreign audience was broached to the C.W.S. last year by "Kooperativa förbundet," the C.W.S. of Sweden. K.F. has itself produced a number of interesting films, and has also arranged shows of C.W.S. films in Sweden.

Limitations to their effectiveness are, however, evident when propaganda and instructional films intended for English audiences are shown abroad. English, it is true, is spoken throughout the world, and is familiar to a very large proportion of Swedes in particular. The "language of the film," too, is said to be internationally understood. But it is not to be expected that any audience will be very interested in a film with a text or sound accompaniment entirely in a foreign language; whilst the appeal of a publicity film may not be so easily grasped by people with a different psychological make-up and ways of living.

The new film which "Kooperativa förbundet" has prepared shows how these problems can, to a large extent, be overcome. From a series of extracts from C.W.S. films has been created a Swedish film on English life, fully understandable to Swedish audiences.

Our English Friends is the title of the film. In a lively and gripping fashion it describes English conditions in general and British cooperation in particular.

Glimpses of the motley life in the metropolis are contrasted with peaceful pictures of the English countryside. The co-operative movement is displayed both at work and in lighter mood.

An insight is given to the many industrial undertakings owned by the C.W.S., especially those which the Swedish co-operative movement does not possess–glass works and biscuit factory, for example. The film, too, shows Swedish co-operators some of the ways in which English co-operators spend their leisure time. The producer has also spiced the film with glimpses of amusing traits–amusing to the foreigner, at any rate–in English life.

The sequence of the film is provided by a spoken narration in Swedish. In some places, however, English has been retained to promote effect, as for instance, when an African chieftain is paying a visit to the C.W.S. Variety is added by the interspersion of song and music.

How has it been possible thus to build up a picture specifically for a foreign audience from English films? Last autumn, a representative of "Kooperativa förbundet," Mr. Anders Hedberg, who is by no means a stranger to film production, saw all the films produced by the C.W.S. With his intimate knowledge of England and the English language, Mr. Hedberg was able to select parts of the films that would specially appeal to a Swedish public.

Copies of the selected parts were made of a special material known as "lavender print," from which duplicate negatives ("dupes") can be developed. The negatives were prepared in a film laboratory in Stockholm, where the pictures were pieced together and the commentary in Swedish recorded. The completed film, which is about 1,200 metres long, and takes about 45 minutes to show, was issued for the first time last month.

Horace Masterman, the manager of the Pioneer Cinema operated by the Dewsbury Pioneers Industrial Society, was an innovative and influential figure. His advice was sought by a number of societies involved in cinema exhibition, and he was engaged by the Blackpool Co-operative Society as technical adviser when they established their News Theatre in 1938. He had a genius for publicity, as demonstrated in his campaign for RKO's The Little Minister *(1934). A further award was made to him in 1937 by Columbia Pictures for his publicity scheme for Frank Capra's* Lost Horizon.

*   *   *

Film Publicity Prize
Co-operative Cinema Manager's Distinction

FIVE cinemas, all within a few yards of each other, cater for the film needs of the fifty-four thousand people of Dewsbury. One is the Pioneer Theatre, owned by the Dewsbury Co-operative Society and managed by Mr. Horace Masterman, who has lived up to his name by securing the highest award offered by Radio Pictures Ltd. in a national "exploitation" competition in connection with the film, "The Little Minister."

In his publicity scheme, Mr. Masterman demonstrated the advantages held by a co-operative cinema manager, provided he could secure the active support of other sections of the society. Members of the Dewsbury Society total a quarter of the population and therefore represent the majority. By utilising to the full the facilities afforded by the society's trading organisation, appeals were made simultaneously from different angles to the largest body of cinema patrons.

By a fortunate coincidence the film was shown during the town's shopping week, and it was agreed that co-operative participation should take the form of a window dressing competition, in which all windows should feature in some way "The Little Minister." Mr. Masterman supplied the necessary photographs, stills, cut-outs and posters, and over a period of several weeks detailed attention was given to reducing ideas to practical form. Correctness of detail became almost an obsession. A letter was even addressed to the Provost of "Thrums" for particulars of the correct tartan, a plaid of which was featured in the tailoring display.

By this time grocers, butchers, drapers, milliners, tailors, chemists, tobacconists, and decorators were co-operating in the scheme. The transport department was offered a prize for the best vehicle display, and the dairy manager arranged for special milk bottle discs to be used throughout the week. Approximately sixty thousand of these discs carried the shopping-week slogan—"'Little Minister' Shopping Week—Let the Co-op. Minister to Your needs"—into the homes of the people.

Nearly sixty thousand dividend warrants, due for issue, were also over-printed with the slogan.

Post, press and poster were used to influence that greatest of advertisers, public opinion, and, in the words of Mr. Masterman, "although 'The Little Minister' proved rather high-brow for the mills of Dewsbury, business was very good and the whole advertising scheme cost only £12 more than normal."

Mr. Masterman's success in the competition is particularly noteworthy, as he had to meet keen competition both in London and the provinces. He has allocated half of his prize of £50 to the society's sports fund as a token of appreciation of the co-operation of the employees.

Appendix K: from *The Millgate* October 1936

Whilst recognising the initiative of some societies in undertaking local Co-operative filmmaking, this article demands central coordination and financing through the setting up of a national film body (here called a "National Co-operative Film Society"). Frank Cox had made some films in the early 1930s for the London Co-operative Society and, in the year following this article, commenced a series of innovative 16mm sound film productions for the Political Committee of the LCS. It is notable that he includes cinema in a broader scheme of media which, he argues, the Movement must not neglect in terms of publicity and promotion. The Reynolds *to which he refers is the Movement's Sunday newspaper,* The Reynold's News.

* * *

A NATIONAL CO-OPERATIVE FILM Society
By
Frank H. W. Cox.

IT is a fact which brooks no denial that the weapons of progress and propaganda in the hands of our opponents are far superior to anything we possess. Why this should be, when we have so ably proved our ability to produce and distribute goods equal, if not better than they, is one of the queer problems with which our Movement abounds.

Another fact which we shall have to face very shortly if we do not alter this state of things, is that capitalist enterprise will soon be in the position to call a halt to all our activities. That will be where we "get off," as the Americans say.

Until we stop being fifty years behind the times and until we take advantage of radio, Press, and films to the fullest extent of which we are able we shall remain at the mercy of capitalism. True, our Press has made a gallant effort lately and every credit is due to those who were responsible for this. But here our wonderful democracy fails us again. Only part of the Movement has helped although all will benefit. Radio is a tougher proposition but not insurmountable.

In the cinema, however, we have a tool ready to use, but like the Press, only usable when backed by fully co-ordinated effort.

In appealing for a National Co-operative Film Society at the Brighton Conference I had previously demonstrated that this form of propaganda could be shown practically anywhere, without restriction, and at a cost within the reach of quite small societies. There are various film societies up and down the country doing this very thing, and we have lately noticed co-operative societies taking it up in a more or less haphazard way. Some are making their own films and some are showing library films, but of real co-operative feature films, very few exist, and those were made for Russian audiences and therefore appeal to only a limited few.

The cinema of to-day serves two very useful purposes to the capitalist State. Purposely so, we are only too well aware. It is a soporific and helps to keep the masses satisfied with their lot in life. Films are made which show the ease by which the rise from obscurity to fame is accomplished by the right attitude towards one's employer, &c.: the reward of virtue and the inevitable punishment of crime; the boosting of imperialism, and the glories of war. But the cause of war and the cause of crime are *not* shown. The thoughts and actions of the average inveterate cinema-goer are subtly influenced by what he sees on the screen, and in the adventures and escapades of his favourite actor or actress he finds escape from the dreary drudgery of his ordinary everyday life. And we are content to leave this weapon almost entirely in the hands of our enemies.

If a film tells a story which is vividly true even if it only depicts the ordinary workaday world; if it portrays the poignant human emotions which are the common lot of all humanity, then it can be used to tell some of the wonderful stories behind the make-up of our Movement, and when we venture into the realms of things to come we have a story of Utopia to portray that the makers of ordinary films dare not show. We have such a story to tell that would make the efforts of Wells and Korda seem like the fairy tales they are.

In 16mm. sound film we have a material which is *not* expensive. Your local co-operative halls could be equipped at a price which would not reach three figures, and in such a manner that the ordinary use of the hall would not be interfered with. It is easily portable and could be used in several halls or taken into guildrooms or public halls. It could be used for election propaganda or trading purposes. The taking of local events, opening of new stores, fetes and outings could be features of your shows. In fact its possibilities are endless.

All this is possible at present and you can do it as an individual society. But the films which tell the stories must be produced by co-ordinated effort and our greatest necessity is a film unit to supply these films.

I certainly do not advocate voluntary effort for the production of these films. It has been tried and found wanting. One could just as soon expect to see *Reynolds* produced by this means. However, we have amongst our amateur dramatic societies plenty of talent, and we have learned from Russia how to make use of natural acting by picking types to take those parts which they themselves fill in their daily life.

A very modest outlay would suffice to fit up and equip a studio for the production and processing of films. One-tenth of a penny in the pound of sales would provide more than sufficient money for such a studio equipped with cameras, lights and scenery for indoor sets, a laboratory for processing, and workrooms for the editing and production of films besides the payment of the necessary salaries.

We should not copy the methods of existing film companies in production. These are wasteful in the extreme. Huge salaries are paid to people who stand idle for hours, or who, perhaps, are never used at all. Fabulous sums are paid for stories which, in the resultant film, are scarcely recognisable. Money flows like water into every pocket but of those who do the manual work, in fact the status of a film is usually determined by the amount of money which has been spent on it. All this is symptomatic of private enterprise.

The directors and producers we should require would be picked for their understanding of our problem, not the cast-offs of private enterprise we usually tolerate in the Cooperative Movement. Our actors and actresses should be chosen for their human qualities and should be definitely sympathetic to the Movement.

For outdoor settings the whole countryside is ours, and with a little guile it is possible to make use of the city streets. The Cooperative Movement has its own farms, fields, and workshops which could be used to the fullest extent, and the ships and other transport facilities of the Wholesale Societies could be used in many romantic settings.

Such a film society is no longer an insuperable problem. It is easy of accomplishment, and the only difficulty which stands in the way is the lack of understanding and a totally erroneous idea of the cost involved.

Good luck to the educational secretaries who are already tackling this job; may their efforts meet with every success. A big push from the right direction might have the effect of starting an investigation into this matter by the Co-operative Union.

In concluding, I would suggest that this investigation should *not* be conducted into capitalist film production, but that we should strike out into this new field on our own initiative and resources so that, instead of trailing behind, we shall for once be in the van of progress.

A report by Joseph Reeves, newly appointed to the Workers' Film Association, on the first film production under the "Five Year Film Plan" of the four London Co-operative Societies – London, Royal Arsenal, South Suburban, and Enfield Highway. Reeves had been a key instigator of the scheme while he was Education Secretary at the RACS and, interestingly, provided the draft scenario of the story. In the following year, the Realist Film Unit completed two further commissions for the Movement – Voice of the People for the joint London Societies, and People With a Purpose for the RACS – with Reeves at the WFA remaining a key figure in the productions. In the final film, the character is named May, not Mary as described in the middle of the report.

*   *   *

Advance Democracy

A Film which Illustrates the Struggle of the Workers to Obtain Economic Redress

If we are not satisfied with the films provided by Hollywood the only alternative is to make our own films. If we make our own films they must serve our own ends. We cannot spend nearly as much money as Hollywood does in the making of films, but what money we have to spend can be used for the purpose of making a type of film which in its own sphere has great artistic merit.

The documentary film is the product of the desire of those who wanted to use the visual medium for educational and propaganda purposes, but who had little money with which to satisfy their needs. Artistically, the documentary film is as effective as the Hollywood glamour film.

The four London societies did a bold thing when they decided some 12 months ago to set aside a sum of £1,000 for five years for the purpose of producing one film a year of a documentary character. When the production committee was appointed, we soon decided that our films to be of value must not deal with narrow and specific problems, but with the broad issues of life in which the average man and woman are interested. Indeed, we were anxious that the films should be in their way gifts to our age and generation.

I was appointed technical secretary to the committee, and advised that the films should be made on standard stock to start with, so that when they were reduced to 16 m.m. stock, there would not be all those imperfections which the direct method of recording exhibits.

I wanted the film to illustrate the struggles of the workers to achieve social and economic freedom, and I was asked by the committee to provide a very rough scenario. This I did and it became the basis of the film which has now been made.

It is called *Advance Democracy*. The film opens with a comparison of the way food is provided for the workers and for the rich, which is used to introduce us to Bert and Mary, the two characters in the story. Bert is a dock worker. He works a crane, and although he hates the idea of war and international conflict, does not concern himself very much about how things can be changed so as to prevent international antagonisms. His wife, on the other hand, is a member of a women's guild, and she has been led to believe that co-operation is a much more effective way of life than the way of competition, and she advises Bert to listen-in to a wireless talk which is to be given by the Rt. Hon. A. V. Alexander on this subject.

Bert reluctantly agrees. Alexander delivers his broadcast talk. He speaks about the sacrifices of the Tolpuddle Martyrs which paved the way for the modern trade union movement, and of the early efforts of the Rochdale Equitable Pioneer Society. He speaks about how the co-operative movement has grown and how its service to the workers has become more valuable. The ramifications of the co-operative movement are shown on the screen. Finishing up his talk, Alexander warns his listeners that democracy is being threatened by the growing power of fascist countries, and pictures of Hitler's ruthless dictatorship are shown.

Bert, who has postponed the completion of his football coupon to listen is visibly affected by the broadcast talk, which is followed by a relay of dance music from a well-known hotel. He switches the music off in disgust, and we then see him discussing the matter with his workmates. He advises them and they agree to go to the great May Day demonstration at Hyde Park.

At this point in the picture, some fine choral music is reproduced under the capable guidance of Benjamin Britten. The Norwood Co-operative Choir sing appropriate songs of the workers, and the picture finishes on this note.

The picture has been produced by Mr. Ralph Bond in association with Mr. Basil Wright, the Realist Film Unit having produced the film under the guidance of Film Centre. The musical accompaniment was arranged by Benjamin Britten, and the radio set used in the broadcast talk was loaned by the Co-operative Wholesale Society, and it was a Defiant.

JOSEPH REEVES.

Appendix M: from *The Co-operative News* 9 November 1940

Following considerable expansion in the resources devoted to film publicity by the CWS in the late-1920s, it was increasingly likely that the society would look towards providing its own cinema requirements. Throughout the 1930s it commissioned the services of Publicity Films, a leading commercial production company. In 1940, it rather unsportingly poached producer George Wynn and lighting cameraman Harry Waxman from that company to work for the newly established CWS Film Unit. Waxman stayed for only a short period before being drafted into the RAF Film Unit, and eventually embarking on a distinguished career in the British feature film industry. It is noteworthy how much technical detail is contained in this report. I have found no evidence that the film Here's Health *was ever completed.*

*   *   *

C.W.S. Putting Co-operative Story on the Cinema Screen

"CO-OPERATIVE NEWS" SPECIAL.

SURPRISING things are happening these days at the C.W.S. tobacco factory, Manchester. It always has been an interesting place. Few factories attract more parties of visitors. But for the past few weeks the tobacco-producing scene has been dominated by something with a far greater human interest—film production.

Yes, the C.W.S. tobacco factory has taken on all the glamour of a film studio. All the paraphernalia is there. Blinding lights, cameras, miles of wire, shirt-sleeved operators, a brisk-mannered producer with his staccato commands—in fact, here is the scene made familiar to us ordinary cinema goers by the many films purporting to show us the scenes behind the scenes.

Of course there are actors. They are the factory employees engaged in tobacco production. They act as they work. And one day in the near future we shall see the story of the movement's own fragrant weed portrayed from the screen of our local cinemas. For then the Film Production Unit of the C.W.S. Publicity Department will have completed its first picture.

Film propaganda has, in fact, become a serious thing with the C.W.S.

Those excellent "shorts" screened in our local cinemas and dealing with co-operative productive phases have been the work of professional London studios. **What the C.W.S. has done has been to acquire these same facilities for itself. Personnel from the big London studios and the most modern camera and lighting equipment are now in the service of the Wholesale Society.**

Remember that delightful film entitled "Rose of the Orient" giving the romantic and interesting story of the co-operative tea leaf? It was produced by one well known in the big studios as George Wynn, who has been responsible for many previous publicity film productions for the C.W.S. His first contact with the movement in this way was in 1931. Now he has a more intimate and lasting association as producer for the C.W.S. Film Unit.

The name of Harry Waxman brings to mind several big film releases to those on the inside of production. For in connection with these films Mr. Waxman had the important role of chief cameraman. To-day he is associated with co-operative film production as the cameraman engaged by the C.W.S. Film Unit.

Equipment

If the names mean nothing to we laymen, a glimpse at the equipment (although you couldn't take it in at a glimpse) would certainly impress.

Let us survey the camera gear. The Unit comprises three cameras. The first, a Mitchell camera, which has been accepted as the standard camera in all the Hollywood and English studios. It features an amazing variety of lenses and tripods. The cost? Well, add another £1,500 and you have the purchase price of a Spitfire! A Newman-Sinclair automatic Kiné, regarded as Britain's most complete contribution to the technical side of film production, comes next, and third, there is the De Vry Automatic—an American hand-camera created for work where the stand camera cannot be used.

Lighting is one of the most important aspects of film production and the C.W.S., in its purchase of Mole Richardson lamps as used in all the first-class British and American studios, G.E.C. floodlamps, Kandem spot and floodlamps, up-to-date portable switchgear, and hundreds of yards of cable, have left nothing to chance in this direction. The scene, which was being "shot" at the tobacco factory, was bathed in dazzling light, the product of 20,500 watts. But this, the engineer assured me, was almost a black-out compared to the capacity of the full range of lamps.

"Perfection in reproduction under almost any conditions is ensured by these three cameras," Mr. Wynn told me as he paused for a breather between "shots" at the tobacco factory.

"No commercial enterprise in the country has a unit like this," he declared. "We have a first-class team of technicians and their equipment is second to none."

Actual production would be centralised at Manchester, but until the time comes for erecting a C.W.S. studio, first-class facilities were at the disposal of the Unit at a major London studio, where editors, sound technicians, and full studio equipment would be put to work on C.W.S. productions.

Mr. Wynn emphasised that all the unit's productions would be on the full-size 35 mm. film, from which 16 mm. copies could be made for use by co-operative organisations using the smaller projector.

The next big job to be tackled by the Unit was then described to me. This will be a film of general interest and educational value dealing with the war-time problem of choosing the most economical and nutritious foods.

The story has already been written, and the title, "Here's Health," chosen.

The film will be a splendid national service to the country in the lessons it drives home.

"Last 'shots' will be a fine piece of co-operative propaganda depicting the co-operative store as a mecca of all who search for health and economy in their food purchases," I was informed.

I left the tobacco factory-cum-film studio definitely impressed by the manner in which the C.W.S. is tackling this new form of co-operative education and propaganda.

Appendix N: from the "Introduction" to the *Catalogue* of the Workers' Film Association, 1945

Joseph Reeves, former Education Secretary of the RACS, was founding Secretary-Manager of the Workers' Film Association. He was a leading propagandist for the use of film by workers' organisations, having first introduced cinema technology as an educational aid within the RACS as early as 1920. This article provides an excellent summary of the film work of the Association during the war, a crucial time of progressive thinking and radical options. Reeves was elected to Parliament as a Co-operative-sponsored candidate for Greenwich in 1945, and in the following year the WFA was transformed into the National Film Association, to which Reeves acted as an adviser. Only three of the nine films commissioned by the WFA in its first year have so far been traced. The film, Labour on the March, *eventually evolved as* Their Great Adventure *(1948), produced by the CWS for the subsequent National Film Association.*

*   *   *

SUCCESS OF WORKERS FILM ASSOCIATION

by JOSEPH REEVES
Secretary-Manager

IN 1938, the Trades Union Congress and the Labour Party, believing that visual propaganda on behalf of the social ideals for which they stood had a great future, decided to form an organisation charged with the task of using this medium to the full. The Workers Film Association was the result of this piece of foresight and careful planning. The first year of film work revealed the need for and the value of propaganda and education by the film in a manner which surprised even the promoters. Nine films were made, a small library of films installed, and sound projectors sold, resulting in an actual trading profit of £250. And then the war came and high hopes were dashed to the ground. But it was decided to carry on even if only with a nucleus staff. Film shows were few and far between and the black-out made even the most enthusiastic hesitate before arranging a film show.

When Soviet Russia came into the war in 1941, a great change occurred. The W.F.A. was entrusted with the distribution of the great majority of sub-standard sound films, prepared by the Soviet Government for distribution in this country. This meant a piece of hasty improvisation. The W.F.A. was reorganised to distribute and exhibit films and with the registration of the Association as a Co-operative Society, its future looked far more rosy. By the end of 1942, after one full year's working, the annual balance-sheet revealed a surplus of nearly £1,000. The parent bodies were amazed and gratified. Here was a respectable sum for development, in spite of the fact that some of the services provided were offered at half the price of those offered by the trade. How was it done?

During the year, the Czechoslovak, Chinese, Polish, and Norwegian Governments entrusted the W.F.A. with the distribution of their films, and to its library were added films from the Film Department of the London Co-operative Societies, the five London

Co-operative Societies, the Woodcraft Folk, the Co-operative Wholesale Society Ltd., and Paole Zion. The Association was also entrusted with the exclusive distribution of "Our Film," made by the film workers at Denham Studios as a contribution to the war effort and in appreciation of the heroic struggle of the Soviet people against Nazi aggression.

A Film School was held at Oxford for one week, at which 60 students attended, and week-end film schools, conferences, and special film exhibitions were arranged.

Mobile outfits were set up to travel from place to place showing films as required by workers' organisations, and during the year nearly 550 such shows were given directly under the auspices of the Association, which included a series of conferences arranged by the Trades Union Congress, and a series of one week's showings by Co-operative Societies, Anglo-Soviet Friendship Committees, etc. Altogether 13,672 reels were distributed during the year.

The catalogue of films published by the Association increased and supplementary lists were issued, which included a series of full length feature films, until 222 films were listed, which means that there are now over 600 films in the library. Agents were appointed all over the country and a branch library established in Scotland under the auspices of the Scottish Co-operative Wholesale Society Ltd.

Negotiations were instituted with the Co-operative Union Ltd. whereby that important federation of co-operative societies should join the Association as a full member. Wartime conditions resulted in the breakdown of the negotiations, but the National Association of Co-operative Education Committees Ltd. and the Scottish Co-operative Wholesale Society Ltd. applied for and were received in full membership as partners in the Association. So there we are, a federation of national federations, registered on a non-profiting-making basis, for the use of visual aids to illustrate the important task of placing the workers' social aspirations on the screen.

An Advisory Committee was appointed to assist the Management Committee in making known W.F.A. services. The Workers' Travel Association Ltd. and the Holiday Fellowship Ltd. joined the Advisory Committee, and as a result the Association was invited to provide weekly programmes of films at hostels supervised by these bodies on behalf of the Ministry of Supply.

Sound projectors were provided for the General and Municipal Workers' Union and the Slough Co-operative Society, while other societies have placed deposits with the Association for projectors as soon as they become available.

A series of short films have been ordered by a number of co-operative societies, and consideration is now being given to a proposal for a film which can best be described as "Labour on the March."

Agreements have been reached with the Co-operative Wholesale Society Ltd. and the London Co-operative Society on the production of standard and sub-standard films required by the Association or its constituent members.

Co-operative Societies and other workers' organisations have been invited to become Associate Members, and already over 100 have responded. For an annual subscription of one guinea they are supplied with copies of the W.F.A. Bulletin and Documentary News, and all publications issued by the four national parent bodies relating to film propaganda and education.

To-day, the W.F.A. has 900 sound films and has recently added 500 silent films to its library. During the General Election loudspeaker equipment to the value of £10,000 was sold to Local Labour Parties, which added considerably to the efficiency of their electioneering campaign. Mobile units are touring the country giving film exhibitions in every county.

THE W.F.A. HAS COME TO STAY

Appendix O: from *The Co-operative Education Bulletin* September 1955

The Co-operative Education Bulletin *was issued monthly by the Education Department of the Co-operative Union for the benefit of the Education Committees of retail Co-operative societies. It carried views and information on all aspects of Co-operative education and training, and offered an important forum for debate. This article on running a film society is a typical example, whereby a successful Co-operative educational venture is reported for the consideration of other committees who might wish to undertake the support of a film appreciation group. There was a notable expansion in the film society Movement after the war, and Co-operatives featured prominently in that growth. The Slough Co-operative Film Society was inaugurated in the period immediately after the Second World War and was well-established by the mid-1950s, with a membership of 91. Its president was Michael Redgrave.*

* * *

ORGANISING A FILM SOCIETY

This helpful article has been contributed by Mr. J. F. Pontin, Education Secretary of the Slough Co-operative Society. The enterprising programme and policy followed by the Slough Co-operative Film Society, deservedly brings that Society frequently into local and national prominence.

AIMS AND ACTIVITIES

The aim of a Film Society in broad terms is to encourage people:

(a) to appreciate good cinema through the presentation and exhibition of films not normally available;
(b) to become discriminate in their choice;
(c) to foster film appreciation by lectures and discussion.

Bearing in mind that, in the main, film societies are catering for an intelligent membership who are aware of this comparatively new art form, the programme of films is booked on individual merit and not for any particular subject matter. Language difficulties need not be considered a bar to enjoying films from the continent—for in the majority of cases these films are available with sub-titles.

The work of a Film Society should not consist only of a series of viewing sessions. It should also give consideration to the development of specialised activities—for example the forming of a Scientific Film Group catering for the interests of teachers, doctors and people connected with learned Societies, or to further the needs of young people for whom the sponsoring of a Junior Film Club is to be commended. A recent experiment carried out in Slough proved that there was a demand for such an organisation; of 140 young persons between the ages of 8 and 15, seventy registered with us to join our Junior Film Club.

A further important activity—although a very expensive one—is the making of amateur films.

The impact of the cinema on our behaviour, our standards of living, is sufficiently well-known to cause us to consider its influence on the community at large. Thousands never read a book, listen to music, visit an art gallery or show any signs of appreciating the many facilities available which are provided by adult educational organisations. Many of these come into contact with the "moving picture" possibly once or twice a week. The "moving picture" is here and here to stay, whatever the scope or dimension it may take. To ignore this important educational medium and consider it a waste of money is to blind oneself to the importance of the impact of film on the community.

Any Education Committee with a 16 mm. projector should therefore give the question of the formation of a Film Society their most earnest consideration. Such a Society may be developed independently or, preferably, with other local organisations and, in particular, it is recommended that contact be made with the local education authority to assist.

OUR EXPERIENCE AT SLOUGH

In Slough, the Education Committee has promoted a Co-operative Film Society which is open both to members of the local Co-operative Society and to the general public. To the Co-operative society as a whole, a Co-operative Film Society can have considerable prestige value and bring in to the society people who, while aware of the existence of a Co-operative organisation, may not necessarily associate with it. The majority of our local Film Society are also members of the retail society—perhaps some five or six per cent. not being members. No distinction is made between them; they enjoy the same membership rights, pay the same membership fee and serve on the committee which is elected annually. This in itself is a demonstration of democracy working with the blessing of a Co-operative education committee.

In the first two sessions direct representatives were appointed by the Education Committee. However, it was found that at the end of the second session it would be possible to make a direct grant to the film society and allow it to be responsible for its own business. This is most important. From the film society members, we have found people who have a genuine interest in the film society movement and who are prepared to be actively engaged in the running of the film society.

Taking it for granted that a projector is available (we have a G. B. Bell Howell), accommodation is the next important matter. The accoustics of the room are vitally important and it is necessary to ensure that the place of screening is

(a) suitable for projection;
(b) reasonably warm;
(c) that the seating can be well spaced.

We are using a Travelling Self-Erecting Tripod Screen which is floodlit with coloured lights controlled from the projector. As near as possible our aim is to give the best possible presentation.

We have twelve committee members who are allocated definite positions. Apart from the Chairman, Vice-Chairman, Hon. Secretary and Treasurer, a Membership Secretary and a Guest Ticket Secretary are appointed. It is advisable also to have a Publicity Officer who will be responsible for maintaining friendly relations with the local press, the local library and will deal with programme notes and the display of stills at appropriate places. Our Annual General Meeting takes place at the end of the season, giving plenty of time for arranging the programme for the following session, etc.

PLANNING THE PROGRAMME

At present we are working on the basis of ten shows with two special evenings for which an additional charge is made. Last year we held a dinner with a prominent personality to lecture—this was followed by a film. This year we held a "Members' Evening," with a bar and buffet, and had with us on this occasion two well known film stars and producers. It was supported by the Mayor and Mayoress and was filmed by the local Borough Council's Cine-Photographer.

The cost of tickets for these functions was 6s. 6d. per head (guest tickets 7s. 6d.) and both were very well supported. One hundred members and friends were present at our dinner in 1954 and ninety-eight attended the buffet-social evening this year.

The selection and booking of the films is the next item to be cleared. The excellent monthly magazine *Film and Filming,* the invaluable *Film User,* and publications available from the British Film Institute, should be subscribed to. These publications will help in the important job of choosing your programmes and will give the committee a background to their job in hand.

Publicity, and the right kind of publicity, need not necessarily be expensive. In our own case the two local weekly papers are always prepared to give advance information concerning our forthcoming shows, and the *Slough Observer* in particular is an excellent example of the friendly relations that exist between the paper and our Society. A press advertisement at the commencement of the season, and a duplicated letter to educational and cultural bodies will also prove of use in obtaining members. We have a special arrangement with the local Public Library whereby a supply of programmes is available on demand and information to hand regarding membership, guest tickets, etc.

Having printed the membership tickets, guest tickets and programmes, we are ready for the first show. (Here I would add that we are supported by a number of organisations including the I.C.I. Sports and Recreation Club, and International Club and two of the local Guilds. These bodies—there are eight in all—have an associate membership with us).

At the end of each film performance we encourage open discussion on the film. This, however, is not very easy unless two or three members are prepared to give a lead in such discussion.

FINANCE

How should the Society be financed? In the case of the Slough Co-operative Film Society, membership costs 16s. (the Federation publication, *Films*, is supplied to members inclusive with subscription) and a limited number of guest tickets are available at 2s. each. Our income from membership fees may be in the region of £65 and approximately £12 from the sale of guest tickets. A grant of £75 is made by the Education Committee. Allowing for hire of films at approximately £60 for the session, hiring of accommodation, publicity, printing and affiliation fees (some £16) it is not possible for such a body to be completely self-supporting unless the subscription is considerably higher than 16s. per member. It should be pointed out, however, that there are a large variety of films available which can be obtained free of charge which would reduce the approximate figure quoted above of £60.

AFFILIATIONS AND SOME LEGAL MATTERS

Already there are some 16 Co-operative Film Societies in operation throughout England. (As far as I am aware there are none operating in Scotland or Wales). The majority of these are in membership of the Federation of Film Societies and the British Film Institute. The constitution of a Film Society is submitted to the Federation for approval and according to the constitution may enjoy full membership or become associate members. The Society must not espouse the cause of any political party or be a profit-making body. This is important if clearance is to be obtained from the Customs and Excise authorities for exemption from Entertainments Tax. Royalties are payable to the Phonograph Performance Ltd., for the use of any gramophone records played during shows, and a check should be made with the manager or secretary in charge of the hall used to see it is licensed by the Performing Rights Society Ltd. Further a Film Society might be liable for accidental bodily injury to any of its members or guests—if the owners of the hall have not accepted liability pay a visit to your C.I.S. Branch Manager, who will be pleased to arrange cover for a few shillings. The risk of damage of films can also be covered and it is advisable to include this in any policy you may have. It is anticipated that the Education Committee having their film equipment covered against theft, damage, etc., such a policy could include the risk to films.

No person under 16 years of age can be admitted into membership or as a guest to the shows. It should also be borne in mind that 16 mm. film shows are private shows and are not open to the public; and under no circumstances should persons other than *bona fide* members or guests be admitted. For guests, tickets can only be obtained through an individual member in advance of the actual performance and must not under any circumstances be obtained in the hall when the show is being held.

All Film Societies are strongly advised to join the Federation, and enquiries in this matter should be addressed to the Hon. Secretary, Mrs. M. Hancock, 35 Priory Road, Sheffield 7. Help and advice will be gladly given and useful publications and film lists are supplied from time to time to members. Every year a national viewing session is held in London with regional viewing sessions and weekend activities are arranged on a regional basis. A Central Booking Agency operates for the benefit of Federation members. Membership of the British Film Institute provides among its many advantages a 25 per cent. discount on National Film Library films and reduced prices for its publications.

DEVELOPING FILM APPRECIATION

In conclusion, a few words on film appreciation. The development of objective criticism and understanding of films is the most important aspect of a Film Society. The danger of monthly viewing sessions (film shows) where members merely come and go—not making any contribution or meeting fellow members on common ground—should be avoided as far as possible. The creative work of art which is seen by the eye and the supplementary power of sound is, for the viewer, a discovery. Each member reacts differently. Knowing what the member thinks is therefore important—thus in encouraging discussion each member's experience is shared and the film in all its aspects better appreciated. It also provides a first class training ground in objective discussion within our own emotional and intellectual limitations. It sharpens our perception, aids our judgment and plays its part in harmonising our own localised experiences with the world at large.

Recommended Publications

Indispensable to any committee considering the formation of a Film Society—"Forming and Running a Film Society" (2s. 3d. post paid from the Hon. Secretary of the Federation of Film Societies); "Critics' Choice" (monthly); Film Bulletin (monthly); "Sight and Sound" (quarterly), available from the British Film Institute, 164 Shaftesbury Avenue, W.C.2. Also recommended is the new monthly "Film and Filming" (1s. 6d.), from 21 Lower Belgrave Street, Buckingham Palace Road, S.W.1, and "Film User" (1s. 6d. monthly), from 174 Brompton Road, S.W.3.

Film Catalogues

This is by no means a complete list but they form a good basis on which to choose a selection of films. In a number of cases the films available are provided free.

Films de France; Archways Films Ltd.; Central Film Library; Plato Films Ltd.; Gaumont British Ltd. Contemporary Films Ltd.; Film Traders Ltd.; National Film Board of Canada; Imperial Chemical Industries Ltd.; United States Information Service; Gas Council; Petroleum Film Bureau; Sound Services Ltd., British Transport Films; National Coal Board.

A complete list may be obtained on application to the British Film Institute.

As the article indicates, the Co-op were pioneers of television advertising, and showed some innovation in their "game show"-style spot adverts at a time when initial advertisers were cautious. The reputed rate of £1000 per screen-minute made many businesses wary of investing in all but simple and brief presentations. It is interesting to note the elaborate plans set in motion by the Publicity Department of the CWS to communicate the basis of the promotional activities to individual retail societies – a necessity for a movement comprising approximately 1000 societies, and a contingency not required by a unitary trading concern.

*   *   *

C.W.S. AND COMMERCIAL TV

Quick off the mark with grocery and provision minute "spots"

THEME IS "SPOT THE LIKENESS"

BY A "NEWS" REPORTER

COMMERCIAL television's first programme will be broadcast from the I.T.A. London transmitter on Thursday next and within the first week of showing, on Wednesday, September 28, C.W.S. products will be on the screen.

The C.W.S. minute spot will be on the screen some time between 7 and 8 o'clock and in that minute the C.W.S. publicity department has had to devise a brief and telling sales presentation which will get home with a punch. How this will be done was explained to a "News" reporter this week by Mr. Frank Churchward, C.W.S. publicity manager.

It will carry the title of "Spot the Likeness" and will have all the attractions of a panel game. Viewers will see in quick succession three figures each holding a C.W.S. product prominently labelled. There will in fact be two or three features common to all three but one will be less obvious than the others.

The voice reading the script will specifically call attention to the fact that all are holding C.W.S. products "but of course, that is too obvious" and will then give the correct answer denoting the key feature—a brooch or a ring—which the viewer will not see so easily. With the presentation of each figure there is a four-line jingle naming the product displayed

It seems an awful lot to crowd into a minute but, of course, the script goes simultaneously with the pictures.

A COSTLY BUSINESS

As every minute of commercial advertising is said to cost somewhere in the region of £1,000, the advertiser must make the most of the time. Not only have platinum-studded seconds to be paid for but the services of an announcer, action-characters in the shot, and cost of film production.

The C.W.S. has booked time on the screen as far ahead as it is possible at the moment and similar reservations will be made with the Birmingham transmitter which is scheduled to open in January, and at Manchester later on.

There has been a most careful tie-up with retail societies within the range of the London transmitter. Societies have been notified of the dates of the broadcasts and it is expected they will exploit the situation by arranging special and attractive displays of the products featured.

Details to societies

In this connection the C.W.S publicity department has produced a first-class broadsheet which is being posted to all branches in the area covered by the London transmitter which will give staffs the fullest details about the TV programme.

It is a matter of congratulation that the C.W.S. is so far advanced with its TV plans. The "News" is informed that the film laboratories, faced with a spate of extra work for the TV spots for a considerable number of firms, are in a state of chaos so far as production is concerned. All the C.W.S films for the various spots are already made or decided.

The voice heard on these C W.S. spots will be that of Patrick Allan, the well-known radio voice known to millions by his "Shilling a Second" broadcasts from Luxemburg and now appearing in "The Desperate Hours" at the London Hippodrome.

Film Title Index

Film Archive Index

Film Credits Index

Country of Production Index

[Unless indicated otherwise – as below – the
country of production in catalogue entries is
England.]

Australia   166

Austria   127

Scotland
1, 7, 10, 11, 16, 17, 28, 41, 73, 79, 100, 103,
107, 110, 111, 116, 124, 126, 132, 133, 175,
        182, 187, 197, 199, 204, 205, 212-214,
   223-225, 229-231, 237, 245, 248, 250, 266,
                                                 267

Sweden   132

Wales   2

Co-operative Society Index

Brand Name Index

Product and Industry Index

Geographical Index

General and Miscellaneous Index

Selected Bibliography

For a more detailed discussion of the history and development of the Co-operative Movement, and of the aims and activities of the workers' film Movement, the following may be useful:

Attfield, John. *With Light of Knowledge: A Hundred Years of Education in the Royal Arsenal Co-operative Society, 1877-1977* (London; West Nyack: RACS/Journeyman Press, 1981).

Birchall, Johnston. *Co-op: the people's business* (Manchester; New York: Manchester University Press, 1994).

Bonner, Arnold. *British Co-operation: The History, Principles, and Organisation of the British Co-operative Movement* (Manchester: Co-operative Union, 1961).

Burton, Alan. "The Emergence of an Alternative Film Culture: The British Consumer Co-operative Movement and Film before 1920" *Film History* 8 (December 1996): 446-456.

——————. *The People's Cinema: Film and the Co-operative Movement* (London: National Film Theatre, 1994).

Cole, G D H. *A Century of Co-operation* (Manchester: Co-operative Union, 1944).

Gaffin, Jean and David Thoms. *Caring & Sharing: The Centenary History of the Co-operative Women's Guild*, second edition (Manchester: Holyoake Books, 1993).

Gurney, Peter. *Co-operative Culture and the Politics of Consumption in England 1870-1930* (Manchester; New York: Manchester University Press, 1996).

Hall, F and W P Watkins. *Co-operation: A Survey of the History, Principles, and Organisation of the Co-operative Movement in Great Britain and Ireland* (Manchester: Co-operative Union, 1937).

Hogenkamp, Bert. *Deadly Parallels: Film and the Left in Britain, 1929-1939* (London: Lawrence and Wishart, 1986).

Jones, Stephen G. *The British Labour Movement and Film, 1918-1939* (London:

Routledge and Kegan Paul, 1987).

Kinloch, James and John Butt. *History of the Scottish Co-operative Wholesale Society* (Manchester: Co-operative Wholesale Society, 1981).

Macpherson, Don (ed). *Traditions of Independence: British Cinema in the Thirties* (London: British Film Institute, 1980).

Mercer, T W. *Towards the Co-operative Commonwealth: Why Poverty in the Midst of Plenty?* (Manchester: The Co-operative Press, 1936).

Richardson, Sir William. *The CWS in War and Peace 1938-1976* (Manchester: Co-operative Wholesale Society, 1977).

Ryan, Trevor. "'The New Road To Progress': the use and production of films by the Labour movement 1929-39", in James Curran and Vincent Porter (eds), *British Cinema History* (London: Weidenfeld & Nicolson, 1983).

Yeo, Stephen (ed). *New Views of Co-operation* (London; New York: Routledge, 1988).

For a wide-ranging collection of essays on historical aspects of the Co-operative Movement compiled to commemorate the 150th anniversary of the Rochdale Equitable Pioneers Society, see *North West Labour History Journal* 19 (1994/95). For a recent general appraisal of the Co-operative Movement since 1945, see *Journal of Co-operative Studies* (special edition) 79 (1994).